PRAISE FOR TAHOE DARK

"ONCE AGAIN, BORG HITS ALL THE RIGHT NOTES FOR FANS OF CLASSIC DETECTIVE FICTION in the mold of Dashiell Hammett, Raymond Chandler, Ross Macdonald, and Robert B. Parker."
- *Kirkus Reviews*

"I CAN'T RECOMMEND THIS SERIES HIGHLY ENOUGH... THEY. ARE. THAT. GOOD." - *Kittling: Books*

"TAHOE DARK IS PACKED WITH ACTION AND TWISTS. THE SURPRISES JUST KEEP ON COMING...THE FINAL SCENE IS ANOTHER TODD BORG MASTERPIECE." - *Silver's Reviews*

"A COMPLEX, INTRIGUING, NAIL-BITING THRILL RIDE TO THE VERY END." - *Tahoe Mountain News*

PRAISE FOR TAHOE BLUE FIRE

"A GRIPPING NARRATIVE...A HERO WHO WALKS CONFIDENTLY IN THE FOOTSTEPS OF SAM SPADE, PHILIP MARLOWE, AND LEW ARCHER" - *Kirkus Reviews*

"A THRILLING MYSTERY THAT IS DIFFICULT TO PUT DOWN ...EDGE OF YOUR SEAT ACTION" – *Silver's Reviews*

PRAISE FOR TAHOE GHOST BOAT

"THE OLD PULP SAVVY OF (ROSS) MACDONALD...REAL SURPRISE AT THE END" – *Kirkus Reviews*

"NAIL-BITING THRILLER...BOILING POT OF DRAMA" - *Gloria Sinibaldi, Tahoe Daily Tribune*

"BORG'S WRITING IS THE STUFF OF A HOLLYWOOD ACTION BLOCKBUSTER" – *Taylor Flynn, Tahoe Mountain News*

"ACTION-PACKED IS PUTTING IT MILDLY. PREPARE FOR FIRE-WORKS" – *Sunny Solomon, Bookin' With Sunny*

"I LOVED EVERY ROLLER COASTER RIDE IN THIS THRILLER 5+ OUT OF 5" – *Harvee Lau, Book Dilettante*

PRAISE FOR TAHOE CHASE

"EXCITING, EXPLOSIVE, THOUGHTFUL, SOMETIMES FUNNY"

– Ann Ronald, Bookin' With Sunny

"BE WARNED. IT MIGHT BE ADDICTING"

- Gloria Sinibaldi, Tahoe Daily Tribune

"OWEN McKENNA HAS HIS HANDS FULL IN ANOTHER THRILL-ING ADVENTURE"

- Harvee Lau, Book Dilettante

PRAISE FOR TAHOE TRAP

"AN OPEN-THROTTLE RIDE"

- Wendy Schultz, Placerville Mountain Democrat

"A CONSTANTLY SURPRISING SERIES OF EVENTS INVOLVING MURDER...and the final motivation of the killer comes as a major surprise. (I love when that happens.)" *– Yvette, In So Many Words*

"I LOVE TODD BORG'S BOOKS...There is the usual great twist ending in Tahoe Trap that I never would have guessed" *– JBronder Reviews*

"THE PLOTS ARE HIGH OCTANE AND THE ACTION IS FASTER THAN A CHEETAH ON SPEED" *– Cathy Cole, Kittling: Books*

"AN EXCITING MURDER MYSTERY... I watch for the ongoing develop-ments of Jack Reacher, Joanna Brady, Dismas Hardy, Peter and Rina Decker, and Alex Cross to name a few. But these days I look forward most to the next installment of Owen McKenna."

- China Gorman blog

PRAISE FOR TAHOE HIJACK

"BEGINNING TO READ TAHOE HIJACK IS LIKE FLOOR-BOARDING A RACE CAR... RATING: A+"

- Cathy Cole, Kittling Books

"A THRILLING READ... any reader will find the pages of his thrillers impossible to stop turning"

- Caleb Cage, The Nevada Review

"THE BOOK CLIMAXES WITH A TWIST THE READER DOESN'T
SEE COMING, WORTHY OF MICHAEL CONNELLY"
- *Heather Gould, Tahoe Mountain News*

"I HAD TO HOLD MY BREATH DURING THE LAST PART OF THIS
FAST-PACED THRILLER" - *Harvee Lau, Book Dilettante*

PRAISE FOR TAHOE HEAT

"IN TAHOE HEAT, BORG MASTERFULLY WRITES A SEQUENCE
OF EVENTS SO INTENSE THAT IT BELONGS IN AN EARLY TOM
CLANCY NOVEL"
- *Caleb Cage, Nevada Review*

"TAHOE HEAT IS A RIVETING THRILLER"
- *John Burroughs, Midwest Book Review*

"WILL KEEP READERS TURNING THE PAGES AS OWEN RACES
TO CATCH A VICIOUS KILLER"
- *Barbara Bibel, Booklist*

"THE READER CAN'T HELP BUT ROOT FOR McKENNA AS THE
BIG, GENEROUS, IRISH-BLOODED, STREET-WISE-YET-BOOK-
SMART FORMER COP"
- *Taylor Flynn, Tahoe Mountain News*

PRAISE FOR TAHOE NIGHT

"BORG HAS WRITTEN ANOTHER WHITE-KNUCKLE
THRILLER... A sure bet for mystery buffs waiting for the next Robert B.
Parker and Lee Child novels"
- *Jo Ann Vicarel, Library Journal*

"AN ACTION-PACKED THRILLER WITH A NICE-GUY HERO, AN
EVEN NICER DOG..."
- *Kirkus Reviews*

"A KILLER PLOT... EVERY ONE OF ITS 350 PAGES WANTS TO GET
TURNED... FAST"
- *Taylor Flynn, Tahoe Mountain News*

"A FASCINATING STORY OF FORGERY, MURDER..."
- *Nancy Hayden, Tahoe Daily Tribune*

Titles by Todd Borg

TAHOE DEATHFALL

TAHOE BLOWUP

TAHOE ICE GRAVE

TAHOE KILLSHOT

TAHOE SILENCE

TAHOE AVALANCHE

TAHOE NIGHT

TAHOE HEAT

TAHOE HIJACK

TAHOE TRAP

TAHOE CHASE

TAHOE GHOST BOAT

TAHOE BLUE FIRE

TAHOE DARK

TAHOE PAYBACK

TAHOE PAYBACK

by

Todd Borg

THRILLER PRESS

Thriller Press First Edition, August 2017

Library of Congress Control Number: 2017905977

ISBN: 978-1-931296-25-0

Cover design and map by Keith Carlson

Manufactured in the United States of America

For Kit

ACKNOWLEDGMENTS

Editing and cover design.

This is what professional book presentation is about.

No matter how imaginative a writer is with words, he or she still needs professional help with editing. Professional cover design is equally important.

In fact, of all the arts, it may be that writers are the people most dependent on these magicians who step in and make your work readable and understandable.

For editing, my wizards are Liz Johnston, Eric Berglund, Christel Hall, and my wife Kit.

For cover magic, Keith Carlson.

And for support of all kinds, Kit is always there, backing me two hundred percent.

Thank you all, more than I can say.

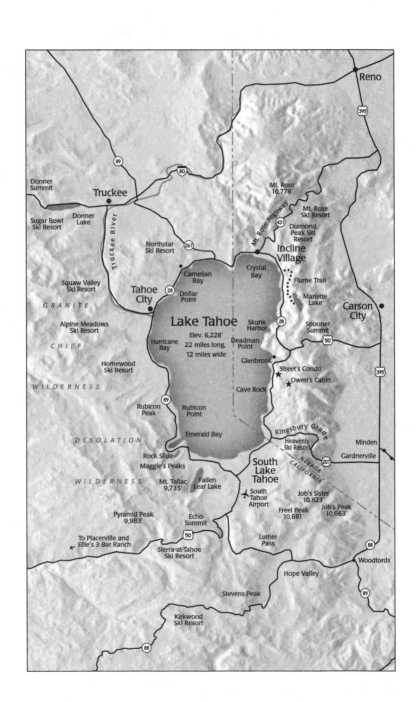

PROLOGUE

The person with the gun said, "Get out of the boat."
The woman hesitated.

"Go!"

The woman's hands were tied behind her back. She had no way to catch herself if she lost her balance. She lifted her foot up and set it on the edge of the boat, her dress sandal teetering. The waves were large, and the boat bounced against the rocky shore. The woman made a wobbly step onto the boulders of Fannette Island.

"This isn't something to joke about!" In another situation, her husky voice could have come off as tough. But it was filled with strain and the vibrato of fear.

"Shut up and hike. Up over those rocks. To the side of that big tree. See where the granite rises up? There are steps to the left, cut into the rock. Follow them. They go up and around."

The person with the gun wore a long rain jacket and dark pants that were hard to see as twilight began to render the roiling storm clouds invisible. The captive woman wore a stylish, red cotton wrap that provided no rain protection. Under it was a starched white shirt with a wing collar designed for a bow tie, but it was open at the neck. Her shirt tails hung out over a shiny black skirt of thin, sinuous fabric that wrapped her bare legs and rippled in the wind. The woman's open-toed sandals were made of narrow leather straps. It was an ensemble suitable for the restaurant from which she'd been taken at gunpoint, not for climbing a boulder-strewn hill of granite on an island in Emerald Bay during an evening storm. A violent shiver shook her body.

The June storm was unusually cold, even for Lake Tahoe. Clouds like charcoal smudges grappled with each other as they raced around the mountains above. Above the Sierra Crest, a sudden orange light appeared in the dark sky. A narrow opening, like a tear in the viscous, misty fabric of water vapor, let in a bit of sunset glow. Then, just as quickly as the light appeared, the sky was dark again.

The icy rain, an intermittent drizzle before, grew intense. The wind-driven spray was violent enough to sting exposed skin.

The captive woman cried out, "Why are you doing this? Why?!" The word stretched into a long, mournful wail.

The captor reached up and flipped on a headlamp. The blue-white LED cast a bright cone of light through the sparse, island forest. When the victim slowed, the captor prodded her in the back with the gun.

The victim whimpered. "I don't deserve this."

"Keep going."

After a minute of hiking up steep steps, they came to an open area of rock. Now that they were above the trees, the wind was ferocious. The rain came in waves. At the top of Fannette Island, looming in the dark, was the stone tea house, nearly 100 years old. It was built by Lora Knight, the same woman who built the Vikingsholm Castle on the west end of Emerald Bay. The one-room building perched at the highest point on the island, on the edge of a granite cliff that dropped down to the water.

The tea house no longer had a roof or door or glass in the window frames. But the stone walls, with their irregular, crenelated top edge, still stood strong.

"Over there," the person with the gun said, the words nearly lost in the roar of the wind, directing the woman to the outside of the tea house. The captor had the woman stand facing the corner closest to the cliff.

"The ground drops off below you, so don't try anything or you'll take a backward dive onto those rocks below."

The victim appeared frozen in place on the thin ledge. Trying to escape the wind, she leaned forward against the tea house corner, pressing her shoulder against the stones, her cheek against the rough, rain-soaked rock.

The captive woman pleaded. "I'm sorry about what I said when you called. I'll do what you wanted." Her voice betrayed her terror.

"Too late," the person with the gun said.

The captor angled the headlamp so that the beam shone briefly in the captive's eyes, keeping her night blind. The woman's hair was soaked, and it drooped down around her face. Her wet clothes stuck to her wet skin, which glistened in the light.

The captor pulled a packaged coil of thin line from a pocket. It was paracord, a type of weave that was originally developed for parachutes. It was sold at countless places, marketed as utility line for hunters and campers. This version was rated for 750 pounds. The captor pulled the cord out of the package.

"I'm going to put this line around your ankles. If you even twitch, I'll shoot you in the leg, and you'll fall off the cliff. It won't be a quick, painless kill. It will be agonizing. And no one will hear a gunshot out on a deserted island in this storm."

"I don't understand. Why are you…"

"I'm not going to tell you again."

The captor looped the line around the woman's ankles, then tied a slip knot and pulled the cord tight.

The captive woman jerked and shook with fear. "If you let me go, I'll make you rich. Seriously. You have no idea how much money I have."

"Shut up." The person with the gun took the coil of paracord and tossed it up and over the top stone on the corner of the roofless tea house. The line fell inside the tea house and landed on the floor. The captor stepped through the open doorway, inside the single room. There was no worry about the woman trying to get away. With her wrists tied behind her back and her ankles tied with a line that went up and over the wall of the tea house, there was no way she could escape.

The captor was wearing a heavy backpack containing a battery and a waterproof electric winch. It took just two minutes to make the preparations, connecting the battery cables, tying the lines, getting the angles right. The captor had previously climbed up and found a smooth groove next to the cornerstone at the top of the wall. A flick of the wrist put the line in place.

The captor carried the backpack out of the tea house.

"Don't do this," the prisoner said with her mouth against the cold wet stone. "You don't need to kill me."

"I'm not gonna kill you," the captor said. "You're going to die all by yourself. Exposure. Hypothermia. Mental stress. Especially mental stress. That's what's going to kill you. That's what should kill you after what you've done. You're going to live just long enough to consider how bad you screwed up. You had a chance to do right. But you ignored that chance."

"I mean it," the woman pleaded. "I'm very, very sorry. I can't tell you how sorry. I'll give you whatever you want."

The person with the gun ignored the statement and bent back as if to shine the headlamp at the dark storm clouds. "The weather forecast says that this rain will turn to snow by morning. There's a high wind and high surf warning on Tahoe for the next fifteen hours. Ridgetop gusts on the Sierra Crest are predicted to be over one hundred miles per hour. No one will be out here tonight. No one will find you. You'll be frozen solid by morning. They'll be talking about your death grimace for years. You should make a good example for anyone else. Everyone else."

"Please! Don't you hear me?"

The captor planted a foot to the side of the woman's sandals, then pulled on the woman's arms, tugging her off balance.

The woman screamed. "What are you doing!" as she fell over, helpless with her wrists tied behind her back.

The captor broke her fall. The woman hit the ground with a relatively soft impact that would give her hip and arm bruises but nothing more.

The captor reached into the pack, found the electronic remote, and pressed a button. A high whirring sound came from the winch inside the tea house. The paracord snaked up and over the wall of the tea house. It drew tight around the woman's ankles and then began lifting her up, feet first.

She screamed. But her voice was small against the gale winds whipping over the Sierra Crest and down into the Tahoe Basin.

When the woman was hoisted upside down and raised high enough that her head was four feet above the ground, the captor released the remote button. The winch stopped. The woman's skirt flipped inside out, draping down over her head, leaving her legs bare from her ankles to her underpants.

While the woman swung in the breeze, her screams gradually getting softer, the captor went back inside the tea house, disengaged the paracord from the winch, threaded it through a piece of one of the window frames in the tea house, and tied it off.

The winch and battery went back into the pack, and the captor went back outside.

Next, the captor reached into the pack and pulled out a roll of duct tape and three red roses. The flowers were not fully mature, their petals closed. The thorns were hard. The headlamp beam shined on the roses. The captor lifted up the woman's skirt to uncover her head

The captive woman saw the roses in the headlamp beam. She gasped. "What are you doing?! I don't understand!"

"Yes you do," the captor said. The captor crammed the roses into the woman's mouth, the flowers and stems sticking out either side. "One of your victims fell for your roses, your story. Because of you, his last hours were torture. This is your payback, dying the same way."

The woman's agonizing, guttural cry was lost in the wind as the captor wrapped duct tape around her head to hold the roses in place.

Next, the captor took out a silver necklace from which hung a little pendant shaped like roses. The captor poked it into the woman's cheek, stuffing it in with the real roses.

The captor pulled one last item out of a coat pocket. It was a tight roll of paper about the size of a cigarette. The paper was made of cotton, and the message on it was written in waterproof ink. The captor stuffed it into the woman's cheek next to the necklace. The thorny rose stems, taped into the victim's mouth, would prevent her from using her tongue to push the necklace and paper out.

After the captor walked away and was hiking down toward the boat, the upside-down woman, too cold to even try to form words with the roses in her mouth, managed to scream and shake her head violently. The movement dislodged the necklace and paper roll from within her cheek. The necklace fell down the cliff. The paper roll bounced off a rock, tumbled through the night wind, and landed in the lake.

ONE

I was sitting in my creaky desk chair, my feet up on the chipped desk surface. I'd managed to get through much of the day ignoring the substantial stack of bills for which funds were in short supply. Because a cold front and storm had come through the night before and dropped a couple of inches of June snow over Tahoe, I spent much of the day hiding indoors, sipping hot tea.

Now I was using up the remaining time before Sierra Nevada Pale Ale hour by perusing a heavy, hardbound monograph of paintings by the Spanish painter Joaquin Sorolla, Spain's national treasure before Picasso took over the position. I'd paused on the two women in "Walk On The Beach" when a knock sounded on the door, a triple bump-bump-bump as if someone used the heel of their palm.

Spot had been asleep, lying on his side on the spotted, splotchy, black-and-white camo rug, custom-designed for a Harlequin Great Dane. At the sound of the knock, he rolled onto his chest, propped up with spread elbows, his head up, watching the door. Apparently his doggie detection powers hadn't determined that we had a familiar visitor for whom he would jump up and greet with wagging tail. So he was motionless, except for the tiny flickering disco flashes that emanated from his faux-diamond ear stud.

I didn't immediately answer the knock because the women in the painting – Sorolla's wife and daughter, dressed in grand white dresses, hats, and fancy shoes, yet strolling on the sand just inches from the rolling waves – had such powerful personalities that I was captivated by their world, and I wanted to remain in it. But eventually, the sway of elegant women and beach lost out to the pressures of daily work.

"C'mon in," I called out.

Spot and I both waited as the door opened.

A short, thick man in his fifties stood in the opening. I could see part of a fat-tire mountain bike in the hallway.

The man was breathing hard. Maybe he was excited to see me appreciating art. Or maybe Tahoe's high elevation and the hike with a bike up the office stairs had cranked his heart/lung system up to the highest setting. What didn't fit was his over-the-top sports uniform, a skin-tight, shimmery, yellow-and-orange-and-blue bicycling spandex that showed off every bit of body flab. The man wasn't obese, but he had enough rolls and folds to give a cardiologist financial anticipation. The outfit seemed, to my naïve view, like something that only a person in supreme shape would have the guts to wear out in public. The presentation was vaguely humorous. Then again, maybe this man was just beginning a fitness regime, and the uniform was an attempt to embarrass himself into getting in shape. I reminded myself that I shouldn't be so judgmental.

The man rolled his bike to the side of the door, leaned it against the hallway wall, and stepped through the doorway.

"Mr. McKenna?"

"That's me."

"Are you available to work? I'd like to hire you. How much do you need to start?"

He was frowning, and he couldn't have telegraphed any more awkwardness if he'd been wearing a magenta tutu and figure skates. Awkward facial expression, awkward speech, awkward body language, awkward posture.

"Let's slow down a bit," I said.

"I don't understand. Does that mean you're not available?"

"I might be. It depends on what you need. We have to talk first and get to know each other a little bit. There are different kinds of investigation, and I don't do all of them. So please come in and introduce yourself and let's chat a bit."

Now the man seemed even more agitated and worried. He took a step into my office. "I need help. Something terrible has happened."

I thought of showing him my book. Maybe Sorolla's women on the beach would calm and soothe him. But he didn't appear to even notice the beautiful art monograph. Shocking.

Spot stared at the man, but still saw no need to move from his comfy new rug. The man didn't appear to have even seen Spot. Spot probably thought it was his camouflage setting that made him invisible, a unique experience for any Great Dane, especially one with Harlequin coloring.

But then the man sensed something. He jerked his head toward Spot, a sudden shock of alarm widening his eyes and creasing his brow. After staring for a couple of intense seconds, he appeared to arrive at the thought that my dog, although a 170-pound carnivore with large fangs, might be benign.

The man softened. He took a deep breath as if my dog gave him an opportunity to change the subject away from his stress. He said, "I love dogs. But I've never seen one so, you know... really large." He held his hand out and took a step toward Spot. "Are you friendly? You won't eat me, will you?" His voice was calmer.

"He's friendly. Meet Spot. Spot meet our visitor, Mr..."

"Douglas Fairbanks," the man said. Although Spot was still lying down, Fairbanks didn't have to bend over much to pet him.

"Like the swashbuckling movie star who played Zorro?" I said.

"Yes," the man said, "minus the swashbuckling and the charm and the enthusiastic personality and, of course, the beauty. The name is the curse of my mother, who had an incurable crush on the man. When she married the jerk who became my father, she apparently thought to mitigate the situation by naming me after the famous and charismatic Douglas. Thank you, mom. What a gift to constantly suffer that comparison."

After three little strokes along the top of his head, Spot closed his eyes and began panting. With some effort, Fairbanks lowered himself down next to Spot and sat on the edge of the Harlequin camo rug, the better to pet Spot. Fairbanks had his legs stretched out straight in front of him the way a little kid often sits.

He spoke as he pet Spot. "E.B.White wrote a little poem about these dogs. Something like how if one were in a city, one would have to be insane to keep a Great Dane."

I said, "White wrote about pigs and spiders in Charlotte's

Web, right? So he might not have been a Great Dane expert. They could be perfect town hounds. Of course, it would help if you had an apartment of ten thousand square feet and an indoor running track. Even so, it's probably a good thing I live at Lake Tahoe."

"Of course. The lake and all," Fairbanks said, nodding, still petting Spot.

Sorolla-inspired or not, all the soothing and petting going on seemed to be working on both man and beast.

"Likes to swim, does he?" The man's hand looked small between Spot's ears.

I said, "Not so much. Spot thinks the lake is for drinking. And, on warm sunny days, running along the beach at high speed at the water's edge, a raucous display of canine daring as he ventures six or sometimes even eight inches into the surf. A brave dog, that one."

Fairbanks nodded, then frowned and looked very serious again. He was still petting Spot with his right hand. So he reached his left hand up to massage his forehead, literally wiping the frown off his face.

"What can I help you with?" I said.

"My friend is gone. My... my girlfriend. She's missing."

"How long has she been gone?" I asked.

"Twenty..." he looked at his watch, "twenty-seven and a half hours. I last saw her at lunch yesterday. She went out for a smoke and never came back."

"Maybe she got a phone call and had to rush off?"

"No. She would have told me. She had nothing on her schedule. For a long time, she'd planned on coming to the Tahoe Mountain Bike for Charity event and was so excited about it that she cleared her schedule through to next week."

I gestured at the chairs in front of my desk. "Why don't you have a seat?"

The man struggled to stand up. He did a slow gyration of his hips to unkink his back, then pulled one of the chairs back a bit and sat down. "What do you need in order to find her? You do find missing people, right?"

"Sometimes," I said in my most reassuring voice. People

run away. Those who are left can't bear to consider that not only did their loved one voluntarily leave, but it may have happened because the person leaving could no longer stand to be with the person remaining.

"Let's start with where you're from," I said.

"I'm from Las Vegas."

"Douglas Fairbanks from Vegas," I said as I wrote on a yellow pad.

Fairbanks nodded. He unzipped a blue belt pack I hadn't noticed against the riotous backdrop of his cycling uniform, pulled out a business card, and handed it to me. It said, 'Fairbanks Insurance Brokerage.'

"Your girlfriend?" I said. "What is her name?"

"Isadore. With an E." Fairbanks pronounced it with a hard A sound like Isadoray.

"And her last name?"

"It's just Isadore. One word. She says that in Greece, it's mostly a man's name, and they pronounce it differently. But her mother liked the French version."

"Where is Isadore from?"

Fairbanks hesitated. "I don't actually know. Part of our relationship has been based on the idea that we are free spirits not tied down by our pasts. We are future focused."

As I looked at Fairbanks, all nervous energy trussed into an elastic outfit that was much like a full-body, day-glo, advertising banner, I couldn't quite see him as a free spirit. He looked captive to the branding concept of a bicycling sports conglomerate.

"If you had to guess at Isadore's home location?" I said.

"I'd guess the Bay Area. She's got that worldly sophistication. She even mentioned going to see obscure plays in little upstairs theaters. We don't do stuff like that in Vegas. We see floor shows. Big, grand spectacles. We like stars in gold lamé attacking the stage with relish, backed up by big bands and backup singers in matching costume. But plays are so, you know... small and arty and intellectual. So San Francisco."

I wondered at his ability to praise Vegas shows when his girlfriend was missing. And I wondered where Tahoe was on the spectrum. We didn't watch much in the way of gaudy shows or arty plays. We mostly just went hiking and biking and skiing and kayaking.

I said, "Where were you when Isadore went missing?"

"We were having lunch at the Sunnyside restaurant on the West Shore. She went outside for a smoke. She had to go out to the parking lot." He sounded irritated.

"Because the rules are strict," I said.

"Yes. Isadore says you can't even smoke outdoors in most parts of Tahoe because of forest fire danger. So she went out, but never came back." In addition to his sadness, he sounded angry.

In the window light, Fairbanks's face looked florid. The skin of his scalp shone rust-pink through a sparse forest of gray hair, each stiff fiber a relatively thick tree trunk cut off an inch above the forest floor. There was a measurable distance between each hair. His head made me think of a pink scrub brush.

"Is Isadore a mountain biker?" I asked.

"Yes. She's signed up for the Black Diamond Downhill Sprint."

"Yet she smokes."

Fairbanks looked embarrassed. "I know. It doesn't make much sense. But I think her cigarette smoking was mostly for show. I don't think she inhaled."

"Part of her sophistication?"

"Yes. Or no. I don't know. But when I saw her puff on her cigarette, I never saw her take a deep inhalation."

"Is it possible that feigning smoking allowed her to step away at odd moments? To be by herself or make a phone call or check email in private?"

Fairbanks frowned, a deep network of worry lines across his forehead. He seemed to be looking inward, making reassessments. He didn't answer.

"What was Isadore wearing?" I asked.

He thought about it. "She had on dress sandals and a black skirt that was all swishy-like, very sexy. And a white men's shirt with the bow-tie collar. Only she wasn't wearing a tie. I guess it's some new fashion thing, women wearing formal men's shirts. Over the shirt was a red coat. Medium length. Like a smoking jacket that Douglas Fairbanks the actor would have worn."

"How old is Isadore?" I asked.

"She's twenty-nine years and eleven months. I know because I've been planning a special birthday gift for her thirtieth." Fairbanks paused, then said, "I know what you're thinking. A beautiful young woman and an older man with some money. But really, Isadore is very devoted to me. I don't think it would be too much to say that she loves me."

"Has she said that?"

"You mean, has she come right out and said, 'I love you?'"

"Right," I said.

"Well, no. But in my experience, women don't just say 'I love you.' Especially sophisticated women. It's not, you know..."

"No, I don't."

He paused. "Isadore is tamped down. It's part of her sophistication. Telling me personal thoughts would be much too gushy. Don't get me wrong. I'd love it if she loved me. Even more if she told me. But I respect that she is staying true to her style. I wouldn't want her to fake gushiness."

"No, fake gushiness wouldn't be sophisticated."

Fairbanks narrowed his eyes. "You're mocking me. You think that a young woman wouldn't spend time with an older man unless there was a financial arrangement that benefited her."

"Is there a financial benefit for her?"

Fairbanks looked incensed. "No." He took a deep breath. "Well, yes. Not in the sense that I pay her to spend time with me. She spends time with me because she thinks I'm... that I know stuff."

"What kind of stuff?"

"Well, I know how to make money."

"In insurance," I said.

"Yes. That's no small thing. It's hard to make money in insurance. In anything. A man who can do that has valuable skills. And women appreciate a man who can make money."

For a brief moment I flashed on the times that Street Casey had told me that she didn't care about my smallish income as an investigator. With her Ph.D. and her growing reputation in entomology, she often pulled down hourly consulting fees that exceeded my per diem charges. "And men appreciate women who can make money, too," I said.

"Yes, of course. But I don't think Isadore makes much money."

"Did she ever tell you her occupation?"

Fairbanks looked uncomfortable. "I asked her once. She said she worked in finance. But when I later talked to her about stocks and bonds and real estate investment trusts, it seemed like she didn't really know much."

"So you think she was spinning her background to make it look more substantial than it really was?"

Fairbanks paused. "Let's just say that Isadore is probably not an investment banker or anything like that."

I nodded. "Could she have voluntarily run away?"

"No. Something happened. Some kind of accident or something. Like she ran out into the road to rescue a kitten and got hit by a car and was thrown into the ditch."

The image Fairbanks painted was more vivid and striking than anything any potential client had ever told me.

"Did you look in the nearby ditches?"

"Yes. I mean, no. There aren't really ditches next to the street where the restaurant is. But I ran along the road, shouting her name."

"So you think she had an accident of some kind."

"Of course." Fairbanks seemed shocked that I could be so dense. "What else could have happened?"

I paused.

I said, "Maybe someone intended to harm her."

TWO

Fairbanks looked horrified at my suggestion. "No one would want to harm Isadore. People love Isadore."

"Do you have a picture of her?"

Fairbanks shook his head. "No, she has a thing against pictures. She told me that the essence of a person is degraded when the person is reduced to pixels. I said that there were video cams everywhere you go. But she said that still pictures, posed and all, are the worst kind."

"If you have no pictures, can you describe her?"

"She has hair like dark chocolate, shoulder length, set in big waves. Hazel eyes. She's about five-seven, almost as tall as me, and maybe one hundred forty pounds. The most noticeable thing about her is her beauty. She could be a model. Although she's not skinny like most models. She has actual curves like a real woman."

"Does Isadore have any identifying marks?"

"Yes, a tattoo of three red roses on the outside of her left ankle. She got it because it symbolizes love, the most important thing there is."

"Can you think of any reason that Isadore would disappear of her own volition?"

"You mean, just leave me without any notice? No. Emphatically no." Fairbanks studied me as if wondering if he should find another investigator.

"Anything unusual in Isadore's life recently? Problems? Financial troubles. Depression?"

"No. Certainly not depression. Isadore is very happy. She always has a good attitude. As for finances, I've solved those questions for her. She knows she can ask me for anything."

"Do you give her an allowance?"

He looked shocked. "Absolutely not. We don't have that kind of a relationship. We are just close. But she knows she could ask for anything."

"How does she know that?" I asked.

"I told her. One night, I said, 'If you ever have financial concerns, just tell me. I'll give you whatever you need.'"

"Has she mentioned any disagreements with other people?"

Fairbanks shook his head. "Everyone likes Isadore. She's the life of the party. She's the girl people want around if they're after a good time. She knows how to make people laugh. And she even sings and plays the piano. Jazz standards. I can't imagine anyone having any serious differences with her."

"What about non-serious differences."

More head shaking. "Again, people love Isadore. The only possible issues could be ones of envy. Let's face it, there are probably people who resent her beauty and charm. Her piano playing, too, I suppose."

"But not enough to make her suddenly disappear?" I said.

Fairbanks looked shocked. "Of course not! You're talking kidnapping? That's not possible. What would be the point? Ransom? I suppose someone could send me a ransom demand. But no one has contacted me. If she has family somewhere, someone could demand that they pay a ransom. But I don't believe she was kidnapped. I can't bear to think it."

"You said you don't think that Isadore is working in high finance. What do you think she might do for a living?" I asked.

"I'm guessing that she doesn't have a regular job. I wondered if she could maybe earn a living as a lounge singer. But even though she's good on the piano and such, she's private-party-good, not professional-good. My guess is she probably manages investments of some kind. Maybe rental properties."

"You think she owns houses or apartments in San Francisco? Wouldn't that take a fortune?"

"She once mentioned something about one of those online rental agencies. If you are clever and focused, you can take a tiny, rented, studio apartment and decorate it very nicely and then re-rent it out night by night for a good profit. It doesn't take any more capital than a rental deposit to rent more apartments. I don't imagine it's easy, but she's very smart. She could do well."

"It sounds like you're not sure of her financial situation."

"That's true. I'm not. But she drives an Infinity. She wears nice clothes. She talks of vacations in many places. She has a top-model mountain bike. I get the sense that she's comfortable."

"How long have you known Isadore?"

"We met at a party in my condo six months ago during the Christmas holidays. I'd invited several friends from Vegas. They brought other people I didn't know. The crowd was something."

Fairbanks said it with pride as if having a crowd of strangers come to a party was a mark of achievement.

"Anyway, there was a group of young women who showed up. I felt like the avuncular host, and I kept my distance. The truth is, I'm not actually interested in much of what young women talk about. You know, music and movies and fashion and celebrities and restaurant trends and weddings. Not one of them talked about poetry, which is my interest. But Isadore singled me out and spent some time asking me about my experience in Tahoe. We hit it off immediately. That was practically the best day of my life. William Butler Yeats wrote about how it's the eyes that perceive love. Well Isadore was a striking sight in her little black dress, which I learned that night is called an LBD. We had a drink together, and she looked into my eyes, and said she could tell I had soul. I mean, Isadore could have had any man at the party, and instead she chose me. How lucky is that? No woman had ever told me that I have soul."

I decided not to ask if the other men at the party had condos in Tahoe and knew how to make money.

Fairbanks went on to tell me about how Isadore ended up playing the piano, and then later, with the music system playing '80s' hits, they danced, and then they went out on the deck and looked across the lake at the lights on the far shore. Fairbanks said the night "shimmered with romance."

I didn't hear all of the words, so distracted was I by the never-ending gullibility of older people who are set upon by younger, beautiful sharks cruising for prey. Otherwise sensible, intelligent people are so desperate to hear words of affection that they believe them. Their heartbeats get erratic, and their breath gets short. And it only takes one magical evening before they upend their lives, open their bank accounts, and sleep with a smile because some gorgeous youth has spoken tenderly to them.

There are many variations. But the most common version is the wealthy older man smitten with a young woman.

The predators are sometimes calculating and sometimes operating instinctively, having learned from adolescence that they have a certain magic with older, unhappy, and often homely introverts. The predators frequently turn to high-end prostitution and live well off a few clients. But the cleverest ones aim for the highest prize of all. They cull a rich mark out of the pack and, using technique no less strategic than that of a champion chess player, they move in together for a time. Whether it's a standard marriage or what the courts consider a civil union, if the relationship dissolves, it can bring them an astonishingly lucrative separation agreement.

The problem with my musings was that it didn't explain why Fairbanks's young girlfriend had gone AWOL.

"Where was Isadore staying in Tahoe?"

"My place. My condo has two bedrooms."

"She stayed in a separate bedroom?"

"Yes, I already told you that I'm, you know... respecting her space."

"Have you filed a missing persons report with the Placer County Sheriff's Office?"

"You mean the police in Tahoe City? Yes. Tahoe law enforcement is a complicated subject. The sergeant said that Tahoe has five counties. You want help from the cops, you have to do a research project first. Anyway, I went to them first thing yesterday. They said I should wait. So I was back there at one today. Then a cop named Santiago suggested that because I have my place on the South Shore, maybe I should contact you."

"How did Isadore get around?"

"She drove up in her Infinity. But she mostly leaves it at my condo and rides with me."

"Was she riding with you yesterday when you went to lunch in Tahoe City?"

He nodded. "Yeah."

"Where is her car now?"

"In the parking lot at my condo."

"Do you have a key for it?"

"I remember her tossing her key into the ceramic bowl by the door where I keep my keys. It was kind of like a symbolic gesture. Like, hey, I'm living here. So when in Rome…"

"Where is her mountain bike?"

"Still strapped to the roof rack on her car."

"What do you drive?"

"I have a BMW. Orange. Like California Poppies. The color's a little loud, but it makes it easy to find in a big parking lot. And it's often got my bike on the roof rack, too."

"But you rode your bike here today."

"Yes. I was so stressed when I got home from Tahoe City. I've learned that when I'm really bent out of shape, the only thing that helps is going for a ride. So I put on my gear when I got home from Tahoe City and rode over here."

"Was it your plan to participate in the Tahoe Mountain Bike for Charity events?"

"Yes. I was thinking of signing up for three events. Not the Black Diamond races, of course. That's for the young people. I'm fifty-five. But they have events for all age levels."

"I saw that you have a mountain bike. You're also into road racing?"

"No. Just mountain biking. I'm pursuing a training regimen. My goal is to eventually get into good enough shape to enter the more difficult competitions. I figure that, because I'm in the older age group, I might have a chance. Why do you ask about road racing? You think I should try that, too?"

"I thought you were into road biking because of the threads you're wearing."

Fairbanks frowned. "I don't understand what you mean."

"I only commented because the mountain bikers I know are more like snowboarders. Looser gear, not the tight style or the bright colors, either. Your gear is more for road racing, right?"

Fairbanks looked down at his clothes. His face got pink.

"You okay?" I said.

"Now I understand some things. I… This is embarrassing. A friend in Vegas said his roommate had moved out and left his biking stuff and did I want it. I said sure. It fit great. But every time I go mountain biking, I get these looks. I'm not very with it when it comes to fashion. And Isadore... That explains why she seemed uncomfortable one day. Oh, wow, I'm such a loser. I've been wearing the wrong thing. Isadore probably thought..." he broke off in distress.

"Not to worry," I said. "Fashion always changes."

Fairbanks seemed to have imploded. His face was now a deep crimson, and he looked profoundly depressed. "I'm remembering more looks I've gotten. How will I face those people if I see them again?"

"Seriously," I said. "Don't stress about it. Let me ask you a personal question."

Fairbanks nodded.

"Are you married?"

He hesitated. He looked down at his left hand where there was no ring and no indication of a previous ring. It took him a long moment to shift his focus from his fashion embarrassment. "Yes," he finally said. "Thirty years. We have an arrangement."

"Which is?"

He seemed to think about whether he wanted to tell me. "My wife is an intelligent, thoughtful, and kind woman who prefers other women to men. It took us a decade or so to work out the best approach. We own our insurance brokerage jointly. I handle the broker issues, and she takes care of billing and appointments and most of the paperwork. We've always lived in the same house in Vegas. We still attend certain social functions together, especially those with business clients. It's like a brother/sister arrangement. We are cordial and accommodating to each other's needs. But there is no love. We're like roommates. We have separate living quarters at home. Except for our household account and the brokerage, our finances are separate. Our rule is that we don't bring our personal friends into the household. I respect the privacy she desires with her companions, and she respects mine. We don't keep our personal inclinations secret, but we don't advertise them, either. It has worked very well over the years." Fairbanks gave me a probing look. "You probably know that for people with substantial income, being married has tax advantages."

I nodded. "Does your wife know Isadore?"

"She knows of her, but they haven't met."

"And Isadore knows of your wife?"

"She knows I'm married and that my wife and I have an open marriage. But we haven't discussed any of the details."

"Is there any animosity between your wife and Isadore?"

"Of course not. Each respects the other's hands-off approach. I won't say it's easy. It's like what Lysander says in A Midsummer Night's Dream, 'The course of true love never did run smooth.' I never thought our love would be perfect, and Lysander describes that perfectly. But it's been good. The bard's poetry is apt."

"I thought A Midsummer Night's Dream was a play. I don't remember poetry in it."

Fairbanks looked scornful. "All of his plays are poetry."

"Oh. Earlier, it seemed you had a pejorative attitude about Isadore going to see arty plays. Yet you quote Shakespeare. Weren't his plays the essence of arty?"

Fairbanks looked shocked. "God, no. They were spectacle. Gaudy spectacle. Yes, he was a poet, and poetry is the essence of art. But four hundred years ago, Shakespeare's plays were like Vegas shows today."

His statement surprised me. I said, "I doubt that scripts of Vegas shows will be studied hundreds of years from now."

"Of course not." Fairbanks looked at me like I was a dense child. "You're missing the point. In Shakespeare's days, his plays were the most popular shows in England. His comedies were bawdy and raucous. And the acting company members who owned shares made a great deal of money. It was very much like the most successful production companies in Las Vegas today. But at the time, he was just considered a playwright and producer. Successful, but not recognized as a particularly special poet. It was only hundreds of years later that Shakespeare came to be regarded as a genius poet."

"How is it that you know all of this stuff?"

Fairbanks gestured toward the Sorolla monograph on my desk. "How do you know about painters? You read books. Maybe you studied art history in college."

"Were you an English major?"

Fairbanks nodded. "Some of it has stayed with me. Especially the Shakespeare, which I love."

"Are you a writer?" I asked.

"No. I wanted to be. But my high school English teacher said I had the heart but not the art. He told me that to achieve success, a person has to find an intersection of interest and aptitude. It was a harsh thing for him to say, but it was good that he said it."

"Insurance satisfied both requirements? Interest and aptitude?"

"Yes. My interest in making money and my aptitude for business-loss mitigation. Shakespeare was as much a businessman as a writer. He happened to be very good at both. And when people find love, they find that he put it into words better than anyone in the last four hundred years. Anyway, now, with Isadore, I've finally felt the love of a woman."

"How deep is your relationship? Are you intimate?"

Fairbanks looked shocked. "Why would you think that?"

"Sometimes that's what men and women do when they feel love."

"Well, not us. I mean, you know... It would be wonderful if that came to pass. But I wouldn't want Isadore to feel pressure. I want to be her support man, her Rock of Gibraltar. But I would never push her toward a sexual relationship. That would be up to her. When she's ready. If she's comfortable."

I paused, thinking about the best words. "You are a smart man, so I know you have considered the possibility that Isadore has chosen you as a lonely heart with a bank account. I'm asking you to consider it again."

Fairbanks looked angry.

"You are suggesting that the love of my life is a con artist, a thief?" Fairbanks's eyes flashed almost as if they were lit by fire. "You are committing the worst sin possible against me. Impugning the character of the person I love." He stood up, turned, and walked out of my office, closing the door fast. I heard the sounds of hard footsteps as he rolled his bicycle down the hall to the stairs.

Spot turned his head and looked at me, then looked back at the closed door. He lowered his jaw, rested it in the space between his paws, and made a long sigh.

THREE

Irealized that I probably lost my client. I definitely lost my chance at an advance retainer. But maybe I could do something useful.

I called the Placer County Sheriff's Office, gave my name, and asked for Jack Santiago. The secretary put me through.

"Hey, McKenna," he answered.

"Sergeant. I just had a man named Douglas Fairbanks in here looking for his paramour, a woman named Isadore who went out for a smoke yesterday at the Sunnyside restaurant south of Tahoe City and didn't come back."

"I talked to him," Santiago said. "He was in yesterday, back today, stressed like a piano wire. So after he filled out a missing persons' report, I gave him your number and said you were good at finding people. I hope that was okay."

"Yeah."

"Any news on the missing woman?" I said.

"No. You know how these things usually go. In another day or two, she'll probably walk in his front door. Nevertheless, we're doing the usual routine. I sent a deputy on a walk-and-talk at the restaurant. Fairbanks said there'd been no threat against her, and he hadn't received any ransom demand. Then again, he didn't know much about her, didn't know if she even had a family. What kind of relationship is that? And even if she were a victim of foul play, Fairbanks would probably be our number one suspect, right?"

"Yeah. What was your sense of his relationship to the missing woman?"

"I think this guy is dreamy over a young woman, and he doesn't want to face the fact that she took a hike. He's what, fifty something and doesn't exactly look like the movie star he was named after. And he said his girlfriend's twenty-nine and beautiful and goes by a single name. Where's the stability in that?

But I'll let you know if we hear anything."

"Thanks much."

I hung up and looked at Spot.

Without any inflection or enthusiasm, I said, "The health benefit of a peripatetic lifestyle, especially in the form of frequent W-A-L-K-S has been widely recognized. Perhaps you would like to join me."

Spot jumped up as if I'd stood up and grabbed my jacket or pulled jerky out of my desk. He turned toward the door, staring at the knob.

"How did you know? Oh, never mind."

His wagging tail banged against the closest chair, the one Fairbanks had been sitting in. When I turned the knob and pulled the door open, he pushed out fast.

We'd just gotten down the stairs and walked out into the parking lot when I saw Sergeant Diamond Martinez hurrying down Kingsbury Grade, his Douglas County Sheriff's SUV going about ten over the limit.

I waved.

He hit his brakes, swerved off onto the far shoulder to gain some turning room, then pulled a U-turn and came back up to the parking lot of my building. He stopped fast enough that his tires made scraping sounds on the gritty pavement.

Spot ran to Diamond's window, stuck his head inside, and Diamond gave him a headlock rub. Spot wagged hard enough to make Diamond's patrol unit do a perceptible wobble.

I walked up and leaned my elbow on the top of his vehicle. "Hey, sarge."

"Why does that nickname always give me a vague sense of something in the movies?" he asked.

"I don't know. Probably there've been some super smart and devastatingly handsome characters on the big screen who were called sarge. Guys who exude personality and magnetic sex appeal. So, of course, that would remind people of you."

Diamond was silent for a moment. "Now that you've explained it, it makes perfect sense." Diamond said it as dryly as it could be said.

"Then there's your emotional intelligence about people,

which relates to my question of the moment."

"Some kind of big favor you must be about to request, all this ego buffing."

"I just had a potential client named Douglas Fairbanks in my office. His much younger girlfriend named Isadore went missing yesterday. After I talked to Fairbanks a bit, he got mad and left. I'd like to ask you about it because you know more about love poems than most."

"Love poems being critical to the case?" Diamond said.

"Maybe. In the space of a few minutes, Fairbanks quoted poems from E.B. White and Yeats and Shakespeare. The White poem wasn't about love, but the others were. Do you think that reveals anything?"

"Maybe." Diamond shrugged. "Dead white guys from back east, two of them way back east, one of them way back in time."

"You think dead white poets are overrated?" I said.

"No. Those guys were great. But not my specialty."

"Your specialty being..."

"Dudes like Cervantes. Juana Inés de la Cruz. Pablo Neruda. Octavio Paz. And, of course, Juan Felipe Herrera."

"Never heard of Herrera," I said.

Diamond flared his nostrils. "The current National Poet Laureate of the United States. Poor migrant farm kid goes to UCLA, Stanford, Iowa Writers Workshop, writes two dozen books, TV shows on PBS, becomes a professor at UC Irvine. The list goes on."

"Is that all. Which leads to my question. My potential client stomped out of my office, angry because he thought I was disrespectful of his relationship with his missing girlfriend. I'm wondering what it means that when his girlfriend goes missing, he talks poetry. Any thoughts?"

"Yeah," Diamond said. "You can learn a lot about a guy from his connection, or his lack of connection, to poetry. If he's willing to reveal elite tastes, he's probably a truth teller."

"You lost me," I said.

"What historians call the high culture/low culture divide is significant. The assumption is that high culture is the best of what humans create. But the reality is that low culture has a larger influence. If you want to make an impression on lots of people, you'll have a much better chance with Hallmark verse than with serious poetry. Same for rock and roll versus classical symphonies or opera. Street dancing versus ballet. Action movies versus stage plays. TV shows versus books. Who reads books anymore, anyway? Bunch of strange people who prefer silence and contemplative thought. How weird is that?"

"What does that have to do with Douglas Fairbanks?" I asked.

"If I were a shrink, my quick psychological profile of this guy would be that he's not a bullshitter or a poser."

"Because he likes poetry."

"Right. Think about it. A guy who admits to a fondness for stuff like love sonnets or still-life painting won't lie or fake up his resume to impress a girl. Confessing to liking that stuff would result in a lot of women thinking that he was a wimp and maybe gay and certainly not a manly guy into sports. Lots of women go for jocks. Always have, always will. Therefore, at some level, the fact that Fairbanks reveals his connection to poetry tells me he's genuine and thoughtful and truthful. Is he a guy you'd like to have a beer with and talk football? Maybe not. Is he a guy you'd want for a serious, life-long friend you could always count on? Maybe."

"You think he could be a killer? Could he, as we speak, have this missing woman tied up in some cellar, torturing her for some twisted reason?"

Diamond shook his head. "I don't think so. A guy who walks out of your office in a huff sounds like a classic romantic, a good guy, maybe a goofball who's no fun to hang out with, but someone whose heart is made of good stuff."

"And you can tell all of this without ever having met him because he likes poetry?"

Diamond nodded. "Of course."

FOUR

Street Casey's lab was across and down from my office. One or two blocks, depending how one measured. Spot and I jogged.

As we got close, Spot's tail was on high speed. Partly to see Street. Mostly to see Blondie, the Yellow Lab that Street rescued after Blondie's owner was incapacitated by dementia.

Spot ran up and reached his paw out to swipe at Street's door. Before he could add claw marks to the previous ones, the door opened, and Blondie raced out, jumping at Spot and then racing off toward the trees.

"Good timing opening the door," I said to Street and then bent down to kiss her.

"Blondie alerts to an impending visit by His Largeness in a subtle way," she said, a bit of sarcasm in her voice.

I raised my eyebrows.

"She leaps up from wherever she is, sprints for the door, and jumps up on it, clawing it, whining." Street pointed to the door's inside surface. "See? Claw marks almost as deep as the ones Spot leaves on the outside."

"Dogs are hard on a building," I said.

"Are you done for the day?"

"Ready for my evening beer." I told Street about my visitor and how he was distraught over his missing girlfriend. "He seems like a very sensitive guy. Quotes love poems. I worry that maybe his girlfriend simply walked out and that he's much more invested in her than she is in him."

"The story of many relationships," Street said. "Let me know how it works out."

"I will. And you? Are you still working?"

"Yes, but with little focus. I've been thinking about our plan to give me self-defense training."

"I can begin any time you're ready."

I'd frequently thought about Street's father, who was on the run from the Missouri Parole Board. He'd threatened Street back when he was convicted of murdering her brother twenty-some years ago.

I said, "Your aunt believes he's coming after you. I believe the threat to you is real. I think you should be living with me and have Spot with you all the time, at work and at home. You've said that's too constraining, and I respect that. But that makes me even more determined to turn you into a self-defense warrior."

"Oh, right," Street scoffed. "Street Casey, ninja entomologist."

"It sounds catchy," I said. "Maybe you should put that on your business card."

Street smiled, but she looked wan and exhausted. "The truth is, I've been getting bad feelings," she said.

"How so?"

"It's probably just my mind playing tricks on me. But sometimes I think someone is following me when I drive. Three or four cars back. A dark vehicle. Like an old sedan. And sometimes at home, Blondie will lift her head and stare at the wall. She furrows her brow with concern. Once in the middle of the night, she ran out of the bedroom and began barking. I went out and watched her in the dark. She was barking at the kitchen door. The outside light was on as always, and when I peeked out through the blinds, I couldn't see anyone. But her bark was insistent. That was one time when I really wished Spot had been with me. Not to let him out because someone could shoot him with a gun. But it would have been nice to know that if someone broke in, he'd be there to take the man down. Blondie is very alert and focused, but if I had a home invasion, I think she'd just bark at the man."

I took Street's hands in mine. "Blondie has become very attached to you, and she might be more protective than you think. But please take Spot. He'd love to live with you and Blondie. Did you order the burglar alarm we talked about?"

"Yes. They're scheduled to install it tomorrow. I'm also getting the panic button you mentioned. It dials nine one one and sends a GPS signal for my location. Of course, I have the emergency nine one one button on my phone, which is always with me. But the panic button is smaller. I can have it in my pocket or around my neck. If I'm attacked, I might be able to get to it when I couldn't get my phone out. Of course, this all might be an overreaction. Maybe sounds and glimpses in the rearview mirror are just products of my state of mind."

"Maybe not. Best to be prepared."

"I know I can stay with you. But despite my fear of my father, I can't shake the fear of losing my independence. That's something that dogs me from my childhood. When you run away at fourteen to escape abuse, you know that the need for independence is hard-wired into you. Being cautious and prudent is good. But taking too many security measures starts to feel like a kind of prison."

"Whatever you want," I said.

"So I want to get serious about the self-defense training."

"Anytime," I said. "Let's start now. Right here."

"I can't. I have a phone appointment in half an hour, and I'm still not fully prepared. But maybe this evening would work if you're free."

"I'll be at the cabin. In fact, I'm overdue for some obedience work with Spot. So maybe we'll dive into some bite training while we wait for you."

"Bite training?" she said. "That sounds ominous."

"If the training works, it's very ominous for anyone on the receiving end."

"Okay. I'll call when I'm ready to come up the mountain."

We kissed again, and we got the dogs in from the woods, and Spot and I left.

FIVE

Spot and I were beginning his bite training at my cabin when the phone rang. I answered it.

Street said, "I stopped home at my condo, and I'll be up the mountain soon. Is there anything I should bring or wear?" She sounded tense.

"You okay?" I said.

"Yes. I… It's just that once again, I got that uncomfortable feeling."

"Someone following you in your car?" I asked.

"No. More like when I got home and parked and got out with Blondie, I had the feeling that someone was watching me from the forest behind my condo building."

"But you didn't see anything specific," I said.

"No. I didn't peer into the woods, either. Of course, I want to know if he's out there. It would be better if he doesn't know I'm on my guard. If he comes at me and I surprise him with my preparation, then I'll have a better chance, right? But if he thinks I'm being very careful, he'll be less likely to make a mistake. Does that make sense?"

"Yes. Unless you can lock yourself up in a castle that no one can get into, your best approach is exactly what you say. Be as prepared as possible for any eventuality, but don't telegraph that. Be casual and let him think it will be easy to attack you. By the time we're done training, he'll get the surprise of his life."

Street didn't say anything for a moment. "Should I wear anything in particular? My workout sweats or something?"

"No. We want you in your everyday clothes and shoes. Any moves you learn to make need to feel familiar and comfortable in your standard clothes, both your lab clothes and your business suits. So choose one approach for this evening, and then you can choose something else for our next session."

"Okay. It'll be a few minutes before I get out of here."

"No problem. His Largeness and I are working on a lesson called Grab The Weapon Hand. But, of course, we'll quit when you get here."

"Perfect. See you soon."

"Street?"

"What?"

"Be very careful. Your sense that someone is watching could just be nerves as you suggest. But he could be in the trees outside your condo as we speak."

"Got it."

"I love you," I said.

"Thanks. I need you to." She hung up.

I turned back to Spot.

"Okay, boy. Ready for a go?"

He looked at my right front pocket where I had stashed jerky.

I pulled on the custom dog-bite sleeves with leather-wrapped plastic gauntlet and hand protection extensions and showed them to Spot. He understood that this meant he could chomp down on me, something he did with disturbing enthusiasm. When a 170-pound dog bites hard, it is a bone-crushing force. Only the integrity of the sleeve keeps your arm in one piece.

I put my hands behind my back, backed up to the kitchen counter, and felt blindly among the weapons I'd assembled. I had two knives, which I'd chosen because they had the dullest edges of any in the rack. I also had an equally dull, 18-inch-long, Civil War bayonet without the rifle, a large scissors with rounded points, a leather-covered sap, a Taser, my old revolver with the broken firing pin, and the miniature baseball bat.

I got the fingertips of my right hand around the leather sap. Leaving my left hand behind my back, I shouted, "Weapon Hand!" as I swung my right arm around and up.

Spot reacted in an instant. His head snapped upward, and his jaws clamped shut around the sap. He jerked it out of my hand, and chomped it repeatedly, no doubt enjoying the feel and scent of the old leather.

"No, boy, you don't grab the weapon. You grab the arm with the weapon." I held out my arm and pointed to it.

Then I reached for the sap. He held tight.

"C'mon, Largeness. You want a treat, you gotta play by the rules."

He glanced at my pocket, munched down on the sap one last time, then tossed it on the floor.

I picked it up, wiped the saliva off on my jeans, and put it back on the counter.

I backed up to the table and, once again working by feel behind my back, picked up the same sap again but with my left hand.

I shouted the command, "Weapon Hand!" My arm came around fast, sap raised high.

Spot snapped his head up again. This time his jaws clamped around my forearm. He bit down hard. Even through the bite sleeve and padding, I could tell I'd be bruised tomorrow.

I let go of the sap. It fell to the floor. I reached out with my foot and pulled it back.

"Okay, Spot, let go of my wrist." He did, reluctantly enough that he maybe liked biting me. "Good boy!" I pulled out a bit of jerky and tossed it to him. He snapped it out of the air. A string of saliva did back flips on its arc toward the far wall. I flexed my left wrist, hoping it wasn't damaged. I'd know better after I removed the sleeve and heavy padding.

"Let's do it again, Largeness. This time, I'll pull out both hands at the same time, so you'll have to notice which hand has the weapon."

I knew Spot wouldn't understand what I meant. But I hoped he'd get the sense that he had to pay attention. Spot was looking at the pocket where I kept the jerky. Like all students, he could appear enthusiastic about learning if the reward was tasty enough. But like most students, he would never get accepted at the doggie equivalent of an Ivy League school. He was more street smart than book smart.

I put my arms behind my back and moved up against the counter. With my right hand, I picked up the Taser. If it were charged, it could deliver 50,000 volts, enough to paralyze man or animal. If it had a compressed air cartridge, it could shoot two sharp darts deep into flesh and deliver its incapacitating shock.

But its battery was discharged, and the cartridge was removed.

"Weapon hand!" I shouted as I brought both arms out, the Taser held high in my right hand.

Spot did the head snap, and grabbed my left wrist with what seemed like vengeance. Probably, he was newly motivated by his love of jerky.

"The other hand, Spot." I waved the Taser with my right hand. "This hand!"

Spot was still chomping down on my left arm. He looked, let go of my left hand and lunged for the right, biting down hard on my wrist.

The padding and plastic protection kept his fangs from piercing my flesh and bones, but the pressure was like I imagined if I got my hand caught in a hydraulic press. I could only imagine what it would be like if he bit down really hard.

"Good boy! You've got the chops, dude." I threw him another piece of jerky.

On the next try, I grabbed the old revolver in my left hand.

"Weapon hand!" I brought my hands out faster than before, trying to make them a blur.

Spot grabbed my lower left arm with such a violent motion that the gun flew out of my hand. It bounced across the floor and hit the wood stove with the solid clank of metal on metal.

"Good boy, Spot!"

I heard a knock at the door.

Spot never took his eyes off my pocket.

I gave him a piece, he swallowed, then turned to the door and made a deep woof, his tail wagging.

The door opened and Blondie rushed in, jumping up against Spot's side, making little squealing sounds, spinning in circles just as she had at Street's lab a couple of hours before. Spot turned, too, swatting at Blondie, his paw on her back.

"Outside, Spot." I pointed at the open door. The dogs raced out.

"How's the new training gig going?" Street said as she stared at my arms swaddled in padded bite sleeves. In contrast, she was wearing a sleeveless top despite the cool weather at my cabin's elevation of 7200 feet. But Street had a superlative metabolism that was sufficient to keep her warm with very little help from clothing.

I bent down to give her a kiss. "It's amazing what a hound will do for dried, salted beef."

"What's the training?"

"I pull my arms out from behind my back. In one of them, I have a surprise weapon. I shout, 'Weapon Hand!' and he is supposed to grab the hand with the weapon, causing the attacker to be immobilized or maybe drop it or cry 'uncle.'"

"You said 'supposed to.' Does that mean that he doesn't always grab the correct hand?"

"Right. It depends on how focused he is on the jerky. Too much focus, and his brain turns to mush, and he can't keep his eyes off my jerky pocket. Too little focus and..." I paused. "Now that I think of it, he never has too little focus on jerky."

"If his focus is just right," Street said, "he grabs the hand with the weapon?"

"Pretty much. Although sometimes he grabs the weapon instead of the hand."

"Do you think you'll ever be in a situation where you can give him that command?"

"Probably not. But maybe it comes in handy someday. More likely, it gets him paying attention to what I say."

"So he can get some jerky," Street said.

"Yeah."

Street paused as if thinking.

"What are you thinking?" I said.

"It's just that this training seems static. Like it's all about someone who is just standing there, and they suddenly pull out a weapon, and Spot just happens to be nearby. So you shout, and he grabs the person's arm."

"You're thinking that people would normally be moving when all this happens," I said.

"Right. The bad guy might be running toward you or running away. He'd pull out a weapon. Spot would be moving, too. So it would all have to happen on the run."

"Good point. Okay, we'll do a test with me running." I went to the door, put my thumb and forefinger in my mouth and made the whistle that means treats.

Ten seconds later, the dogs emerged from the forest across the road. Blondie was still out front. Spot closed in. Blondie dodged to the left, then shot to the right and went back into the trees. Spot tried to follow. But like a big truck, he had to make a larger arc, and he was once again far behind.

"Hey, Largeness."

Spot made another turn, this one on track to bring him on a large, fast curve toward us.

I held a piece of jerky in the air. He charged up to me and made a quick stop. He was panting hard, giant tongue dangling, the tip doing the little flip motion, flicking drops of saliva into the air. I tossed the piece to him. His teeth clicked as he chomped down.

Blondie watched from a distance as if she understood that the jerky treat was some kind of unspoken communication taking place between the large man and the large dog. Her wariness suggested that she sensed that running into the scene might be dangerous.

"Okay, Spot, Street thinks that our training should be dramatized by movement."

Spot stared at me with focused eyes and ears, trying to divine any hint of where and when the next jerky treat would appear.

"Street?"

"Hmmm?"

"For this exercise, you should come here and hold his collar."

"Okay." She walked over and got a firm grip on it.

"You'll hold him in place while I take one of the weapons and run across the road. You should give his chest a shake to get him excited. You've seen how I do it." I turned and looked across the road toward the forest, gauging distances. "When I reach the pavement, drop your hand next to his head as you've seen me do." I lowered my voice to a whisper. "You shout out, 'Find the suspect.' Then give him a fast pat on his rear. He'll probably take off running toward me. Because he knows it's me, he'll probably be running more for play and jerky than for a suspect takedown. Nevertheless, I've still got on my bite sleeves, which he knows are okay to chomp on. I'm thinking that if I time it correctly, I can shout out 'Weapon hand' as I lift up the weapon. Perhaps, he'll understand that this exercise is like before only with me running."

"Owen, I'm not sure this is a good idea. Now that I'm visualizing this, it seems like you could get hurt. What if he doesn't bite on your bite sleeve?"

"I suppose it's possible, but so far he's been very good at understanding the difference between where my body is protected and where it isn't. Plus, he never bites down very hard. It's like he understands that this is all an exercise. So I'm not worried."

"You're sure?" Street said.

"No, I'm never sure. But that's what I think. And I think your thought that the exercise should include movement is smart."

"Okay. But I don't want to think that my idea led to an injury."

"Don't worry," I said. "I'm sure I'll be fine."

Street looked skeptical.

"Okay, Spot," I said. "You hang with Street and come for me when she gives you the okay."

I went inside, got the revolver with the missing firing pin, and brought it outside. "Ready?" I said to Street.

"Yes, I guess so."

"Give him the command when I get to the road."

"Got it," she said.

"When he sees me run, that will make him excited. But give him the chest shake anyway to get him more primed."

Street kept hold of his collar with one hand, then tried to vibrate his chest with her other. "Okay, Spot! You're going to take the gun from the big bad guy! Are you ready, Spot?!"

"I'm off," I said. I sprinted away, across the little front yard of my cabin and toward the road.

I heard Street shout, "Find the suspect, Spot! Take his weapon!"

I sensed the sound of paws and claws scraping the dirt as he ran after me. I kept the revolver at my chest so he couldn't see which hand held it. I ran fast. I knew Spot could run maybe twice as fast as my fastest sprint. It wouldn't take him more than a few seconds to catch me. I kept my head turned sideways so I could see his approach in my peripheral vision. As I got to the center of the road, I sensed he was almost on me. Holding the revolver in my left hand I swung my left arm out and up. I shouted, "Weapon hand!"

In an instant, I felt his jaws clamp down on the bite sleeve that covered my left arm. For a tiny moment I was very pleased that Spot had done exactly as I wanted. But in an additional, equally tiny moment, I realized that his high-speed motion had transferred from his jaws into my arm.

I also realized that Spot was probably going 30 miles per hour when he grabbed onto my arm. By comparison, I was relatively stationary. He'd leaped into the air as he chomped down onto the bite sleeve. His fast motion made him fly past me, the drag of my arm in his mouth spinning him around 180 degrees. When his motion reached the limit of spinning him around, it jerked me forward off my feet and into the air. The fact that I outweigh his 170 pounds by an additional 45 seemed not to matter. The huge difference in our speeds made him the sling and me the projectile being whipsawed around. I was jerked off my feet, lifted up, and thrown forward at high speed. Spot let go as I flew past him on an upward arc, over the far edge of the road.

My curve crested, then crashed down, and I landed well off the road. My shoulder plowed into a tree, my chest thumped hard enough to knock much of the air out of my lungs, and I came to rest face down in the dirt and pine needles.

In a moment, I sensed Spot sniffing and poking with his nose, full of excitement over this new game.

"Owen! My God, Owen!" Street called out as she ran toward me. She knelt at my side. "Are you okay? Are you alive?" I felt her touch the back of my head and neck.

"Yes, I'm fine."

Street rubbed my back, bent down and kissed my temple. "I never dreamed that would happen!" she said. "I couldn't believe how fast Spot was going when he locked onto your arm. It was like you were shot out of a catapult."

"Yes, it kind of felt like that."

"Do you think your bones are broken?"

"No, I'm fine." I pushed up from the dirt.

Spot was excited and happy. Wagging his tail.

"He wants to do it all over again," I said.

Fifteen minutes later, I was sitting in my rocker. I'd pulled off the bite sleeves. Touched enough body parts here and there to establish that I was still in one piece. Street had gotten me a beer. The passage of time made some of my body parts much more sore. The beer made other parts more comfortable.

The dogs were lying on the floor.

"After those gymnastics, you gave him more jerky," Street said, looking at Spot who was quickly moving toward sleep.

"Reward for a job well done," I said.

"His focus on food that's bad for him reminds me of you."

"Ah. But jerky has the all-important salt and preservative nutrients and is chewy as a bonus."

"But he doesn't chew."

"Yes, there's that. Anyway, to Spot, I'm just the food caterer. So I need to focus on which junk food helps most with obedience. I'm pretty sure my dog training wouldn't be as successful using broccoli as a treat."

Street made a dismissive grunt. Despite the sunset hour, she was still not wearing any wrap over her sleeveless shirt. I reached out toward her and touched a fingertip to her bare shoulder and traced the ins and outs of firm, thin muscles.

"Any more sense of anyone watching you as you came up the mountain road?" I asked.

She shook her head. "Nothing bothersome but my nerves."

"Self-defense training will help that," I said.

"I don't want to get a gun. That would make me too nervous. You once said that there are many non-gun skills that are good to have. You also said there was a simple but devastating thing that even a small woman can do to stop even the biggest attacker."

"Yes, that's true," I said. "There's no guarantee that you can pull it off, although it's not particularly difficult. But if you can do it, it will stop a giant in his tracks."

"What is it?"

"Gouging out his eye."

SIX

S treet looked at me in shock.
   "The sun is setting, but there's still enough light to go outside and try some moves." I picked up the bayonet off the table and brought it outside. The dogs came back outside with us.

Street's eyes widened when she looked at the bayonet. I put my hand on her shoulder and then rubbed her back. "Are you okay with this?"

She nodded, determined if unsettled. "Yes. I want to learn whatever it takes to protect myself. But what if my father is in the trees watching? He'd learn about my preparations."

"If he had followed you up here, the dogs would find him and make a lot of noise."

"Good," Street said.

"Okay. Let's start with principles of self defense. The first principle is to get used to being uncomfortable and scared. Once discomfort and fear become familiar, they can be oddly reassuring. You won't waste energy on the distress of discomfort. Instead, you'll focus on preparedness. The second principle is to develop an explosive reaction. You don't carefully gauge a threat situation, decide on the best response, and then react. You immediately explode in action. You are violent. You are a bomb that goes off. When the explosion hits your attacker, it is the surprise and size of your reaction that disables them more than the actual moves you make."

I waited to see how Street responded. She looked very somber.

"Do you want me to continue?"

She made a slow nod.

"In essence, an attacker can do just three things. One, he can kill you. Two, he can hurt and torture you and then kill you. Those both produce the same result. Three, he can really scare you even though he intends to let you live. In the first two cases, if you fight him, you may get even more hurt before he kills you. But you might also get away."

"I see where you're going with this," she said. "With a serious murderer, there is no reason not to fight. And if you die, you might want to die sooner rather than later."

"Exactly," I said.

"So what about the attacker who just wants to scare you but doesn't intend to kill you?" Street said. "I would think that if you fight that person, you might push him over the threshold and he'll kill you even though that wasn't his original intent."

"That can happen. But in all of the murders I've investigated over the years, the evidence suggests that the killers had intent before they committed murder. Even when we see evidence that the victim fought back, we see prior intent. The important thing to remember is that sometimes the victim who fights back gets away. We've even seen it happen with serial murderers. A killer can commit a string of murders, and then one of his victims suddenly fights back and gets away."

Street looked very somber. "I should always fight back."

"With a potential murderer, I think so, yes. If someone merely wants to steal your money, then it's best to give them what they want. But I think it's good to assume that whenever someone comes after you with what looks like intent to murder, they are going to follow through. I believe the best approach is to assume you have nothing to lose in fighting and everything to gain."

Street thought about it and seemed to steel herself. "Okay. I'm ready."

"When someone attacks you, there is an order to your priorities. First, if at all possible, run away. You can run faster and farther than anyone but a young, serious athlete. Certainly, your father could never catch you. And after you are running, yell for help. "

"What if he is holding me so I can't run?"

"Then you try a diversion. If you have a free hand and that hand is holding keys or something else, use them as a weapon if possible. A key can be stabbed into someone. If you are being held on the ground, a handful of dirt or sand can be thrown into the attacker's eyes. If you have any opportunity to hit him in the throat, do it as hard as possible. Use your knuckles. Your goal is always to startle and hurt him enough to loosen his grip. Then you run away."

"What if he has a gun?"

"You still run away. Immediately. Explosively. Don't talk. Don't try to negotiate. Just sprint away. Maybe he shoots you. Maybe he misses. Maybe he hits you but you can still run. Always run. That's your most effective defense."

"What if he sneaks up behind me and puts a knife to my throat? If I move, I get my throat slit."

"That is one of the worst cases, but it isn't hopeless. Now I don't want you to be startled. So I'm going to tell you each thing I do before I do it."

She nodded.

I continued, "Let's say someone surprises you and puts a knife to your throat. Knives are much scarier than guns. That means that, when it comes to creating disabling fear in a victim, an attacker with a knife has an advantage over an attacker with a gun. We're naturally terrified of knives."

I held up the bayonet. "I want you to notice that this has really dull edges. So as long as I don't stab you with it, we can use it for demonstration."

Another nod.

"First, I'm going to step behind you, reach around and put the dull blade of the bayonet up against your throat. I want you to feel the cold metal. If you know what it feels like, then you won't be so startled if it ever happens."

"I understand."

I did as I said. When the cold blade touched her neck, she made a little jerk, and her body went rigid.

Holding the bayonet in place so that she could begin to get a bit of familiarity with how it felt, I spoke from behind her. "A knife against the throat terrifies by its feel and the knowledge of what it can do. The attacker with a knife counts on it to paralyze you. But the knife is no more deadly than a gun pointed at you from ten feet away. You want to memorize that feeling of metal against your skin." I moved the bayonet across her throat for emphasis. "Every time you think of what that feels like, tell yourself that it is just another deadly weapon. I don't mean to sound flip. But when you put it into the same category as a gun across a room, you won't be so paralyzed by the knife."

"Okay. So if I'm not paralyzed by the knife, what do I do?"

"What you do is watch and listen for an opportunity to startle your attacker. Then you can create a diversion, push away, and flee. For example, let's say your attacker is moving a bit or even just talking. That may give you an opportunity to glance down and see the placement of his feet. Before you make your big move, you relax your muscles. When he feels the tension go out of you, he'll loosen his grip on you. Then you explode, and he won't be ready. You can stomp the top of his foot."

"His instep."

"Right. Even if he's wearing heavy shoes, it's likely to give him serious pain and distract him long enough for you to get away."

"Got it," Street said. "What else?"

"Assuming he's behind you, an elbow punch backward into his gut can be very effective. It won't give him serious pain like a foot stomp, but it might make him loosen his grip on you."

"But what if I still can't get away?"

"Rotate toward him. Even if he maintains his grip on you, you can often spin around if you do it suddenly and forcefully. If, after you stomp his foot, he still has the knife at your throat, you'll have to make a quick judgment about whether or not he's loosened his grip a bit. You might do the foot stomp and elbow punch in succession."

Street tipped her head sideways to look down at my feet. I felt her muscles tense as if she were about to rotate. She was getting a feel for possibilities even though I still had the bayonet at her throat. This pleased me, because when a victim can even think about possibilities, that dramatically increases their odds of escape.

"Now, imagine you've rotated toward him, even just a bit. If you have some distance between you, punch him in the throat."

"Like a fist punch?"

"Any kind of punch will do if you aim for his Adam's apple.

The most effective punch is with your knuckles. Bend your fingers so your knuckles make a sharp point." I held out my hand and showed her. "Even a mild blow with your knuckles to his throat can break his trachea. That will be severely disabling."

"You said to use a throat punch if I could get some distance between me and my attacker," Street said. "What if I can't get any distance? Maybe I rotate and I'm still right up against him? Should I knee him in the groin?"

"You can. But that is the one move that men are most prepared for. It's easy for him to raise his knee toward the inside and block the blow. Better to use the heel of your hand to strike under his chin. Men don't expect that. And it can often be done when you're pinned."

"Show me."

I had Street rotate so that she was turned toward me. But I continued to hold her tight. Her head was below my chin. Mixed scents of sweat and stress and even fear rose around my head.

"Now you just have to figure out which side of your head my chin is on. Then you lean a bit away from my face and slam the heel of your hand up against the bottom of my chin."

Street did it in slow-motion, the heel of her hand connecting with my chin and slowly pushing up as my teeth clenched shut and my head tipped back.

I said, "Even a weak woman can do it hard enough to break an attacker's teeth, maybe cut through his tongue, and jar his brain. The effect is similar to someone falling and striking their chin on the ground. The blow will stun and disorient."

Street turned around so that her back was once more against me. I held the dull bayonet against her neck. She made more slow moves, using me as her attacker, acting out the foot stomp and elbow gut-punch and rotation and knuckle punch to trachea and heel slam to my chin.

"Now let me get some props and we'll try it at full speed," I said.

I went inside and pulled my old motorcycle helmet off the top shelf in the closet. I grabbed two towels and a pillow. In my tool drawer were some elastic shock cords.

Back outside, I rolled one towel into a tight roll and set it on the ground. "This is my foot." I used the shock cords around my body to hold the pillow against the front of my stomach and chest. I pulled on the helmet, which was a full face model. I tucked the other towel around the lower bar of the helmet, padding it.

"Don't try the knuckle punch to my Adam's apple. My head will be tipped too far forward, and my helmet is in the way. But I think you can practice the palm heel slam under my chin. You'll hit the towel on the helmet. The pillow will allow you to practice an elbow punch to my abdomen."

So I held her from behind, bayonet to her throat. She struggled a bit, then relaxed like a pro so that any sudden movement would be a surprise. Next, she foot-stomped the rolled towel, gut-punched me with her elbow, rotated and slammed her palm heel up so hard against the towel on the helmet that my head bounced back and I felt stunned.

Without even realizing it, I'd let go of Street. She pulled away from me and sprinted away up the road. After a few seconds, she turned and came back.

I was taking off my padding and helmet. "That was excellent," I said. "You gave me a headache and my stomach hurts. If you'd stomped my foot instead of the towel, I'd be in trouble. I'll need to rest before we try it again."

"Now that I've been through a test run, I can replay it by myself." She seemed to turn inward, thinking. Then she went through the moves in the air, assaulting an imaginary attacker. Foot stomp, elbow gut punch, rotation, palm heel chin slam. When she was done, she said, "We can practice these again, later. Let's move on to the big item on the self-defense list."

"The eye gouge," I said.

"Right."

SEVEN

I heard my phone ring from inside the cabin. I went inside to answer it.

"Owen McKenna."

"Sergeant Bains calling. I was talking to Santiago at Placer County, and he said you and he have talked about a missing woman. I thought I'd give you a courtesy call."

I said, "A man named Douglas Fairbanks was in my office this afternoon asking about his girlfriend who went missing in Tahoe City yesterday at lunch. The woman we're looking for is five seven, brown over hazel, one-forty, and has a tattoo of three red roses on her left ankle."

"That's the woman in question. This morning, the El Dorado Sheriff's office got a report from a boater in Emerald Bay. The caller said there was a body hanging upside down from the outside southeast corner of the tea house on Fannette Island. I went out there with two of our men. We found a woman hanging from a line that was tied around her ankles and stretched up over the top of the tea house wall."

"Dead?"

"Very. Close to frozen, too. Her skin was crunchy stiff, but I could tell she was still unfrozen inside. She was late twenties or early thirties, about five-six, one thirty, long brown hair, and had the red rose tattoo you mention on her ankle. Eye color is obscured by lividity."

"In other words," I said, "the pooling of blood happened in her head because she was upside down when she died. Or turned upside down right after she died."

"Apparently. Her neck was also ballooned out. It was not pretty. So we know she wasn't strung up post-mortem. She was strung up to die. There was no ID on or near the body. We don't yet know cause of death. But that cold front that came through was serious. So it looks like the cause of death could be hypothermia. Either way, we've got homicide first degree. Whoever put her there is a nasty piece of work."

"Any other details?" I asked.

"The victim had three red roses duct-taped in her mouth."

"The killer is sending a message," I said.

"Yes. And the line holding her was thin. One of my deputies is a rock climber. He said it was paracord. The line went up over the tea house wall and was tied off on one of the window frames."

"Paracord?"

"Yeah. A specialty line made of a certain weave. Green in color. Although I guess it comes in other colors as well. Thin but strong enough to hoist a woman. He thought it was probably seven hundred fifty-pound test."

"Any sign of sexual assault?"

"No. The woman's clothing wasn't torn. Her skirt had flipped upside down because she was hanging by her ankles. Her underpants weren't torn. And there was no bruising near the groin. So probably no sexual assault. Besides, when have you ever heard of an assailant putting underwear back on his victim?"

"Right," I said. "The man who came to my office said her name was Isadore, just the single name. But he doesn't know any more about her identity or where she's from."

"Quite a name," Bains said. "I'll see if we can find any match between the name and this corpse. What's the suspect's name?" Bains asked, following the assumption that any man romantically involved with a murder victim is automatically a prime suspect.

"Douglas Fairbanks."

"Like the movie star? That sounds as fake as Isadore."

"Yeah, but I think it's real."

"Address?"

"He got mad at me and left before I could get local contact info. So I don't have anything but a phone number and a business address in Vegas. If I locate him, do you want me to inform him of the woman's death?"

"Well, it's police business. But you're an ex-cop, so you may as well. Let me know what you find out."

"Will do."

We hung up.

EIGHT

Street had come into the cabin and heard my conversation.

"Was that about the woman your client was looking for?"

"Yes, I think so." I explained what Bains had said, leaving out the description of lividity and the fact that the victim was hanging upside down.

Street looked stressed. "I need to keep a broader perspective. Here I am fussing about a potential problem, while your client's girlfriend is found dead."

"You're not fussing."

"Do you want to call your client?"

"In the morning," I said. "Shall we resume self defense?"

Street nodded. She seemed distracted by the news of the dead woman. I thought it would help if we got to work.

I said, "Again, I should reiterate that the simplest and most effective response to a dangerous threat is to run away. So as you focus on self-defense moves, always keep that in your mind."

"Sure," Street said. "But if he comes into my lab or condo, I'd likely be trapped, unable to get out the back door."

"True. And when confronted with a threatening invader in your home, killing him with a gun is arguably the best thing to do. Of course, if he comes into your business, that's different, as a business with an unlocked door is considered a public place, and you can't just shoot unless he threatens you with a weapon. All you can do is call nine one one."

"You say a gun is best, but you don't have a gun in your house," Street said.

"True. And that choice, for an ex-cop, is by definition an ill-considered one. But as you know, I live without a gun not because it's smart but because of my past. When I was on the San Francisco PD, I killed a kid. I responded properly during a bank robbery. But it still bothers me. If I carried a gun, I'd be living with the spector of a potential repeat. Of course, most of my friends and former colleagues think I'm somewhere between a wimp and a fool for not carrying a sidearm. My resistance to carrying a gun may be stupid, but there it is."

"I think the same reasoning applies to me." Street pet Blondie as she spoke. Blondie shut her eyes as if to better focus on the sensation. "I've read the statistics many times. Some people, some of the time, save their lives and their family's lives by shooting a home invader. But the vast majority of gunshot deaths from homeowner's guns come from suicide and accidents and even murder where the home invader, more alert than the sleepy resident, gets the gun from the homeowner's hands and shoots him. And even if I were to successfully shoot a home invader at four in the morning, if I later found out it was the neighbor kid looking to steal money, I would never recover."

Street turned and gazed down at the lake, a view as spectacular as any on the planet and sufficient to distract anyone from other subjects. But the evening light on her face showed intense seriousness.

She continued, "If I wanted to use a gun to protect myself from a home invasion, I'd have to have it out and loaded and close to me. But whenever my friend Sally brought her boy Cassidy over for a visit, I'd have to remember to unload and lock up my gun. Or he might find it as he runs around exploring. And then, if I forgot to unlock it and put it back under my pillow before bed, it would do me no good, right? And what about when I go to work and bring my gun along in my purse? I could never let a child in my car or I'd worry about it. I couldn't let a kid into my lab without worrying about it."

"Such is the life of a responsible gun owner."

"And if an attacker surprises me, and I don't have time to grab my gun, I'm out of luck anyway."

"Which brings us to eyeballs," I said.

"So what do I need to know?"

"There are two things to remember about popping out eyeballs," I said.

Street winced at my casual words. But I'd chosen them on purpose in order to start her thinking that the subject wasn't as sacrilegious as people think.

"We value our vision above all our other senses," I said. "That makes it very hard for us to imagine destroying it in anybody. There is also the yuck factor. There's a hierarchy to the wounds we can inflict on others. It's relatively easy to shoot someone with a gun. It's very much harder to stick a knife into them. Popping out eyeballs is most difficult of all. But what I want you to visualize over and over is Tom Casey crashing into your house or lab, or breaking into your car when you're at an intersection. If he comes, he'll have spent years considering the ways to get at you when you are least prepared."

"You mean he might break in when I'm in the shower." Street's voice was small.

"Exactly. He will choose a place and time when you are most vulnerable, when his sudden presence will make you scream and jump and lose control and stop thinking. So the most important aspect of your response is that you stay in control."

Street was making a slow nod. "And I practice that by visualizing a potential assault. Over and over."

"Right. Now imagine Tom Casey with his hands around your neck. He's shouting at you. His face is red with rage. His breath reeks of alcohol. He is determined to strangle you and break your neck at the same time. You will have to do anything you can to make him stop. Anything."

"You're implying that the best way to stop him is to pop out his eyeball." Street was shaking her head slowly, as if she couldn't quite accept the idea.

"In a deadly mano-a-mano attack, yes. Not only is it relatively easy to do, it is psychologically devastating to the attacker. The strongest man loses his strength and resolve, and nearly loses his mind, when he loses an eye."

"I just can't imagine doing it."

"The biggest hurdle is visualizing the act often enough that the concept becomes second nature."

"So how exactly do you do it? And does the eye actually pop out?"

"First, the answer to your second question. No, it doesn't pop out like a grape and fly across the room. There is a bunch of connective tissue holding it in place. But it will pop sideways enough that it tears the optic nerve and the blood vessels, and the person goes blind. It is quite painful. But the reason the person screams in agony is not just because of the physical pain but because of their sudden realization that you've blinded them."

I let the thought hang for a bit.

"As for how to do it, you simply put the tip of your thumb on the person's eyeball and jam it hard back into the eye socket. It doesn't require great strength, but plan to put a real effort into it and make the move as fast as you can. As your thumb dives into the eye socket and you feel it bottoming out against the back of the socket, you hook your thumb behind the eyeball and attempt to tear the eyeball from the person's head. It works from any angle. And if the person scrunches up their cheek to protect their eye, you can still jam your thumb in there."

Street's eyes were open wide.

"It even works when the person is behind you. Let's say your attacker is choking you from behind. You simply reach back with both hands if possible and use your thumbs to feel across his face. When you contact an eye, he'll naturally blink the lid shut. But that doesn't matter. The moment your thumb contacts an eye – either eye – you make the movement as explosively as possible."

Street looked appalled.

I said, "Probably, the person will jerk away hard. But if you've made the move fast enough, you will be successful in destroying his eye even if he jerks away."

Street was holding her thumb out, rotating her hand, moving it behind her head, trying to feel how it might work.

"Let's do a little practice," I said. "I'll get behind you and put my hands around your neck so you can get a sense of it. I'll move slowly so that it won't be alarming and so you can feel the position of my face behind you. Turn like this, away from me," I said. "You don't know I'm coming up behind you. The first sensation you have is my hands around your throat. We'll pause at each step on this practice run."

"And I'll not pop your eye out. I'll just feel for it."

"Good idea," I said.

I stepped behind Street and slowly put my hands around her

neck.

She reached her hands up and behind, feeling my face. I held her farther away. She strained to reach farther back.

"Some attackers will hold you close, and some will hold you far," I said. "If your attacker holds you from behind and keeps his arms straight, you won't be able to reach him. But few will worry about what's coming. And even the ones who hold you far will often lean in close to say something nasty in your ear. Especially if this is a crime they've been planning, they'll want to leave you with some last words before you pass out. So you're ready. The moment they get close, you feel with both hands and get ready for your explosive movement."

I leaned my head closer and whispered into Street's ear. "We all have an instinctive desire to avoid touching the face of someone we despise. So it's best just to think of it as a simple task. Find the eyeball. Take it out."

Street reached her hands back. Her left hand touched my face. The fingers of her right hand touched my temple. Immediately, her thumb found my eyeball.

"Perfect," I said. "Remember this isn't the real deal. Move your thumb until you find the edge of my eye socket. Yeah, just like that. Now imagine how you would plunge your thumb into the eye socket. And when you hit bottom, you squeeze your grip hard, thumb in the eye and fingers grabbing against nose or temple."

I felt Street's hand tense, her thumb trembling against my eyelid.

"Perfect," I said. "You've done exactly what you should. Your attacker thinks he's got complete control over the situation. Yet you are about to take out his eye, which will destroy him."

Street and I went over the self-defense strategy again. Then she and Blondie went home. I felt the pang of loneliness and worry as they drove away. I might be a big, tough, ex-cop, but my emotions were always a bit on edge when it came to Street. She was the life in any room, and when she left, things got very empty very fast.

Spot and I ate dinner and went to bed.

NINE

The next morning, I made a small fire in the wood stove, sat with Spot, and drank two cups of coffee.

I needed to tell Fairbanks that Isadore was murdered. I thought that it should be in person and ideally at his condo so that he was in familiar territory when I crashed his world down around his head. Another aspect of law enforcement is the maxim that a law enforcement officer should observe the reaction of next of kin when they are told of tragedy. You can't do that over the phone.

If I wasn't thoughtful about how I contacted him, he'd figure it out. I didn't want that.

I picked up the business card Fairbanks had given me and dialed.

"Douglas Fairbanks," came the answer after one ring.

I said, "Owen McKenna calling. I'm sorry I upset you at my office yesterday. I have some questions about Isadore. I can come to your place if you like."

There was a long pause while he apparently considered whether he would have anything to do with me. Eventually, he said, "Okay."

"I'm running errands across town. You said you had a condo in town. I could stop by."

"Um, sure. I'm at Lakeland Village." He gave me the number. "Feel free to bring your dog in. He's such a sweetheart. You might get some looks from my neighbors, but ignore them."

"I'll be there in about twenty minutes."

I hung up, brought Spot with me, and headed for Fairbanks's condo.

I turned sideways in the seat after I parked at Lakeland Village and said to Spot, "You want to make a house call? Douglas Fairbanks requests the honor of your presence in his condo." Spot was lying on the back seat. With his droopy bedroom eyes, he looked like a sultry movie star. He reached his head forward and stuck his wet nose on my cheek. I wiped my sleeve across my face, mopping it up some, wishing I had a bath towel.

"Yes, I love you, too," I said, getting out of the Jeep.

I opened the back door, and Spot got out. He had a lightness in his step. He'd never been here before, and new places are a rich source of new smells.

We found the building, went down the walk and up the stairs. Fairbanks opened the door as my knuckles were about to strike the third time. Maybe he'd been watching out the window.

"Thanks for seeing me," I said.

He nodded, held out his arm in a welcoming gesture, and ushered me into his place. As Spot pushed in, Fairbanks bent over a bit and hugged him long and hard. Like so many people, he seemed to sense in Spot a refuge and safety zone. Spot didn't just endure these sudden and extravagant displays of affection, he loved them. I walked into the living room.

It was a standard upscale condo, new carpet, nice abstract wall art, granite counters in the kitchen, a spacious deck with a view of one of the swimming pools and what realtors call a filtered view of Lake Tahoe in the distance.

Eventually, Fairbanks and Spot joined me.

"Have a seat," Fairbanks said.

I sat on a big leather chair. He sat on the leather couch. Across from the couch was a video screen so big that I wondered why he even came to Tahoe. If your focus is the latest entertainment technology with resolution that allows you to count the pores on the actors' noses, you don't need to leave Las Vegas. Tahoe is about lake and mountains and hot sunshine and melting snow and wildflowers. The more indoor distractions, the less point in coming here.

Fairbanks was wearing brown jeans and a tan sweater, a major change from his garish biking outfit from the day before.

Spot, recognizing a source of endless pets, sat on the floor next to Fairbanks and leaned, slightly, against Fairbanks's knee.

"You said you had questions," Fairbanks said. His face was earnest, his manner was sincere, and his voice cracked a tiny bit.

I paused. "I'm very sorry to say that I've got bad news."

Fairbanks looked alarmed. "About Isadore?" His voice wavered and croaked.

"Yes. She was found dead yesterday."

Fairbanks stared at me. The shock on his face, in his eyes, on his brow was profound. Then he began to melt. If he'd been a sculpture at Madame Toussad's Wax Museum and put into the fire, it wouldn't have been much more dramatic. His face collapsed and his shoulders dropped and he lowered his head into his hands and sobbed.

Spot turned his head and looked at me. His brow was furrowed.

After a time, Fairbanks leaned over and wrapped his arms around Spot. The sobbing went on without pause. Then came high-pitched groans. I finally thought to stand up and go over and sit next to him. I put my hand on his shoulder. At that, his melting tipped him sideways away from Spot, and he slowly fell onto my lap.

If anyone were watching, they would think the scene was excessively melodramatic. A director in a stage play would have said that the emotion should be dramatically scaled back in order to be believable. But it seemed that Fairbanks had collapsed into a pit of despair.

I didn't know what to say, so I put my hand on his back and rubbed him.

It took long minutes before his sobbing caught and sputtered, and he coughed. He began to get ahold of his emotions enough to slow the crying. When he finally pushed himself up off my lap, his red, swollen eyes showed a touch of surprise as if wondering how he and I had gotten into such a position.

When he was sitting without support, I went into his kitchen, found a glass, and came back out with water. He took it and drank, making little noises in his throat as he swallowed.

Spot was now lying on the floor next to Fairbanks. He had his head up so his jawbone could rest on Fairbanks's thigh. I'd never considered training Spot to be a therapy dog. But he had the moves and the instincts. Fairbanks put both of his hands on Spot's head, and Spot sighed a deep breath. If this was work, Spot was happy to sign on.

I did what I do best and waited. To those who are patient comes much. I didn't have to wait long.

"Did she suffer?" Fairbanks asked.

"I don't think it was severe, and I don't think it lasted long."

"How did she die?"

"She died of hypothermia, outdoors in that snowstorm two nights ago. I'm sorry to say that she was tied up. So it was murder."

Fairbanks jerked as if struck by a stun gun.

He didn't speak. He was waiting for me to explain.

"She was found on Fannette Island in Emerald Bay."

"What? Oh, my God! How'd she get out there? What was she doing?"

"We don't know. I'm hoping you might know something that would give me an idea of where to look next."

Fairbanks was shaking his head. "I don't know! I have no idea! Isadore was my... you know..." he stopped. He lifted one hand off Spot's head and raised it into the air, holding it without apparent awareness. Levitation of the distraught.

"Douglas," I said. "You said you didn't know what Isadore did for a living or where she lived. But we need to learn something about her if we are to have a clue about where to start looking for her killer."

"I'm embarrassed to admit that I know almost nothing about her." Fairbanks found a tissue, blew his nose, reached for another tissue, wiped, blew, and then wiped again. "Like I told you before, she told me she worked in finance. That's such a catchall term. But I didn't question it. I should have. I suppose I was just so smitten that I didn't want to put her off with qualifying questions. I didn't want to say anything that might make her, you know, be uncomfortable with me."

I waited, having learned that if you give people verbal space, they will often fill it.

Fairbanks took some time to calm himself. "Isadore was an engaging, wonderful woman. Very smart. Quick with words. She made me laugh, and, believe me, that's not an easy thing to accomplish. And she was physically beautiful as well. Like one of those Greek statues of the perfect idealized woman, Aphrodite. In the beginning, I thought that she wasn't something I could ever aspire to touch or have. In fact, the first time I saw her, I thought of that Yeats poem where he says that beauty is indifferent to the solitude of an old man. That living beauty is for younger men."

Fairbanks took several deep breaths. "But after much more time together, I began to hope that I could do what I've never done, that I could touch beauty. I dreamed that my solitude would be broken if only for one night."

Fairbanks clenched his jaw as if steeling himself. "You said she was tied up and died from exposure. How was she tied up?"

"Her body was hanging from the corner of the tea house."

"Hanging! Oh, my God! Do you think it could have been suicide?"

"It doesn't appear to be. She was hanging by her ankles."

Fairbanks looked astonished. He shook his head. "I… I don't understand. She was upside down?"

"Yes."

"But that wouldn't kill her. At least not for a long time."

"It was at night, and it was cold and snowing," I said.

"That's horrible! Why would someone do that?"

"We don't know. We're hoping you can give us an idea. Can you think of anyone who may have wanted to hurt her?"

Fairbanks shook his head. "I didn't really know people in her circle. The few times I was with her and people recognized her, they were always warm and friendly. I got the feeling that people really liked her."

I made a perfunctory nod. "Earlier, you told me that you believed she just went by the single name Isadore and that you didn't know anything that would shed light on why she disappeared. Now that you know she was killed, does anything else occur to you? Were there any animosities that Isadore spoke of or hinted at? Any tensions or problems in her past?"

"No. Nothing. I'm so sorry. The truth is that we were new to each other, and it was one of those whirlwind relationships. The focus was on us, on the moment. We avoided talking about our pasts. The desire to be in the moment was one of the ways we connected. Now she's dead, and I can't help you at all. I'm worthless."

"You're not worthless, Douglas. You're in shock. You will probably think of things at a later time."

"What happens next?"

"California law requires an autopsy. The results will give us an idea of how to look for her killer."

Fairbanks seemed distracted by a thought. "Isadore wasn't a large woman, but she was strong. She would have put up a good fight. How would someone hang her by her ankles? That would take a great deal of strength."

"That's a good question. Maybe there were two or three men who lifted her up and tied her in place. Did Isadore ever talk about rock climbing? Or camping or mountaineering?"

"No, why?"

"Because she was tied up with paracord," I said. "It's a thin kind of line that sportsmen use for a variety of purposes."

"It doesn't sound familiar," Fairbanks said. "The Isadore I knew was a sophisticated woman. I'd guess she was urban to the core. I just assumed she lived in a good-sized city, ate at nice restaurants. I can't make a picture of Isadore camping or rock climbing. Except for her bicycling clothes, her other clothes were all what she'd wear in the city, not in the forest."

"I want you to think about those places where you remember people recognizing Isadore. Those places were in Tahoe, right?"

"Yes. Isadore and I first met in Tahoe, and every time we've met since was in Tahoe. Tahoe was our thing. On our second or third meeting, I said she could stay at my condo. I even gave her a key. The only places where we went where she bumped into people she knew were in Tahoe. Restaurants and such. I'll try to remember where."

"Go to those places. Try to find people who knew her. If so, get their names and contact info."

Fairbanks nodded.

"How did you and Isadore contact each other?"

"We had each other's cell phone numbers and email."

"May I have hers?" I asked.

"Yes. I'll write them down."

He got a little pad of paper, wrote, tore off the sheet, and handed it to me.

The email address was a Yahoo account, which would be very difficult to access.

"I see that the area code for the phone number is from the Bay Area," I said.

Fairbanks nodded. "I sort of casually asked her about that because, of course, I was curious. She said that she often did business in the Bay Area, so it helped her to have a number that connected her to the Bay Area. When she told me, she seemed to take care that I not assume she lived there. Although that's what I thought, anyway."

"Did she know you lived in Las Vegas?"

"Yes," Fairbanks said. "I told her I was an insurance broker there. That was another one of those times when I sensed that she didn't want to know my personal information. It was like she wanted me to be her vacation friend, and it would be special because we wouldn't let the rest of our worlds enter into our magic vacation world. So other than explaining to her about my open marriage, I never brought up my other life again."

We sat in silence for a bit.

"Will you continue to look into this?" Fairbanks said. "I'll pay whatever you charge. I want you to find her killer. I need you to find her killer."

"Yes, I will." I paused, thinking. "I wonder if you have a piece of Isadore's clothing."

Fairbanks frowned. "What for?"

"I'd like to do a search of Fannette Island."

He stared at me. "Oh, you mean, you want one of those search and rescue dogs to smell Isadore's clothes and then look for anything with her scent on the island."

"Right."

"Do you know someone who has such a dog?"

"Yes, but I was thinking of using my dog."

Fairbanks looked at Spot, then back at me. Spot watched his eyes, then turned to look at me, too.

"Is he, you know, trained at how to search?"

"Sort of. He's not a professional. But he makes up for his amateur status with enthusiasm."

Fairbanks turned back to Spot. He leaned forward and pet

him, both of his hands going down the sides of Spot's neck. "Can you find out what happened to my girl, Spot? Can you?" Fairbanks turned to me. "You wanted some of her clothes. I'll go get her bag."

"First, get a large zipper-type food bag if you have one. Open it wide, take it into the bedroom where she stayed, and then put an item of her clothing into it without letting it touch the outside of the bag. The clothing can't be fresh out of the wash. It needs to be something she's already worn. A dirty T-shirt. Or a hat or scarf that she's had on her head is even better. When you've done that, wash your hands and then come back out and stay with my hound. I'll go in and seal up the bag."

"I get it," he said. "You want to make it so that when you open the bag and let him sniff the clothing, it will be a new scent."

"Yes. He already knows her scent just being here in your condo. But when I pull her clothing out of the bag, it will give him a clear idea of what scent to look for."

Fairbanks stood and went to the kitchen. He opened a drawer, removed a bag from a dispenser box, and then went down to one of the bedrooms. He moved fast and with purpose as if I'd given him the relief of focusing on doing something useful.

In time he reappeared. "I found her pajama top. Will that work?"

"Yes. Perfect. Pet my dog while I go seal the bag."

He did as requested.

I walked into the bedroom. The open food-storage bag was sitting on the bed. In it was a pink, flannel top. I squeezed the air out of the bag, sealed the seam, and brought it out.

"Thanks. I'll take Spot out to the island and see what I can find."

"Will you let me know? Will you keep me informed of your investigation?" Fairbanks's voice was high and tentative and strangely hopeful. His love was dead, and he would be shaken to the core about it for months to come. But at this moment he was hopeful that I might find her killer.

"Yes, I'll keep you up to date."

"Thanks. Thanks so much. Let me get you a check. I want to

hire you for as long as it takes to solve this."

I gave him a substantial figure.

Fairbanks pulled a check book from a kitchen drawer, wrote me a check, and handed it to me.

"I'll be in touch," I said.

Spot and I left Fairbanks standing at the door, his eyes red and swollen, his worry and pain greater than anything a person should have to confront.

On our way out, two guys were coming into the condo building. They saw Spot and held back. One guy was tall and had a stringy goatee. The other guy was short and clean-shaven and had a flat top greased up firm and shiny.

"Good afternoon," I said. "Don't worry, my dog is friendly." I held Spot by the collar so the men wouldn't be nervous. "Do you guys live here?"

The greased, flat-top, shorter guy looked up at the taller guy.

"I do," the taller guy said. His goatee wiggled a bit.

"I'd like to ask you a question, please. I was just talking to your neighbor Douglas Fairbanks. His friend Isadore went missing two days ago and he's asked me to help. I'm a private investigator." I handed him my card. "Does either of you know her?"

The taller guy said, "I don't really know her, but I met her at a party Fairbanks had a long time ago. We didn't talk more than How-do-you-do. But I've seen her with Fairbanks since then. Is she in trouble?"

"Just missing," I said. "Can you tell me what you remember about her?"

"Well, Isadore's..." He paused.

I waited.

"It's just that anyone would remember her. She's pretty much a ten on the hottie scale." He made a quick glance at the shorter guy. "Fairbanks is a lucky guy."

"Did you ever get a sense that anyone didn't like her? At the party? Or since then?"

He frowned. "No. She's real... what's the word. Vivacious. Fun to be around. I think everyone probably likes her. Except maybe other girls. Or men who put the make on her and got slapped down." He made another glance toward the shorter guy.

"Do you know anyone who's a friend of hers?"

"Other than Fairbanks? No. I don't think locals in Tahoe would know her. She's from out of town. She sort of radiates tourist, if you know what I mean. Although, I've seen her staying at Fairbanks's place a few times. So the tourist thing is probably rubbing off."

"May I contact you if I have further questions?"

"Yeah, sure. I'm the manager at the Mountain Street Grill over in Zephyr Cove. The easiest way to reach me is to call there and leave a message on my voicemail. My name's Kendall Martini, just like the drink."

I wrote it down. "What about your home phone?"

"I don't really have one. I have a cell, but I'm like the only guy in my generation who doesn't live on that thing. I turn it on when I'm expecting something I care about. The rest of the time, it's turned off. Nothing worse than linking turns in the deep pow and getting texts on your phone. Besides, the companies are always tracking everything we do, and I like to keep a low profile."

"Right." I turned to the shorter man. "What about you? Do you have any impression of Isadore?"

"Sorry, man. I have no idea who that is."

I held his eyes for a bit, wondering if he was telling the truth. From Kendall's statement, I would guess that he'd have told his friends about his sometime neighbor who was a hottie.

The shorter man didn't waver.

"Okay. Thanks much." Spot and I left.

TEN

I called Sergeant Bains of El Dorado County.

"Any chance you did a canine search on Fannette Island?" I asked when he answered.

"No. What would we expect to find? We have a victim and the means of murder. We did a grid search. There was nothing else but rock and trees. The murderer left no trace."

"I don't expect there is anything in particular to find. But you never know what a dog will turn up. Would you mind if I took my dog out there?"

Bains paused before he answered. "I remember when you had Ellie Ibsen and her professional avalanche dog search the slide at Emerald Bay. Your dog mostly watched the other dog, as if wondering how in the heck did he do it."

"Right. I could see if Ellie has an available dog. But right now, Spot's the only dog I have. Mind if I have him search?"

"Not at all. You probably know that it's against the law to bring dogs to Fannette Island."

"I thought about that. So as a scofflaw, I might try not to get caught. But I could also invoke your name, which, last I heard, is respected in some circles."

"The circles of perps I've put in jail," Bains said. "Sure bring your dog. Call me and tell me if you find anything."

"Will do."

I next called Diamond. When he answered his phone, I said, "Hey, I was thinking about when we paddled that canoe out to the anchored boats to try and find Evan Rosen and her sister Mia."

"What's it been," Diamond said, "two weeks? Caught that sick bastard with the murder weapon in his hand."

"Yeah. Your paddling energy was impressive. Yet somehow I got the idea that you'd never paddled a canoe before."

"That is correct," Diamond said. "First time for me. Maybe the last. Those things are tippy as a kayak. But they ride higher in the water than a kayak, so it seems they have an even greater chance of overturning. Why do you ask?"

"Because I have a vision of a canoe hanging up under the rafters in your garage. A red one, I think."

"Sí. Good memory. The canoe came with the place when I bought it. And my Green Flame Karmann Ghia is short enough that I can park it underneath the canoe."

"Are you saying you own a canoe but have never used it?"

"Sí again."

"Do you know if it floats?" I said.

"I don't know. I've never tried to float it. Why would I? Anyway, it doesn't have any obvious holes, so it probably floats."

"Does that mean I can borrow it?"

"My unused canoe? Help yourself. What's your plan?"

"I told you about the potential client whose girlfriend went missing. Her body was found on Fannette Island."

"And you want to go out there. But why go to the trouble to come down to Minden and borrow my canoe? You could rent a powerboat and make it easy."

"I don't think they're allowed to pull up at the island. We'd have to drop anchor and swim in."

"Which would be seriously cold this time of year," he said.

"No kidding. Water doesn't come colder than snowmelt."

I thanked Diamond and then called Street.

"I've been doing a little self-defense practice," she said when she heard my voice. "I don't think I'm getting the moves right, but I can tell it's getting me conditioned to the possibility of assault. I'll be better able to react in the right way if it happens."

"That's good. Practice produces the defense pattern."

"Learn anything new about the body they found?"

"Not yet. Douglas Fairbanks gave me a piece of her clothing. I'm going to take Spot out to the island and have him search on the woman's scent. Would you and Blondie like to come? I'll get Diamond's canoe this afternoon and paddle out tomorrow morning."

"We'll join you."

ELEVEN

Spot and I headed up and over Kingsbury Grade. We dropped down 3000 feet and pulled up to Diamond's house just off the town square in Minden, one of the old ranching towns in Carson Valley, and the headquarters for the Douglas County Sheriff's Office, where Diamond was a sergeant.

Diamond was gone, so Spot and I walked down the narrow drive alongside the old clapboard house that Diamond kept in spotless condition. Diamond's backyard was also neat and clean and recently mowed. The little old garage was a bit sway-backed across its roof line, but the siding was freshly painted white, the trim a shiny forest green enamel, and the little window panes were so clear I wondered if they'd been washed that morning.

I let myself into the unlocked garage. Spot pushed in past me, his nose high, air scenting, teasing out hints of all activity during the past few months, whether the smells were of small furry critters or gas for the lawn mower, or fertilizer for the grass or light oil lubrication for Diamond's many tools in the rolling Craftsman carts that organized and housed them.

Diamond's Karmann Ghia, the Green Flame, was parked beneath the hanging canoe.

I found a small step ladder and used it to reach up and unhook the straps that cradled the canoe's hull and hung it from rafter hooks. Lifting up, the canoe seemed lighter than I expected. I took it down, careful not to bounce it on the old classic car, carried it outside, and set it on the grass.

The canoe was a red Old Town, one of the short models, just 14 feet long, with one large space between the seats. There were two seat cushions at one end. Tied to one of the support thwarts that gave strength to the canoe were two dusty flotation vests. Wedged from the seats to the thwarts were two wooden paddles. Spot looked at the canoe, then looked up at me, his brow furrowed with question.

"Yes, boy, you get to go on another boat ride."

I found shock cords and nylon rope in Diamond's garage and used them to tie the canoe to the Jeep's roof rack.

Three hours later, I'd brought Diamond's canoe to the boat inspection station for invasive species and gotten my approval.

The next morning, the newspaper had a big headline about the murder on Fannette Island. Below it was a picture of the victim. The photograph looked like a telephoto shot taken from a boat some distance from the island. The photo was small, grainy, and dark. I guessed that the paper had reduced the photo's resolution and printed it small to make it seem less sensational. But the photo showed a vague image of the victim hanging upside down.

The story accompanying the photo was short.

Murder Victim Found At Fannette Island

The El Dorado Sheriff's Office has confirmed that a body was found hanging from the tea house at the top of Fannette Island yesterday morning. Although foul play was involved, cause of death has not been established. No further information has been released.

I thought about the murder. Maybe the killer had strung his victim up as punishment for terrible deeds, real or imagined. Maybe he realized that hanging a person in one of the most photographed spots on the planet would mean that the press would be eager to print the story and spread it across the country. It could be that the whole point of the murder method was to display the body for the world to see.

I set aside the paper, turned on my laptop, and went to the Google News web page. The story was at the top. Multiple national news sites had picked it up, printed the picture, and written about the situation, focusing on the salacious aspects of a woman in a skirt hanging upside down.

Why display a dead body? There could be several reasons. It might be a taunt. Hey, everybody, check out how I can string someone up, and you can't find me. Or it could be a puzzle. Try to figure out why I did it. Try to guess if I will do it again.

I grabbed Isadore's pajama shirt, and Spot and I got in the Jeep and headed down to pick up Street and Blondie.

Street had packed a lunch in a cooler.

We drove around the South Shore, headed out past Camp Rich, and turned into the road to Kiva Beach, one of the few beaches on Tahoe that allows dogs.

Because it was June, the summer tourist season hadn't yet begun. So there were several parking spaces. I pulled the flotation vests out of the back of the Jeep and handed one to Street.

She held it up, gave it a shake. "An archive of Carson Valley insect history is stored in these spider webs," she said, wiping at the gossamer threads. She plucked something very small from the detritus, held it up to the sunlight and looked at it. "An intact pupa case. Something prevented this poor guy from emerging from his post-larval nap and transformation. Now his remains are desiccated within the case."

"Where I see sticky dead bug stuff, you see a science lesson."

"Science lessons are life lessons," she said. She put on the vest, which was a couple of sizes too big.

I put on mine, which was too small.

"You know these won't save our lives if we go into the drink," she said. "Tahoe's too cold."

"Right. Flotation vests just make it so they can find our hypothermic bodies. But don't worry, we'll stay close to shore for the bulk of our trip. By the time we have to cross the open water of Emerald Bay to get to Fannette Island, we'll have our technique down. We won't overturn."

Street held my eyes. "You're sure about that?"

"Yeah. Totally confident."

"Totally," she repeated slowly as if experimenting with the sound of the word. "Why am I not totally convinced?"

"I totally have no idea."

Street looked up at the trees. "The wind in the branches is strong. It'll be much stronger out on the water."

"The wind is from the west. So if we stay near the west shore, we'll be in the lee. It shouldn't be too bad."

Street lifted the cooler out of the back seat. "I hope you're right."

I untied the canoe from the roof of the Jeep. I lifted it up by the gunwales, turned it upside down, and held it above my head. I carried it out to the beach and across the sand to the water. I set it down on the beach, the bow floating in the water, the stern on the sand.

"This canoe seems smaller than normal," Street said.

"It is. Fourteen feet compared to seventeen for most canoes. But a small canoe is bigger than nearly any kayak." I took the cooler from Street and set it in front of the stern seat where it would sit between my legs. Then I put the cushions in the center compartment and got Spot to lie down on them. Blondie nervously ran back and forth, whimpering.

"I wonder if she's ever been in a boat," Street said. "That's a question that always arises with a rescue dog. What is their past experience?"

"Let's have you sit on the bow seat and we'll try to coax her to sit in front of you, between your knees."

"She certainly seems nervous. But I suppose the worst that could happen is she jumps into the water. And as we all know, Yellow Labs are as at home in the water as sea otters."

Street got into the bow seat. I spread out my jacket on the hull in front of Street for a bit of padding. Together we urged Blondie into the small space. Street got Blondie to sit, and she squeezed the dog between her knees. I handed Street a paddle, put one foot into the stern, and pushed off into the ice cold, choppy water.

As I took my first paddle stroke, I noticed that to the west, dark clouds were swirling over the mountains of the Sierra Crest.

TWELVE

We paddled at a brisk pace, fighting a medium chop. The wind wanted to push us parallel to the waves, a dangerous orientation. We had to make strong strokes to keep at an angle to the waves, quartering them. Street took steady pulls through the water, and I matched my strokes to hers. As with most boats, a canoe is steered from the stern. I kept us as near to the shore as I dared, trying to see through the waves in case the top of any boulder was just beneath the surface.

After ten minutes of quiet paddling, Street said, "What's Fairbanks like?"

"Awkward in every way. Uncomfortable in his own skin. Unsure of how to act or talk. Probably got severely picked on when he was a kid. But smart. Quotes poets."

"Like me when I was young," Street said.

"You're kidding, right? It's hard to see you as awkward."

"Oh, yes. I was the geeky tomboy who was good at science. Kids made relentless fun of me. They called me the pimple science stick because I was so skinny and had such bad acne. I hated school and all of its cliques with their focus on gossip. But I had no refuge at home, either. So I spent all of my time by myself, plotting my escape from town. After my father's conviction, it was a relief to decide that I was old enough and smart enough to run away and take care of myself."

"At fourteen years of age," I said.

"Some kids are forced to grow up early," Street said. "Maybe Fairbanks had a similar youth. Maybe he was the kid who wore the wrong clothes, literally and metaphorically."

"That's more accurate than you might imagine," I said.

We canoed along the west part of Baldwin Beach, came to a row of houses, then came to forest. We followed the shore north toward Emerald Bay. The hardening breeze above the icy water was crispy cold. Now and then a moist pocket of air washed over us carrying scents of verdant spring wildflowers and wet earthy soils where one would find mushrooms.

The shore was made up of rocks ranging in size from small cobbles up to boulders large enough that a party of four could spread out a picnic on top of them. The breeze was shifting. When I stayed very close to the shore, we were still largely in the lee of the wind, protected by the towering trees on the shore. If the waves had been gentle as they lapped against the rocks, it would have been an idyllic setting. As it was, the waves were uneven and, though not large, they sounded angry against the shore.

The forest was foreboding in its depth and breadth. From where we paddled, one could set ashore, walk through the woods to the highway, and, once across the pavement, hike through mountains and over the Sierra Crest for 40 miles without seeing another road or person or sign of human habitation. It was a wilderness landscape mostly unchanged from the last ten thousand years when the Washoe lived in the Tahoe Basin in the summer and hiked down to Carson Valley when the snows set in.

The forest was so close to the shore that it was almost as if we were paddling through it. The trees had frequent dark areas, shadowed by the canopy above. There was a vague sense of threat in those shadowed cavities. If we got out of the canoe and wandered those recesses, we'd probably discover that the wilderness was benign. But with the wind, the woods seemed to be filled with hints of danger. It wasn't the threat one senses with a mama bear and her cubs, nor a pack of hungry coyotes, nor even a mountain lion. It was the imagined potential conflict in coming upon that most dangerous animal of all, an angry man motivated by perceived slights and armed with a deadly weapon, be it gun or axe or a length of paracord.

As if reading my mind, Street said, "The landscape is beautiful. Too bad the subject of our outing is so dark."

"Oh, that," I said as if I hadn't been thinking that very thought.

"You've told me a little about this case you're working on," she said. "But it isn't clear."

So I gave her a more thorough account, beginning with

Fairbanks looking for his missing girlfriend and ending with the body that had been found hanging from the ankles, upside down. "It sounds like some kind of punishment killing. In the victim's mouth were three red roses, taped in place with duct tape."

"Oh, my God. That is twisted." Street sounded horrified.

"Bains said they found no ID. The only notable mark on the body was a tattoo of three red roses on her ankle. That was my first indication that the dead woman was Douglas Fairbanks's girlfriend, because he'd mentioned the tattoo."

Street didn't respond. No doubt she was grappling with vivid images in her mind. I didn't know if I should let her process or try to change the subject. I kept paddling in silence.

It was about two miles from Kiva Beach to Eagle Point at the southern side of the entrance to Emerald Bay. At our leisurely pace, we came to the point less than an hour after we'd left Kiva Beach.

As we rounded Eagle Point and headed through the narrow entrance, the full length of the bay came into view, stretching back southwest for two miles. The mountain backdrop that surrounds the bay rises 3000 feet directly above the water, higher for more distant peaks.

"Fannette Island straight ahead," Street announced.

"The tea house is on the head of the island, so to speak. The trees and rock on the side of the island that we're looking at go from the water up at a steep angle and rise directly to where Lora Knight had the tea house built. I remember it as a square building of rock with no roof above."

"That's exactly what I see," Street said. She seemed to paddle harder. "Lora Knight built the Vikingsholm Castle, which was, I suppose, very self-indulgent even if it became a great example of Scandinavian architecture. But she did good stuff for people, right?"

"Yeah. She supported youth groups and donated to schools and other educational organizations. She and her second husband also provided much of the financial backing of Charles Lindbergh's flight across the Atlantic. That certainly was significant as it proved that air travel could cover great distances."

I steered us along the shore until we got close to the island.

"Time to head across open water," I said. "Feeling stable?"

"As long as we don't tip, yes."

I dug my paddle into the water, did a J-stroke, and steered us out into the deep water.

The wind rose as we headed into the waves. With each stroke, I brought my paddle down deep enough that my hand dipped into the cold water. I pulled hard, and it seemed that Street instinctively did the same. Our canoe sped up.

I saw Street occasionally glance out at the deep water, scanning as if looking for other watercraft.

I sensed her tension. "Worried?"

"Not a lot," she said. "But it would be easy to kill canoers by driving a bigger boat into them and swamping the canoe. If the shore was far enough away, the cold water would ensure that the paddlers never made it back to land."

I realized she was thinking that her father could kill us by ramming our canoe with another boat. My hope was that Street wouldn't worry, but I didn't want to sound dismissive. "I don't see anyone except that boat way out by the entrance to the bay."

"Can you see who's on the boat? I would especially wonder about any boat with a single man."

"No, I can't see."

She nodded and kept paddling.

Despite the waves and wind, we got to Fannette Island in about ten minutes.

"We're about to make landfall," Street said, her voice sounding as if she was experimenting with the nautical word. Or maybe the inflection was just relief that we made it.

I slowed my paddle strokes as we approached the rocky shore, steering us to the left, parallel to the shore in a clockwise direction. I looked for a good place to land and pull up the canoe.

Blondie was staring intently at the shore, as is always the case when dogs are in a boat as it approaches land.

Spot realized he was pointing more toward the lake than the island. He swung his head around to the island side, shifting his weight and causing the canoe to make a dramatic tilt.

Street gasped as we tipped. She grabbed for the canoe's gunwale to stabilize herself. I jammed my paddle into the water, the blade broadside, thrusting it down and in to counteract Spot's movement. As the canoe tipped, the gunwale lowered to the water level. Icy water sloshed into the canoe. Street and I managed to shift our positions so that the canoe stopped tipping and rocked back to its proper position.

"Whoa!" Street exclaimed. "That was a close call." She looked around at the dogs and me. The dogs had instinctively stayed low but were very alert. "What happened?" Street said.

"One of our passengers wanted to get a better look at the island. So he moved his head, which shifted his body, all of which weighs a lot. Blondie almost got her swim."

At the sound of her name, she looked back at me from where she sat between Street's legs.

"It's okay," Street said, giving her a pet.

Spot was placid, ignoring us and watching the island. He had no clue that he could have caused a disaster if we'd been far out on open water.

Street said, "So if we turn again such that the closest land is on the other side…"

"I'll give advance notice, and we'll be prepared. A good lesson."

We resumed paddling.

I steered us along the shore, about 30 feet out.

Fannette Island is a rocky, forested mound about the size of a football field. As Street paddled, she stared up through the trees toward the top of the island.

"How high is the tea house above the water?"

"I remember reading that the island rises one hundred fifty feet above the water. The island must be made of a very tough mound of granite to have resisted the glacier that carved out Emerald Bay during the ice ages."

We came around the far end of the island where the slope was most gradual. There appeared to be no other boats. We were alone in the relative wilderness. There was an indent in the rocks that looked like a good place to land the canoe, so I steered us in.

As we neared the rocks, I back-paddled to slow us. Street stood up. Just as the bow of the canoe touched the rock, she stepped out onto dry land. With her weight out of the bow of the canoe, it rose higher, and she was able to pull it farther onto land.

Spot and Blondie both stood up, ears up, tails wagging, excited about exploring new territory. The canoe was very tippy, balanced between the bow on the rocks and the stern in the water. I turned my paddle upside down and held it by the blade to keep from damaging the blade's thin edge. I pushed the paddle handle down into the water so that it jammed on the bottom and stabilized us.

Spot looked at the uneven rocks, then looked back at me.

"It's okay, boy," I said.

He stepped out carefully, walked over big rocks to smoother land, then trotted away, nose to the ground, eagerly investigating the new landscape.

Blondie hopped out and ran after him.

Street reached in and lifted out the jacket and seat cushions that the dogs had been lying on. They were soaked from that water we took on during our tipping adventure. Now that the canoe was partially on land, the water that had sloshed into the canoe had run rearward and collected at the stern.

I lifted the canoe, tipped it over to drain the water, and set it upside down between some trees so it could continue to drain. Street set the paddles under the canoe. We took off our flotation vests and hung them and the cushions from tree branches to dry.

Looking around revealed a postcard landscape. We were surrounded by water. The end of Emerald Bay was across from us, and the Vikingsholm castle sat nestled in the tall pines about 1000 feet across the water. Mountains rose up around three sides of the bay, a slope that was steep enough that we had to crank our necks back to see the peaks. A bit farther to the left of the bay's end was Mt. Tallac, its cross and northeast bowl white with large snowfields.

"After the dogs?" Street said as the dogs ran by and then raced in the direction of the ridgeline to the top of the island.

"Yeah."

The island looked like it had been lifted from a fairytale and put into place by Disney. There were boulders and Manzanita bushes positioned as if by design, and pines with branches spaced to provide perfect views of the castle and mountains on the mainland. Here and there were overlooks that allowed a view down to the brilliant viridian water close to shore and, a little farther out, the deep indigo water that dropped down to great depths.

Street looked around, peering at the trees, checking behind her.

"You okay?" I said.

She nodded. "In another couple of weeks, when tourist season hits and this island is swarming with kayakers and boaters, it will seem benign. But now, when we are the only people on the island, and we're investigating a murder at the tea house, it seems a bit sinister."

"I suppose."

"You're probably thinking that my worries about my dad affect my perception."

I made a little smile. "Let's hike up to the tea house."

"Where the body was found. I don't think I like this."

THIRTEEN

To the east, the island rose above us in a gradual climb. We found a path through the bushes and discovered granite rocks that rose in steps that seemed natural. Lora Knight must have demanded that her stone workers build a staircase that appeared to have always existed. The steps were perfectly comfortable to climb yet sufficiently uneven and irregular that they didn't appear constructed by anyone other than the glacial gods who originally designed Lake Tahoe and its singular bay and island.

The natural staircase turned this way and that. When it seemed the trail was a dead end, one need only turn and look a different direction and see a new approach, a jumble of rocks that, on closer examination, revealed another nearly perfect flight of steps, climbing up the island's backbone. After a short hike, we arrived at Lora Knight's tea house at the summit of the island.

The small square building, maybe 15 feet on a side, still had solid walls, though the roof had long since disappeared in the 90 years since it was built. The rock walls stood about 12 feet high. The stone masons had constructed the top row of rocks to have points facing up, which gave the tea house walls a sense of crenelations as if on a castle. Each wall had a single window opening that, despite the long absence of glass, framed gorgeous views of mountain and lake. In the northwest corner of the structure was the original fireplace. It was easy to imagine Mrs. Knight's guests taking tea in front of the fire while they celebrated the views after their hike to the island's top.

It was hard to imagine the tea house as a murder scene.

Sergeant Bains had said that the body was hung on the outside of the building, on the southeast corner, opposite the fireplace. They'd found the victim strung up by her ankles.

I walked out of the tea house and looked toward that corner.

The building was built so that its east wall was at the edge of a precipice that dropped almost straight down to the island's east shore. The obvious question was how the killer managed to hoist his victim up above a slope that was so steep as to be like a cliff. As I looked up at the rocks that formed the top of the tea house wall, it was unclear how it was done. The only possibility seemed to be that the killer had positioned his victim outside the tea house and down below it, then run the paracord rope from the victim's ankles up and over the wall at a point where the rock and mortar were relatively smooth so that the rope wouldn't abraid. Then the killer must have stood on the inside of the tea house and pulled down on the line, hand over hand. But to overcome the friction of the line going over the wall would take someone very strong or a pulley system to produce leverage. It would also take someone substantially heavier than the victim who'd been hoisted up.

As I looked up at the stone wall, I was startled by Street's voice.

"You're figuring out how the victim was hoisted up?"

I turned and saw her framed in the tea house window. She had her hands on the sill, her arms braced straight, and was leaning out of the opening.

"Yeah," I said. "Not an easy thing to haul someone up by rope. But it appears that whoever did the deed, tied the rope to the victim, tossed the rope over the top of the wall, and pulled from the inside. Bains said that the rope was tied off on the window frame."

I called out toward the trees. "Hey, Spot! I need you to do a search. Earn your keep. Earn some jerky."

I heard nothing.

"Yo, Largeness. Follow my voice. Want a treat? Come and get it."

Still no response.

"Do you see the dogs?" I said to Street.

"They were here a minute ago. I saw them just down the trail to... Oh, there he is."

She pointed.

I looked. Spot stood about 30 yards away. He was facing us,

but he held his head low, and his ears were back.

Just at that moment, Blondie appeared, trotting up the trail past him. She went into the tea house. "What's wrong with Spot?" Street asked.

I walked toward my dog. "He smells human death. It's happened too many times, so he's sensitized to it and doesn't want to come near."

"Even though the body has been gone for over a day?"

"Yeah. Without a strong rainfall, the scents last a long time."

I got to Spot. "Sorry, boy. I read you loud and clear. Here, have a treat." I pulled out a piece of jerky and gave it to him.

He chomped on it a couple of times and ate it without enthusiasm.

I pulled out another piece of jerky and showed it to him. He looked interested. I put the jerky back in my pocket. "Here's what I need," I said. I pulled the food storage bag out of my pocket, unzipped it, and removed Isadore's pajama top. I put it on Spot's nose. "Smell it, boy. Do you have the scent? Take a good whiff. Now find the scent." I shook his chest for emphasis, then made a pointing motion with my hand at the side of his head. "Find the scent!" I gave him a pat on his rear.

Spot didn't move.

"C'mon boy, find the scent!" I once again put the pajama top on his nose, holding it there for a moment. Then I put it back in the bag.

I took Spot by his collar and walked him toward the tea house. He didn't resist, but he wasn't eager.

"Good boy," I said. "Look for the scent. Find the scent. You want more jerky? Sure you do. Find the scent." I walked Spot over near the corner of the building where the woman had presumably died. I pointed at the ground with one hand and directed him with my other hand on his collar.

"Find the scent, Spot." I took him toward the nearest tree and then over to the closest group of boulders. Spot showed no interest.

Street spoke up. "What do you think he might find?"

"I have no idea. Probably there is nothing connected to her scent but the smell of death. The entire process focuses him on something innately depressing. Dogs have evolved to be focused on people. It wouldn't be out of line to say that dogs worship people. We are their source of food and shelter and a portion of their fun and even meaning, if such a word applies to a dog's perception of the world. So when people die, it is very difficult for them to face. Especially if, like Spot, they've dealt with human death many times."

I tossed the bag with the pajama top to Street. "Why don't you do the same routine with Blondie. She could be as good at this as Spot. Maybe even a lot better. Retrievers make great search dogs. If you put her through the motions, she'll soon figure out what we're doing."

Street opened up the bag, went over to Blondie, and started scenting her on the pajama top.

I noticed that Spot had his head at normal height, but his nostrils were flexing in the same way they do when he has his nose to the ground.

He was air scenting. Left nostril, then right nostril, taking the deep inhalations.

"What do you smell, Spot?" I let go of his collar. I gave him a little smack on his rear. "Find the scent, boy! Find it!"

Spot walked forward toward the edge of the drop-off. He turned his head left, then right, moving slow, sniffing hard. Then he lowered his head as if to sniff the ground. I knew he was zeroing in on the breeze that was coming up over the rocks. Because of the prevailing southwest wind, there would be turbulence, bringing him bursts of scents, and then nothing, and then more.

"What is it, boy? Find the scent!"

Spot looked down over the rocks. Then he moved sideways and found an angled path that wasn't vertical but still very steep. Like most dogs, he had a pretty good awareness of his own ability. I tensed as he picked his way down a split in the rock, a natural depression where water would run when it rained. Twenty feet down, he turned and moved sideways a few feet. To either side the rock dropped away to the lake. His nose was still up, air scenting, picking up possible concentrations of scent. Then he lowered his nose to the ground, moved farther down, paused to sniff a rock, a tiny bit of brush, a patch of dirt.

By the lay of the land, it seemed that anything that had Isadore's scent would have fallen over the cliff. It would be unlikely that something had gotten lodged near where he stood. But I knew never to question a dog's nose.

Blondie came down the steep slope, then turned around and went back up to Street. She knew there was a game of some kind going on, and she seemed eager to get in on the process.

Spot pawed at the dirt, sniffed, then pawed again.

It was an alert. Nothing definite. But it looked like he had found something with Isadore's scent.

I couldn't see how to get next to him. I took a different approach, climbing down using hands and feet. Then I moved sideways toward him.

"What did you find, boy? Did you find the scent?"

I looked where he dug at the ground. All I saw was dirt. Using the side of my hand, I gently brushed at the dirt, sweeping away the top-most layer. There was nothing. I reached toward the little mound of dirt that Spot had scraped up and brushed it back to where it had originally lay. Again there was nothing. "Where is the scent, Spot?"

His nostrils were flexing. He lowered his nose, bringing it close to my hand. Whatever he smelled, it was close. Maybe it was the dirt. Perhaps Isadore had touched dirt and tossed it here. I scraped some more. Maybe I should grab the soil and bag it for later inspection. I swept my hand again. This time I saw a glint of light. A sparkle. Off to the side. Where Spot had reached with his paw but hadn't quite connected. I moved more duff, decomposed pine needles and the fine granitic gravel called grus. My fingertip touched something smooth. I got a grip on it and pulled it out.

It was a silver necklace. White showed here and there. A white plastic necklace coated to look like silver. Costume jewelry. I lifted it up to the light. It had a little pendant, dark with dirt.

"Spot found something!" Street said. "What is it?"

"It's a necklace with a little pendant that has an unusual shape." I rubbed it. "The pendant looks like miniature roses. Three of them."

FOURTEEN

I showed the necklace to Street. She showed it to Blondie, putting it in front of Blondie's nose. "See Blondie. Smell this. This has the pajama scent on it." She pulled out the pajama top and had Blondie sniff it and the necklace again.

"I can see that she has the focus," I said. "Once she realizes what we're after, she'll be great."

I put the necklace into one of the baggies that I always carry to crime scenes.

We searched for another hour, but found nothing else.

When we were all back in the canoe, I steered us around toward the shore of the island that was directly below the tea house.

"Do you think there will be something else to discover?" Street asked.

"No. But why not take a look?"

When we got to the eastern tip of the island, Spot suddenly lifted his head. He appeared to be sniffing the breeze.

Because Street was paddling in front, she didn't notice.

"I think my hound just alerted again."

Street stopped paddling and turned around. "What do you think he's smelling?"

"I have no idea. In a perfect world, he'd be picking up on another scent of Isadore. But it could also be an unusual animal, or some bit of food that picnickers dropped overboard and it washed up on the island."

I turned the canoe to point where Spot's nose was pointing. I paddled toward the shore.

"Watch your dog and see if she notices any scent. We've both seen how she loves to track critters in the forest."

"Why don't they use retrievers for police dogs, finding suspects and such?" Street asked.

"Because they aren't aggressive. They could find the suspect as easily as any dog, maybe better, but then they would just bark at him or maybe want to play with him."

"What about Great Danes? Are they aggressive enough for police work?"

"They aren't as naturally aggressive as German Shepherds or Rottweilers. But their size gives them the advantage of serious intimidation. If a suspect saw a Great Dane running full speed to take him down, he would rather face a mountain lion, which would, at least, be smaller."

Spot had shifted his nose to the left as we moved toward the shore. I turned the canoe a bit to follow, trying to anticipate any dramatic dog movements that could overturn the canoe.

"Then why don't they use Great Danes as police dogs?"

"Too big. And not enough work ethic. Danes would rather snooze with their head in your lap than chase bad guys."

Spot was now focused on a big boulder near the shore. He didn't seem especially interested. But his nose was pointed that way. I made little rudder actions as I paddled.

"We're almost directly below the tea house," Street said.

"And we're pointed upwind. A dog can find a scent plume the same way you and I could see a smoke signal trailing out from the island. As we drift toward the edge of the scent plume, Spot will point toward where the scent is stronger. So I can kind of follow his motions. Look at Blondie. She seems to be sniffing with a particular focus as well. Watch her nostrils. Dogs can smell in stereo. They get a three-D smell picture of the landscape."

Street looked down at Blondie.

Spot held his head up a bit higher. I piloted the canoe toward the place where Spot's nose seemed to point. As we got to the rock, I used the paddle to slow our motion.

When the bow of the canoe touched the rock, Street said, "Do you think I should hop out and look for some foreign object? Or should we get the boat sideways to the shore and let Spot out?"

"The shore is too steep here."

Spot shifted his focus a bit.

"Look over near the root that comes down from that fir tree," I said. "Spot's focused on it. I see a little white object."

"It looks like a cigarette," Street said.

I said, "Douglas Fairbanks said that his girlfriend disappeared from the restaurant when she went out to the parking lot for a smoke."

"If you can shift the canoe to the left a bit, I can maybe get it with my paddle."

I did as Street suggested, and she tried a few times with her paddle and eventually got it on the blade. She carefully pulled her paddle back and grabbed the soggy cigarette off the blade. She held it up toward Spot. "Is this what you were smelling?"

Spot gave it a sniff.

"What do you think this means? Was the victim smoking this... Wait, it's not a cigarette. It's more like a little roll of paper. I can unroll it." She slowly moved it along the paddle blade. "Owen! There's something written on it!" She got it unrolled on the paddle and turned it around.

"What's it say?"

"It's a little poem. It says,
'Red roses of hope
Provided by false promise
Spread wicked deceit'"

"A haiku," I said. "Five syllables in the first line, seven syllables in the second, and five syllables in the third."

Street looked up at me. "This is about roses. The necklace had roses on it. And the victim had roses taped in her mouth. And didn't you say the victim had a rose tattoo?"

"Yeah. So we have a rose motif. I wonder if the victim wrote it."

"Or the murderer," Street said.

"But Spot was sniffing for scents that match the pajama top, right? So that would suggest the victim wrote it."

"Or at least held it in her hand." I pulled out another baggie, opened it, and leaned forward. Street put the little roll into it.

As we paddled back toward the main lake, Street said, "I was thinking about the haiku on the note. That is a great clue. We should be on the lookout for any potential suspect who's into poetry."

"Yeah," I said. "Like Douglas Fairbanks."

FIFTEEN

"**I** have an idea," Street said. "Maybe I'm crazy, but the little necklace with roses reminds me of something. And the haiku reinforces my thought."

"Which is?" I said.

"Can you paddle alone for a minute? I want to look something up on my phone."

So I paddled, and Street got out her phone and started tapping.

We'd come through the entrance of Emerald Bay and turned toward the South Shore when she spoke.

"I just found something amazing," she said.

"What?"

"In your last case, there were people who were murdered in different ways. Because the murders were unusual, you thought they were probably connected. So I was wondering what else, besides this woman's murder, is unusual right now. I Googled 'Tahoe moutain bike festival' and 'Red roses.'"

"You find something?"

"Get this," Street said. "On the festival website, there's a list of sponsors. One of the sponsors of the Tahoe Mountain Bike for Charity is the Red Roses of Hope Charity for Children. "The first line in the haiku is 'Red roses of hope.'

"Now that's interesting," I said. "And the haiku talks about false promise and spreading deceit."

"Do you know if Fairbanks's girlfriend was involved in the mountain bike event?" Street asked.

"Yes, she was. Fairbanks told me that Isadore was up in Tahoe to attend the festival and participate in some of the races."

Street turned to look directly at me. Her eyes looked aflame. "You said that Douglas Fairbanks didn't know much about her, didn't know what she did for a living, didn't even know where she lived."

"Correct."

Street said, "And now we find two pieces of evidence connecting her and her murder to red roses and maybe the Red Roses of Hope charity. If you count her red rose tattoo and the roses in her mouth, that's four bits of evidence."

"And it gives us a motive of sorts," I said. "Maybe it was her murderer who left the necklace and the haiku. It could be that the killer had the necklace and haiku and used them to accuse Isadore of bad faith or fraud or something, but then accidentally dropped them. The writer of the haiku appears angry about some kind of deceit. Like maybe Isadore was raising money for the charity, and the murderer was somehow burned."

"You think the murder was punishment?" Street said.

"Could be. Most murders are about financial greed or crimes of passion, often driven by sex and jealousy. But anger is sometimes a motive." I paddled for a bit. "Is there contact info for the Red Roses of Hope charity?"

"Yes. A Gmail account and a snail mail address."

"The gmail account is impossible to hack," I said. "But one can always visit a mailing address."

"It's on Market Street in San Francisco. With that address, this charity could be a big deal."

"Yeah. Market Street is one of the more expensive locations in The City. Can you do reverse address search on your phone? Put the address into Google and see if an owner pops up?"

"Already on it. Nothing pops up. There is no phone number connected to the address either. So the charity is not advertising its ownership."

"If you want to talk to them, you can't call. You have to send an email or a letter."

"Or go visit their office on Market Street," Street said.

"Yeah." I kept paddling as Street worked her phone. "Does the charity have a website?" I asked.

"Yes, and a fancy one, too. Pictures of poor kids. Stories of children whose lives were turned around by the financial support of loving, caring, supportive Americans. There are three different pictures of the American flag. Here's a photo of a little girl and a reproduction of a letter she wrote. The handwriting is very shaky.

'Dear Red Roses Mom, Thanks for the food and the clothes. Now we are warm at night. Our new apartment has its own fridge. We love you forever."

"Are you thinking what I'm thinking?" I said.

"That it's a little too pat and sweet to be genuine?" Street said.

"I suppose charities are like businesses in that they spin their presentation to make a good impression."

Street paused. "Maybe you should visit the charity's office on Market Street?"

"My thought exactly," I said.

SIXTEEN

When we got back to Kiva Beach, I called Sergeant Bains and told him about the necklace and the haiku that we'd found on Fannette Island.

"I could drop them off at the sheriff's office," I said.

"I'm in town. Let's meet there. Fifteen minutes?"

We got the canoe tied onto the Jeep, loaded the dogs, and drove across town.

Bains was in the parking lot off Al Tahoe Blvd. He said hi to Street. I handed him the baggies with what we'd found.

"The necklace was about thirty feet below the tea house in a depression in the rocks. It had probably fallen near the tea house and slid down the smooth rocks. The haiku was floating in the water at the base of the cliff below the tea house. It probably blew into the water and was kept against the rocks by the wave action."

Bains fingered the bags, turning the items over to look at them.

"The bags suggest they are not contaminated?"

"No, they are totally contaminated. We both handled the haiku, and the necklace has dog slobber on it."

He looked at me.

I said, "Sometimes, when one is poking around in woods and wilderness that the sheriff's deputies have already abandoned, one has to touch stuff to see it. We didn't wear latex gloves. In fact, I had to scrub at the necklace before I even knew it wasn't just another bit of dirt."

"Okay, I get your point. So your dog found these?" he said. "They're awfully small to spot in the woods."

"Yeah. I got the woman's pajama top from her boyfriend and had Spot smell it. He followed the scent and found the necklace and haiku."

"I'm impressed. It's hard to imagine much scent on items like these. And the paper was in the water? That's amazing. The power of a dog's nose is something, huh?"

"Yes, indeed," I said.

I then told Bains what Street had found out about the Red Roses of Hope charity and that I was going to head into San Francisco to track down its address.

"Let me know what you find?"

"Will do."

I took Street home to her condo.

"I'm going to return Diamond's canoe, then head into The City. Would you like to come with me?"

"Yes, but no. I have too much work to do."

"In that case, can I leave Spot with you?"

"Of course." She got out her phone, found the address of the charity, and wrote it down for me.

"Thanks so much," I said. I left Spot. He was happy to collapse on her carpet in front of her gas fire. I kissed Street goodbye. Spot didn't even notice that I left.

I drove up and over Kingsbury, down to Carson Valley, and left Diamond's canoe tied up in his garage where I'd found it. I called him and left a message on his voicemail to that effect, adding that I was heading off to investigate the Red Roses of Hope charity.

While the address for the charity was on Market Street in downtown San Francisco, it was unlikely that I could find a room in The City on short notice, and even more unlikely that I would think it affordable despite the retainer Douglas Fairbanks had paid me.

So I found a hotel near the Bay Area Rapid Transit station in Walnut Creek in the East Bay.

The next morning I rode the BART train to San Francisco, got off at the Embarcadero station, and walked down Market Street. The address for the Red Roses for Hope charity was down a block and a half.

I found the number painted in gold script on a double glass door that was tinted so that it was impossible to see through the glass. I pushed inside.

I'd expected an entry lobby and a desk attendant, or at least a sign box showing tenant names and office locations and elevators that would lead me to Suite 47, as Street had found on the website. Instead I was in a small room looking at a wall of locked boxes like you'd find in a post office. Each box was about 6 by 6 inches and had the word "Suite" and a number. None of the boxes had the name of a business. This facility was nothing but a maildrop, designed for anonymity. There were several hundred boxes.

Based on the address alone, Street and I had both assumed that the Red Roses charity would have substantial offices. Renting out mailboxes on Market Street in downtown San Francisco was probably a lucrative business. It followed the real estate rule about location being the most important thing in choosing where to set up shop. A business seemed roughly as significant as its address.

I thought about trying to pick the lock on the box labeled Suite 47 when the outer door opened and a woman walked in. I made a little smile and nodded at her as I feigned digging in my pocket, looking for my key.

She slipped a key into a box, opened it, pulled out a stack of mail, then shut the box, removed her key, and left.

I fingered the lock on box 47. It was a simple lock, probably easy to pick if I came back with the appropriate tools. But while its contents could be revealing and possibly useful, any mail addressed to Suite 47 would tell me little if anything about the charity and its employees. I couldn't get a search warrant to learn about the charity, because I had no probable cause.

It would be much better if I could wait until someone came to fetch the mail. Then I could follow them and see where their real office was.

The fact that a woman just retrieved her mail suggested that the day's mail may have already been delivered by the mail carrier. But I had no way of knowing whether or not the Suite 47 box had already been emptied for the day. It could also be that the box holder was out of town, not to retrieve the mail for two weeks.

If someone came for box 47, my best approach wasn't clear. If I waited outside, I wouldn't be able to see through the tinted glass.

I wouldn't know which box a person was emptying. If I loitered inside, I might get reported and have to answer questions to the police. Having worked for the SFPD for 20 years, I knew they were thorough, and I didn't want to lose time. Worse, the person who emptied the box would likely see me, making it much more difficult to follow them.

I studied the location of the box. Walking in the front door, box 47 was at about 10 o'clock, four rows up from the floor and seven columns in from the left.

If the front door to the room were jammed open, one could see box 47 from outside at about 4 o'clock. But how to jam the door?

The door had a hydraulic closer attached to the top edge. I pulled out my pocketknife and tried fitting the point of the blade into the Phillips screws on the door closer. They were as stiff as if they'd been spot-welded in place. I'd have to get a strong screwdriver and come back.

I walked back outside to look and see if there was a hardware store nearby, then remembered this was Market Street near the Embarcadero, home of financial institutions and other large companies. And even if there were a hardware store, the owner of box 47 might come while I was shopping for a screwdriver. As I considered the possibilities, another woman came and opened the door. I followed her in and fished for my keys once again, making pocket noise, pulling my keys out, staring at them as if to find the correct one, all just so I could see whether she was headed for box 47.

She opened a box on the opposite side of the room from 47. She left. I stepped out shortly after. It was a charade I could repeat all day. But someone would probably notice and get suspicious.

I walked down the street a bit, thinking, glancing back to see if any of the passersby went through the tinted glass door. I stopped and leaned against a wall, my back to the black granite of an office tower. When I began to think that my loitering would draw attention, I turned around to walk back to the maildrop door. As I rotated, the toe of my shoe caught something heavy and metallic. I looked down to see a four-foot strip of angle iron that had been left on the sidewalk. It looked like scrap hardware that might have fallen off a service truck. Probably someone had kicked it up against the wall so no one would trip on it, there to lie for minutes or months until a good samaritan picked it up and disposed of it.

No reason why I shouldn't be that good samaritan.

It was a weighty piece of metal, like the material they use for sign posts. I carried it down the sidewalk as if it were my cane.

I realized a guy like me could accidentally enter the wrong door, get confused turning around to leave, and accidentally drop the impromptu cane in the process.

So I went into the maildrop room just after a man came out. The front door was still shutting, I accidentally dropped my angle-iron cane so that it fell into the crack between the door and the door frame. The angle iron clattered down against the lowest hinge and prevented the door from closing.

Of course, anyone in such an unfortunate situation would try to retrieve the dropped angle iron. So I reached down to pull it out, then accidentally-on-purpose leaned the wrong way and bent the angle iron into a half-pretzel so that it would be very difficult to remove. The door closer was unable to shut the door. It stood open wide.

I left the maildrop, walked down the sidewalk, crossed Market, and walked back until I came to a bus shelter. By lounging at the bus shelter, I could not only see past the door and into the maildrop room, I could see the box that was four rows up and seven columns over. Box 47, receptacle for mail headed to the Red Roses of Hope charity.

SEVENTEEN

I stood behind the bus shelter.

The maildrop wasn't a crowded facility, but there was a steady, if slow, trickle of people collecting mail. People who, for whatever reason, wanted to appear as if they had a downtown address.

I knew there was a good chance that I could wait all day and never see anyone go to box 47. But the business of detecting is often the business of waiting. So I resigned myself to a long stint. I played mental games to pass the time. I made up biographies for every person who went in to collect the mail. On the fourth person, I ran out of ideas for what he did for a living. Next, I tried to perform the memory tricks I remembered from when I was a kid, like naming the presidents in order. I got up to Grant before I crashed and burned.

A kid came to get mail, the youngest person yet. But he didn't go near box 47.

I tried naming all of the states and their capitals. I was pretty good on the East Coast, probably because I was born in Boston, and on the West Coast, because I'd lived out west for some time. But there were many states in the central part of the country for which I hadn't a clue about where their legislators convened to make law.

A well-dressed young woman whose clothes were a bit revealing came to get mail. It made me wonder if an anonymous maildrop was de rigueur for call girls and escort services. She went to the wall opposite box 47.

On the street cruised a black, stretch limo with very dark windows. It stopped, and the woman climbed in the back door.

I looked back at the maildrop and saw a man shutting the box I'd been watching. Or at least it seemed like the correct box. As he walked away, I squinted at where I thought he'd been, focusing carefully. Then I counted, moving to the left. Seven from the left.

Counted down. Four from the bottom.

My red rose charity man.

Because I was working solo, my hope was that the charity man would walk or take mass transit to his next destination. If someone picked him up in a private car and there was no taxi nearby, I'd be out of luck.

The man was wearing what looked like a tailored suit. He stuffed his thick pile of mail into a leather shoulder bag that probably cost more than my used Jeep. He walked a bit like a man on fire. He was doing a kind of jerky jog while he held a phone to his right ear, his left hand holding the straps of his shoulder bag.

The man's fast walk seemed the rushed pace of someone who was late for an important appointment. Maybe he was talking to the person he was meeting, as he was almost shouting into his cell phone, his words garbled, but his tension clear.

I had to walk fast to keep within a reasonable distance.

The man headed east up Market toward the bay.

After a block, the man seemed to tire and slowed to a fast walk. He glanced at his watch. At the end of Market, he went across the Embarcadero Park and into the ferry terminal building. It was crowded as always. He must have had a pass, as he headed out to the docks, all while talking on his phone. When I saw which ferry he was getting on, I got in line to buy a ticket, handed over my money, then ran to the gate. The gate shut as I approached. I jumped over. The ferry blew its horn as I ran out onto the dock. The dock hand held his forearms up, crossed like a road-closure symbol. I kept running. At the last moment, he swore and stepped aside so that I wouldn't collide with him. Without slowing, I put my hands on the rail and vaulted over onto the boat, which had started to move away from the dock.

People stared at me. Perhaps the man I was following had watched, too.

I looked for him as the ferry headed out into the San Francisco Bay. We were close to the Bay Bridge, which loomed high above, the cars and trucks looking like toys as they crawled beneath the huge cables that rose up to giant silver towers. Then the ferry turned north and sped up to a fast cruise.

It took me ten minutes to find the red rose man. He was in one of the upper cabins, sitting on the end of a bench near one of the scratched, plexi windows. He was no longer talking on his phone. Instead, he had his elbows on his knees, head in his hands, like a man grappling with some kind of bad news.

I stayed back by the rear deck opening. I kept him in sight even though I doubted that he would move until we got to his destination.

The view of San Francisco's skyline was spectacular, the buildings and hills wrapped by misty fog that pushed in from the Pacific and swirled about the bases of the skyscrapers. Soon, we headed into the large open strait that stretched from the main bay out to the Golden Gate Bridge. The rolling swell was larger, and the ferry began to porpoise a bit. The few tourists grinned at each other and grabbed the railings for support. The commuters were oblivious, focused on their phones, their tablets, and the rare newspaper.

The ferry went close to Alcatraz Island, which sits a mile or so north of Fisherman's Wharf. The remnants of the famous prison were still there, tall masonry walls rising above the imposing surf crashing on the rocks below.

The red rose man still had his head in his hands as we approached Sausalito, the postcard village that climbs up the hills. The ferry slowed. It reversed its thrust for a moment, sending low, ponderous wake waves toward the boats in the nearby marina and the floating houses to its north.

The man stood up to disembark. Like before, he was oblivious to those around him. He was easy to tail as he walked the cute little streets of Sausalito. Once out of the business district, he went up roads that climbed in twists and turns like a jungle vine. Despite my high-altitude conditioning, I was soon panting. The red rose man must have been in very good condition.

He stopped at a tall thick hedge that was on the bay side of the street. The hedge was tall enough and dense enough to hide whatever was on the other side. In the hedge was an opening, and the plants grew up and over the opening in a perfect arch. He reached out and used a key to open an arched wooden door. He stepped through and shut it behind him. I heard the click of a deadbolt.

In a moment, there was the sound of another door opening and closing.

I moved close to the hedge gate, wary of hidden cameras, and looked into the hedge. Concealed behind the foliage was a solid wall of stone or concrete. It would be possible to climb by grabbing onto the hedge branches. But it would be messy and noisy.

I walked up the street, looking for an easier way into his yard. In fifty or sixty feet, the hedge came to an end, but the wall continued. Feeling carefully to make sure the wall wasn't topped with broken glass, I grabbed onto the top of the wall and pulled myself up.

Looking over the top, it was easy to see that the spot I was in was completely exposed, visible to dozens of houses on neighboring hills. Anyone who happened to be looking this way would see me climbing the fence.

I went back down the street, looking into the foliage, probing my hand in here and there. I came to a place where the hedge foliage was sparse, damaged from what looked like decades of neighborhood kids climbing through. It was dark inside the thicket of branches, so I couldn't see how best to channel my inner ten-year-old boy's instincts for tunneling through somewhere I wasn't supposed to go.

I reached one leg through a small opening, bent some branches, ducked my head down, and poked it into the foliage. I shifted my hips into what seemed like an impenetrable thicket. My shirt hung up on branches, sharp wood gouging into the side of my neck and threatening to poke into my ear canal. A vine wrapped around my throat, seeming to pull at me harder the longer I held still. Maybe it was a carnivorous hedge, reeling me in for the biggest supper of its life.

I grabbed a different branch, shifted my weight, ripped at the vine that was choking me, and turned so that I was going through the branches back first. Then I popped out into a clearing. I might have been bleeding from multiple wounds, but, assuming there weren't guard dogs waiting, I would live another day.

I looked around. A heavy canopy of tree branches stretched

overhead, and sunset was soon, so I was still in relative darkness.

I pushed through the bushes and trees, slipping through tight spots sideways and raising my arms up as plants scraped at my butt and abdomen. Twice, I got down on hands and knees and crawled under low trees whose branches couldn't be breached without a bulldozer. Marin County jungle might not be as thick as Hawaii jungle, but it was still a jungle.

I came to a driveway that curved up to a three-car garage. Parked in front was a black Corvette and next to it a silver Audi.

To my side was an occasional view of the red rose guy's house, large, low, and modern. Spare windows set in redwood-sided walls with no trim or shutters faced spectacular views across Sausalito to its bay and Tiburon. The sun had lowered behind the coastal ridge to the west. Berkeley and Oakland across the bay were still sunlit, but Sausalito was fast moving toward twilight.

At the downhill side of the red rose man's house was a sprawling deck. Because of the slope of the ground, one edge of the deck was supported by eight-foot-tall posts. The center of the deck seemed to sit on a dome of concrete. The side of the deck closest to me was lit by light coming from inside the house.

I crept around and under the deck, head bent to avoid beams. I moved slowly, peering hard at the dark ground to try to discern any objects that might make noise should I stumble into them. Except for a collection of yard tools leaning against a wall, my path to the other side of the deck was clear.

On the other side of the deck, the landscape was again dense with plants. I pushed through bushes. The top of the deck was easy to grasp. There was a notch in a small tree into which I wedged my foot. I found a branch to provide some support for my other foot, but I put most of my effort into pulling myself up with my arms so that I minimized the likelihood of breaking off the branch with my foot and making a loud snap.

With a fast movement, I let go of the deck with one arm and quickly grabbed the railing above. Moving my foot up to the deck, it was easy to swing my leg up and over the railing. I paused in the growing darkness to look at my surroundings.

The deck had a grand view across the bay, a spectacular collection of a million lights interrupted by large areas of black water. Ferries and ships and pleasure craft twinkled as they crawled across the bay. The multiple lights of the Bay Bridge support cables made shimmering arcs through the night. Beneath them crawled the endless line of vehicles, trucks keeping The City supplied with everything from caviar to gasoline, cars filled with vacationing families from across the heartland, their jaws open with wonder at the sight of San Francisco at night, limousines bringing people to and from the theaters and jazz clubs and dance stages, the occasional ex-hippy in his split-windshield VW microbus with flowers painted on the side coming back to relive memories from his days in the Haight during the '60s.

I turned back to the house and saw that it was a large spread done in 1950's Modern. The entire outer wall was floor-to-ceiling glass. It had a dramatic, overhanging roof. Inside the closest windows was a large room with a shiny maple floor, lit by recessed ceiling cans. The overhead lights also shone on a black grand piano. To one side was a heavy glass table and in its center, a glass vase with three red roses.

In the center of the deck was a swimming pool, glowing blue from soft underwater lighting. It was one of those infinity pools, with the fall-away side where the water appears to flow off the disappearing edge.

The entire picture of a grand house and deck and pool and even grander view didn't make sense. Charity work was about collecting donations of money or other goods and distributing them to the poor or otherwise needy. Charity spoke of used clothing and warehouse storage facilities and dedicated people driving old cargo vans. Charities were effective at motivating even frugal people living on fixed incomes to give small amounts to help people who were worse off. Yet, I'd watched a well-dressed man collect charity mail and followed him to an abode more appropriate to that of a tech billionaire.

I stepped closer to see better through the window wall and saw that the roses in the vase had wilted.

If I hadn't moved close to the window, I might not have seen the reflection that showed movement to my side. I turned as a shovel arced through the night toward my head, its sharp blade about to slice through my neck.

EIGHTEEN

I let my legs collapse and dropped to the deck. I shot my arm up, fingers extended. My palm hit the handle of the shovel as it came down, but I was unable to grab it. My hand deflected the shovel blade just enough to miss my face. The man spun around to swing at me again. I rolled toward him and grabbed his legs. It's the simplest takedown when someone isn't prepared to leap away.

I locked my arms around his lower legs and pulled them to me hard. He couldn't kick and he couldn't catch his balance. He began to fall backward. He tried to catch himself by stabbing the shovel back onto the deck behind him. It hit a big ceramic planter and slipped to the side, and the man went down hard enough to break his tailbone as he hit the deck. He put his elbow out to break the fall and to keep his head from bouncing off the deck boards. I heard him grunt with pain.

The fall stunned him. I scrambled up, rolled him over onto his stomach and pulled his arms behind his back, his wrists crossed over each other. He'd taken off the suit coat and put on a sweater. I put a knee on his arms to hold them in place.

"You're breaking my arms!" he cried with a garbled voice as his face was mashed onto the deck boards. Unlike when I had vaguely overheard him talking on the phone, this time he sounded not so much like a young man as like a kid.

"What's your name?"

He didn't respond. I pulled up on his arms. He moaned.

"Kyle!"

"Last name?"

"Spatt. Kyle Spatt."

"How old are you, Kyle?"

"Eighteen."

"Whose house is this?" I asked.

"My sister's. Dory Spatt. My arms are killing me!"

"Who else is home?"

"No one."

I eased off the pressure but kept my knee on his back, holding his arms in place. "Who do you work for?"

"Dory."

"Does Dory have a tattoo of three roses on her ankle?"

"Yes."

"Who does Dory work for?"

"Herself. She's self employed."

"What kind of business?"

The kid paused. "Different stuff. Investments."

"Like this house," I said.

Another pause. "Yeah."

"Where does the investment money come from?"

He didn't answer. I jerked up with my knee, bending his arms enough that his elbows would be under severe stress.

"Okay! Okay! I'll tell you."

I backed off with my knee. "I'm waiting."

"She runs a charity. She invests the charity's money."

"Did Dory start the Red Roses of Hope charity?"

"How did you know... No. She worked for the owner. But the owner died."

"How?"

"They were out sailing on the bay. On the owner's boat. The owner got his leg caught in a line and fell overboard. He was dragged along. Dory tried to free him, but couldn't."

"And Dory took over the charity," I said.

"Yeah. Dory said the owner had made her a partner."

"Right," I said. "And then Dory took on the name Isadore and upped his charity game to a new level."

Kyle paused. "She thought that name made her seem sophisticated."

"How long ago did Dory take over the charity?"

"I think it was four years ago. When the man died. I started working for her two years ago."

"When did Dory buy this house?"

"About the same time she hired me."

"Two years after she started acquiring money like it was

shooting out of a firehose," I said in an effort to be provocative.

The kid didn't respond.

"The Red Roses of Hope charity is a fake, right?" I said.

Still no response.

"Answer me!"

"I don't know. Maybe. Probably. But Dory is a good person at heart. I really think that someday she's going to give lots to the poor. I mean children. Children in need." Kyle Spatt squirmed underneath me. "You're breaking my arms. Let me up. Please. I won't do anything. I promise."

I patted the kid down, from ankles to neck. I found his ring of keys, his wallet, and his phone. I stuffed them in my pocket. I held his right arm behind his back as he stood, lifting up on it until he squirmed and moaned.

"Open the door. We're going inside."

"I don't have to. You are a trespasser. I have a right to defend myself and my house. This is a home invasion. I could call the cops. You'll go to jail."

"Great idea. Let's go inside and call the cops."

I walked him over to a slider. He slid open the door. We walked into the room with the grand piano.

"Where do you keep tape?" I asked.

"What?"

"Packing tape or duct tape. To tie you up. You make it easy, I won't hurt you. You make it hard, I'll break your arm."

"In the kitchen."

I walked him into a large kitchen with appliances so modern I didn't even know what some of them did, a center island larger than my entire kitchen nook, black granite counters, glossy red cupboards, stone floor, all glowing under ceiling can lights. Over on one counter was the leather shoulder bag, still bulging with envelopes containing the mail, which probably meant money.

"Where?"

"The drawers next to the wine cooler. Second one down."

I walked him over but held him away from the drawers. I didn't want him trying to grab a knife.

There was a roll of black duct tape where he said. I sat him on a barstool at the center island, taped his hands behind his back and his feet to the legs of the stool, positioning his legs so his feet were below the footrest. But they didn't reach the floor.

"That hurts," Kyle said. "This is a really uncomfortable position with my legs just hanging."

"And the stool is tall and narrow. Easy to tip over," I said. "You'd smack your head onto stone tile."

"This is like torture. It's a crime to tie me up."

"Right up there with taking money from donors under the guise of telling them it was for feeding children and then using the money to heat the swimming pool."

"I could scream," he said.

"Sure. And I could pick up the phone, dial nine one one, and report that I have captured one of the principles behind the Red Rose charity scam, guilty of bilking innocent donors. I could explain that the two principals in the business were siblings who had animosity between them and that I believed that Kyle, murdered his older sister Dory."

"What? Oh my God, what are you saying?! Dory was murdered? Was it you? Did you kill Dory?!"

"No, I'm investigating her murder. And you are my prime suspect."

Kyle was moaning again, rocking on the stool. "She wasn't returning my calls. I thought she was blowing me off, again. I can't believe this!"

"So you are going to answer my questions. If I think you're fudging your answers, I call the cops." I pulled out my phone and set it to record.

"State your full name."

He hesitated, staring at my phone as if it were a poisonous snake.

"Kyle C. Spatt."

I made Spatt give a full statement. He answered my questions as if he were on the witness stand, and he gave me all of the sordid details of the Red Roses of Hope Charity for Children. He told me that the charity was bringing in roughly six million dollars a year and that one of Dory's biggest ongoing dilemmas was figuring out what to do with all of the money, $500,000 every month, more during the holidays. He told me how Dory used direct mail advertising and email newsletter marketing with devious techniques to convince potential donors that their contribution was going to save children from dire conditions. He told me how she brainstormed for hours about how to appeal to people's empathy and sympathy. He explained how she ran test mailings to see what kinds of baby pictures got the most response, which vulnerable toddler photos made people write bigger checks.

"It sounds very manipulative, preying on people's emotions and fears and worries," I said.

He nodded. If the news of her murder was stressful, he didn't show it. "One time Dory was talking about the wording on a mailer. She said she always has two goals. First, she wants donors to think that good people want to help others. Second, she wants donors to worry that they or their families could one day need help, too. Like, someday, you might get run over by a bus, and your darling daughter would be at the mercy of the foster system, just like the sad little girl in the brochure picture. So your fears motivate you to send more money. Dory was always like that, figuring out how to play a person so that they would open their wallet."

"Did Dory ever discuss with you the best ways to distribute benefits to the kids who need help the most?"

Kyle shook his head.

"Did Dory ever meet with kids who needed medical help?"

"No."

"Poor kids? Orphaned kids?"

"Look," Kyle said. "I'm sorry. The answer is no. Dory is a… was a scammer. The charity was basically a way to cheat people out of their money."

"You say 'basically.' Why the qualifier?"

"I just say that because that was, you know, her intention."

"I don't understand. A scam is a scam."

"But technically, it wasn't. It was all legal."

NINETEEN

The statement was shocking in its boldness.

"How could it be legal? How did she satisfy the demands of the state governments or the IRS?" I asked. "Surely, she had to jump through some hoops to justify her charity to the authorities. Didn't she have to prove at least some level of giving?"

Kyle was breathing hard. "I don't know how it all worked. But they have some basic systems they use."

"Who is 'they?'"

"I've heard Dory talking to other charity people on the phone. It's like any kind of business. The people in the charity business get together and talk shop. They have meetings. Conventions, even. Like right now there's a mountain bike get-together for them up in Lake Tahoe, where Dory was going when she disappeared. They all go to play in the mountains. But instead of collecting charity, I think they mostly perfect their techniques."

"These scammers have systems for dealing with authorities?"

"Yeah. A bunch of them, as far as I can tell."

"Like?"

Kyle cleared his throat. "Well, one of them I know about is called donation value inflation."

"It has a name?"

"Yeah, I guess it's a standard thing some charities do."

"How does it work?"

"I don't know how other charities do it, but I can tell you how Dory did it. She'd order up ten thousand children's T-shirts for a dollar each. Really cheap shirts she could get in bulk from Viet Nam. Then she had a printing company print something on them like, 'Love Heals.' The printing company charged a dollar for each one. So then she would own ten thousand printed T-shirts, and their total cost was twenty thousand dollars. Next, she'd find some way to give them away, sometimes just shipping them off to another charity like the Goodwill. Or when a natural disaster strikes, like a hurricane, she'd ship the shirts in bulk to a disaster shelter. Maybe some kids get them and use them. But maybe the disaster shelter can't even give them away and they end up in a landfill. The main point was that she'd figure some way to get rid of the shirts and get a receipt for the donation."

"Giving away ten thousand T-shirts might be hard," I said.

"Right," Kyle said. "But it was worth whatever it took, because the whole point was just to get paperwork saying she bought the shirts and then shipped them off."

"So where's the scam?" I asked.

"The scam is that the official word from Dory's charity is that the plain version T-shirts are really worth twenty dollars each and she got them so cheap only because she's such a shrewd shopper. After all, you can go into stores and find kids T-shirts selling for twenty dollars and more. Then she would claim that printing 'Love Heals' on the shirt adds another twenty dollars to each shirt's value. So the Red Roses of Hope charity claims that each shirt has additional value because of the charity's efforts. The total value of the shirts with printing is stated as forty dollars each. So each time Dory gave away ten thousand of them, she claimed a total charitable donation of four hundred thousand dollars."

"For shirts that cost the charity only two dollars each, or twenty thousand total."

Kyle nodded. He looked embarrassed, but he also looked a bit proud. "Yeah, I don't really like my sister much, but she's real smart." He paused. "Was. She was very smart."

He shifted on the barstool. "My legs are killing me. Can't you move the tape so they can be on the foot bar?"

"No. If you want to stay out of prison, keep talking."

He took a deep breath, shutting his eyes. "Dory had a rule. We had to make two donations like this every year. That way she claimed she was making donations worth eight hundred thousand dollars a year. She'd put that on the tax and government forms, and she used that amount to convince her donors that Red Roses of Hope is being super generous. Her paperwork supposedly proved that the Red Roses of Hope donated almost a million dollars worth of goods to children every year, which was most of her net income. The donation value inflation made it look like most of the dollars she collected got sent out to needy kids."

"Where did the rest go?"

He took a deep breath. "I don't know how accounting works. But she talked about categories like executive salaries, staff salaries, office space, supplies, stuff like that. I think that used up the rest of her net income."

"So her net income was about one million a year," I said. "Let me guess. Executive salary means money paid to her. And Dory's staff is you. And the office space is this glorious house, and supplies are things like gas for the Corvette in the driveway."

Kyle grit his teeth. "Right."

"A few minutes ago, you said you thought the charity brought in six million dollars a year. If her operating income was one million, what happened to the other five million?"

Kyle looked uncomfortable. "The main expense for most charities is how the fundraising works. For example, the Red Roses of Hope charity uses a separate company to do all of its fundraising. It's called Fundraising Matrix Systems, LLC."

"A Limited Liability Company," I said.

"Yeah. So when the IRS checks the Red Roses paperwork, they see that Fundraising Matrix Systems LLC raises all of our money. I've heard that most fundraising companies take a large percentage as their fee. In Dory's case, she pays eighty-five percent of gross revenue to Fundraising Matrix Systems."

"A huge percentage."

"Yeah. But as Dory always said, the fundraising company has sophisticated techniques that bring in the money, money that the charity wouldn't otherwise have, so Fundraising Matrix Systems earns its fees. Eighty-five percent of the gross revenue is the five million you're wondering about."

"Okay, so Fundraising Matrix Systems gets five million. Where's the scam in that?"

Kyle swallowed. "Fundraising Matrix Systems is a for-profit company, and it's owned by Dory."

TWENTY

"**Y**ou're saying her Red Roses charity pays a separate company five million a year and that Dory owns that company, too?"

"Yeah. But I don't think her name is listed as owner of Fundraising Matrix Systems. There's some way it's hidden."

"That sounds like laundering money."

"No, it's all legal. And Fundraising Matrix has expenses, too. Office staff and website stuff. But it's mostly automated. The software was set up by a company that specializes in building online stores. The mailers are printed and sent out by a printing company. The office staff is a woman in Oakland who does almost everything except during the Christmas holiday rush. Then Dory hires two temps to help out."

I said, "If you take those expenses out of the five million dollars, that would leave a lot of money left over."

"Yeah," Kyle said. "About four million five hundred thousand. Dory pays income tax on that, so it's all legitimate."

"But it's still a scam."

Kyle seemed to squirm on the bar stool. "I guess I'm just thinking that the people who donate to Red Roses probably wouldn't think it's right that the money they send in goes to Dory's accounts and doesn't actually feed kids or anything."

"Just to be sure I understand," I said, "Red Roses of Hope takes in all this money. Then it gives most of it over to Dory's other company for fundraising. So from the point of view of the state or the feds, Red Roses of Hope charity has relatively little left over to use for actual charity work."

"Correct."

"And of that smaller left-over amount, Dory also paid herself a regular salary. Money that looked, on the books, like operating expenses that any successful charity would have."

Kyle nodded. "And because of the donation value inflation,

Dory could claim that her Red Rose charity gave away most of its net income."

I said, "The inflated value donation is just a figure on a tax form. The money still exists. Where does that it go?"

"I don't know. But stuff like this house got paid for in some way, whether from the charity or the fundraising company. Same for her condo in Hawaii, her cars, other stuff. And when she takes vacations, she's officially doing research to learn how best to do her charitable giving."

"So the vacations get deducted as business expenses," I said.

"Yeah."

"I've always thought that charities were non-profit companies that had to have a board of directors. What about Dory's?"

"Yeah, for sure. Nine friends. Actually, they're really just drinking buddies that belonged to Dory's sorority in college. They all get a stipend for their services, and Dory lets them use this house and the Hawaii condo."

"I've heard of exorbitant salaries for charity executives, but this seems a step above that."

"Totally." Once again Kyle sounded proud of the scam. "Dory often said that while people at the top of big charity companies make big money, it's nothing compared to successful mid-sized charities that don't have lots of employees and real boards of directors. Although I guess in the charity business, they're not called owners."

"What do you mean?"

"She said that charities are owned by the public and the people who run them are called stakeholders. Anyway, she kind of scoffed at her poor charity colleagues who work for the bigger name companies where there's more scrutiny. Those people only make hundreds of thousands per year compared to the successful acts put on by people like her, who make several millions per year. I remember her talking about a guy in New York who claims that his charity provides for the wishes of dying children, while the reality is that he makes over a hundred million a year. All legal because the vast majority of it is paid to his for-profit fundraising company."

I couldn't hide my disgust. "These people are crooks, ethically and morally."

"I agree," Kyle said.

"And you're saying it's legal."

Kyle nodded. "Yeah. I talked to Dory about it once. She said that what makes things legal isn't about what's ethical or not. It's about what legislators vote for to keep the economy going. She said her business generates huge dollars and sends it along through the economy, and that's better than just having that money sit in old people's checking accounts doing nothing."

I made a slow shake of my head. "And that leaves her plenty of money to contribute to the re-election campaigns of legislators who see things her way."

Kyle nodded. "Dory always says that if you're stupid and use a gun to rob a thousand dollars from a gas station, you can go to prison for decades. But if you start a charity and use the standard accounting techniques, you can make millions every year. And the local chamber of commerce might give you a medal for bringing so much money into the local economy."

"You called it accounting techniques. It sounds more like accounting tricks."

"Yeah, I think so," Kyle said.

What he said seemed so unbelievable that I made a mental note to check into the regulations about charities.

After a minute of silence, he said, "How did she die?"

"Somebody tied her up to the tea house on Fannette Island in Emerald Bay, Lake Tahoe. It appears she died of exposure. Hypothermia."

"So the killer wanted people to find her body," Kyle said.

"I think so. There were three roses folded up and stuffed into her mouth. Taped in place."

"What?" Kyle looked appalled. "Why?"

"I'd guess the killer wanted to display her body in the manner that would get the most attention. Can you think of anyone she burned? Anybody who might want to harm her?"

He shook his head. "Certainly there were people who didn't like her. But kill her? No, I can't think of anyone who disliked her that much."

"Where does Dory do her banking?"

Kyle thought about it. "Well, her business checking accounts are at Marin Trust and Savings Bank, both the Red Roses of Hope charity and Fundraising Matrix Systems. That's where I deposit the checks I collect in the mail. I know she also has some savings in other banks. She also invests money through a couple of investment brokers. Stocks or whatever they sell."

"Do you have access to any of the accounts?"

"No."

"Do you pay bills for Dory?"

"No. She's real private. She's never given me any of her computer passwords or anything."

"Where does Dory keep her business records?"

"In her office downstairs. She keeps the door locked. I don't even have a key. I only have access to the checking deposit forms and the copy machine."

"How would you describe what you do for Dory?"

"I'm really just an errand boy in nice clothes. I pick up the mail every day. She makes me wear a suit in case anyone finds out that I'm getting mail for the charity. When I get home, I stamp the checks and make photocopies of them so she has their addresses. Then I enter the amounts on a deposit form, put them all into a blue deposit bag, and take them to the bank. I have a key for the bank deposit drop."

"Are you one of the charity directors?"

"No." Kyle looked off and stared out the windows. "I used to think that when I turned eighteen, she would take me in as a partner. But she's never changed her attitude about me."

"Did she pay you well?"

"No. That always pissed me off. I was learning about the business, and I could have taken on a lot of responsibility. But I'm still just the little brother errand boy."

"Be very glad for that. It might keep you out of prison."

I picked up my phone, clicked off the record function, and scrolled through my contacts. It was after business hours, and I wanted to talk to Sergeant Bains of El Dorado County. I found his cell number and dialed.

While it rang, I opened Kyle's wallet and pulled out his driver's license.

"Hello?"

"McKenna calling. I have information for you. First, almost for certain, the body you retrieved from Emerald Bay belongs to Dory Spatt."

"I thought it was Isadore?"

"Apparently, Isadore was a kind of stage name that Dory used. I'm in Marin County, at Dory's Sausalito home, talking to her brother Kyle who worked for Dory. Turns out that Dory ran the Red Roses of Hope Charity for Children. The brother says it's a scam. It appears that Kyle wasn't much more than an errand boy. But he knows about many aspects of the scam, so the state may well bring charges against him. But for now, he's being cooperative. I'll give you his driver's license number so you will have his descriptors should he attempt to flee."

Kyle's eyes got wide as I said it.

"Ready," Bains said.

I read off the address. "Also take down the address of Dory Spatt's house, where Kyle is living," I said as I looked at Kyle. He told me the address, which I repeated into the phone.

"One more address," I said. I recited the address on Market Street in San Francisco. "It's just a mail drop that Dory Spatt used for the Red Roses of Hope charity."

"You mean," Bains said, "that there's no office? It's just a front to make the charity seem more respectable?"

"Exactly."

"You think the brother had something to do with Dory's death?" Bains said in my ear.

"Probably not," I said as I looked at Kyle.

"Do you have any other ideas about the killer's identity?"

"Not now. But I'll be in touch."

We hung up.

I walked over and looked out at the swimming pool glowing turquoise in the night and the distant lights spread across the San Francisco Bay.

"Can you think of anyone who had disagreements with Dory?" I asked.

"Not that I know of. Dory didn't talk to donors or anything. From phone conversations I overheard, it sounded like people seemed to like her. Sometimes, when she didn't want to go places alone, she would take me to business mixers in the area, places where she could, as she called it, take the temperature of the charity climate. Dory was charming. Certainly with men, of course. But women also seemed to like her. Sure, some of them would give her a kind of look."

"What look is that?" I asked.

"A look of resentment. Like, it wasn't fair that some people win the lottery in the beauty department. Like Dory didn't deserve to be beautiful. But Dory would usually win them over."

"Can you think of any of those women?"

"No. When her sorority friends who serve on her board of directors come over here, I've seen a couple of them give her those looks. But I don't think it was more than envy of her looks." Kyle frowned. "So, do you work for the cops?"

"No. I was hired by a man named Douglas Fairbanks. Do you know him?"

"No. I've heard of the actor. But that person died a long time ago, right? Why would this Douglas Fairbanks hire you to investigate my sister's death?"

"He didn't know she was dead. He just wanted me to find her. He thought he was your sister's boyfriend."

"No, not again."

"She's done this before?"

"Yes. She was – what's that word – narcissistic. She was proud of her power to attract men. Dory loved the way older men would fall for her like she had some kind of magic potion. But it caused her so many problems. Why couldn't she just be satisfied with an ordinary life? She was so smart. Yet, whenever she was presented with a choice, she always took the wrong one."

Kyle's anguish seemed sincere. He continued, "And did she dump this man like the others?"

"Maybe she would have. But she died before that could happen. Tell me, Kyle, why do you think she did this? Why would a smart, beautiful woman be a crook?"

Kyle stared up at the wall in a way that reminded me of Douglas Fairbanks when he stared off.

"When I was a little kid and Dory was maybe sixteen, we

were living in a one-room apartment in South San Francisco. A real shit hole. Our mother worked a day shift at a convenience store and an evening shift as a motel clerk. Mom and Dory had tremendous fights. Dory thought that mom was a failure for not having any money, and mom thought that Dory didn't have a clue about how hard it was to make a living. Mom even taunted Dory, saying that if Dory didn't open her eyes to the way the real world worked, if she didn't get an education and a real job, then she would never have any money, that she would never amount to anything. Dory hated mom's attitude. But then, as Dory got a little older, she discovered the power of beauty and how she could get men to do whatever she wanted. And one day when mom told her to get used to being poor, Dory ran away. She sort of hitched herself to the men who started the Red Roses of Hope. Then, she talked the Red Roses man into hiring her."

"Wait. Were there two guys or one guy?"

"Yeah, it's confusing. I guess the Red Roses charity was actually started by two guys. Then one bought the other out. The remaining one hired Dory before he died. After that, Dory owned the whole business."

"Do you remember hearing the names of those guys?"

Kyle shook his head. "I never knew for certain. But one time she made a crack about them. She said something like, 'the guys were a crazy pair, a real Larcenous Larry and Hustler Harry.' I remembered that 'cause I didn't know what larcenous meant. So I asked if that was really their names. She said she thought Larcenous Larry's real name was Lynn. But then she stopped as if she regretted saying it."

"So she didn't say what Harry's real name was."

"No."

"Did you ever hear Lynn's last name?"

"No. I got the sense that real names were best avoided in case the charity got in trouble with the authorities. Dory always just referred to her partner as 'her partner.' I think that was part of their agreement. That way, no one would ever accidentally find out his identity."

"Was it your sense that Lynn was the partner who hired Dory? Or was he the partner who split before that?"

"I don't know," Kyle said. "I'd guess he was the guy who split, but I don't know why I think that."

"Did you ever see either of those men? Or have you seen any pictures of them?"

"No."

"Did you get the feeling the men and Dory were pals?"

Kyle thought about it. "I don't think there were bad feelings between Dory and her partner. But it wasn't like friends."

"When he died and she took over the charity, did she seem tentative or worried about how she would manage?"

Kyle smiled and shook his head. "No, it was the opposite. She was like a tiger let out of the cage. She charged ahead into her new life like she'd been given the greatest gift. She was so excited, all she did was work. Eighteen hours a day. It's like she realized she could finally make big money, and she was a dynamo about it. It was just two years later that she told me that she was doing ten times the business that her former boss had done. She saw herself as a powerful businesswoman, and she believed nothing could ever stop her from proving that mom was wrong, that mom was the real loser. She wanted mom to eat her words for not believing in Dory's potential."

"Do you think that Dory might have orchestrated the death of her former boss?"

I expected Kyle to shout out a protest at the idea. Instead, he said, "I've wondered about it. But I don't know."

TWENTY-ONE

"Kyle, what records of Dory's do you have access to?"
He shook his head. "Like I said, she keeps all that stuff locked in her office."

I untaped Kyle's hands and legs.

"Show me where her office is."

Kyle stood and stretched, then walked out of the kitchen and into the living room. There was a broad open stairway that went down in stages, turning to the left, wrapping around a hanging art-glass chandelier that was 20 feet tall. I followed Kyle down to another wide room, this one cozier than the wood-floored, grand piano room upstairs. There was a thick-nap carpet, a stone fireplace, and big leather furniture arranged to face a large video screen. Kyle went down a hall with several doors. The first was open and contained fitness equipment. Across the hallway, was an open door. "Guest bedroom," Kyle said.

The room was modest in size but luxuriously furnished.

Kyle walked past and touched the next door, which was next to the exercise room. "This is the utility room." The last door, which was closed, was on the same side as the bedroom.

"This is Dory's office."

There was a doorknob and a deadbolt above it. I tried the doorknob. Locked. The lockset was heavy. I'd noticed that the other doors in the house were oak. It would be difficult to break into. "Did she keep the deadbolt locked as well?"

"Yeah."

"Where did she keep the key?"

"Her key ring was either in her pocket or her purse."

"Does the office have windows?"

"Just one. Like the guest bedroom." Kyle went back to the bedroom to show me. I looked at the guest bedroom's window. It was made of oak, very difficult to compromise from the outside without breaking the glass.

"Did Dory keep her office window closed?"

"When she's gone, yes."

"Where is Dory's bedroom?"

"Back upstairs. I'll show you."

As Kyle led me back to the stairway, I saw a framed poster in the hallway that I hadn't noticed before. It was a large graphic of the Solar system. It showed the Sun, and four small dots representing the four inner-most planets, Mercury, Venus, Earth, and Mars. I knew that beyond the small inner planets were the huge gas giants Jupiter, Saturn, and so forth. But those planets weren't depicted on this graphic.

At the top of the poster were the words, "Earth/Sun Lagrangian Points."

I pointed at the framed piece. "Was Dory into astronomy or astrology?"

Kyle made a little chuckle. "No, not at all. But she kept this print around because her former partner was into this thing called Lagrangian points, and he considered them, like, a guide for certain business decisions. I guess there are Lagrangian groups online."

"Finding meaning in the position of stars and such?" I said.

Kyle shrugged. "I don't know. Dory said that Lagrangian points are places where there's balance. Like, if you put something at a Lagrangian Point, it pretty much stays there. It won't go flying off into space. Or into the Sun. Or whatever happens to stuff out in space."

"What do you put there?"

"I have no idea. I think it was more of an idea concept. Like if you have a big customer, you want that person to be in a balance point. Then you just tweak things now and then to keep the customer comfortable. If so, you'll keep making money. She's got a book on it. Something about going big with the Lagrangian model for business."

It sounded like nonsense to me. I took another look at the poster, and we headed up the stairs.

Kyle took me to the upper bedrooms, all modest in size but with private bathrooms. All had the spectacular views. Dory's was the end one. It contained no business-related items. I glanced in her closet and drawers. There was nothing worth noting.

"You said you made the bank deposits," I said. "If you don't have access to the sales records, how did you do it?"

"I just fill out the deposit slips."

"So you have access to the deposit books. Where are they?"

"At the kitchen desk. I'll show you."

He walked back into the kitchen, opened a drawer near a small desk area, and pulled out a long, narrow, booklet and handed it to me. It had printed, self-carboning pages, the kind where one writes on the white copy and it transfers to the yellow copy underneath.

About half of the slips had been filled out. The top, white copies had been torn out and submitted to the bank with the checks. The yellow, carbon copies were filled with names and dollar amounts. I scanned down them. The dollar amounts were mostly under $50, with the most common figure being $23.43.

"Why this unusual amount?" I asked, pointing to the slip.

"Dory's mailer has this page with little boxes next to amounts. Donors can check one of the boxes to show how many children they want to save. Dory put the twenty-three, forty-three amount because the specific unusual amount makes the idea of saving a child more real than just a general twenty or thirty-dollar figure. She says there's psychological studies on how that works. But I can say from experience that when she started printing the unusual amount on the form, the response rate went up."

Kyle handed me a mailer.

It was a large format envelope. On the front was a picture of a young girl about two years old with large, sad, brown eyes. She stood barefoot on a dirt street. In the background was a rusted garbage can tipped on its side, garbage strewn about. A rat scavenged near a fast-food container. Next to the garbage can lay a homeless woman, unconscious, dressed in rags. Near the child's feet were two dirty syringes. On her face was a look of fear.

Printed on the envelope near where the address would go were the words, 'Official Business. It is a Federal Crime to interfere with mail delivery. This mail is only for the recipient listed.'

In the lower left corner of the envelope, below the picture of the little girl, it said, 'You can save this child's life with just

$23.43.'

On the top of the envelope was a message in script, printed in metallic gold. It said, 'Find Your Thank You Gift Inside!'

Inside the envelope was a brochure with more pictures of children. There was also a slip of paper with another photo, this one of a young boy in tattered clothes looking up at an American flag. The caption said, 'Even the poorest children have dreams. You can make those dreams happen with your help today! Just $23.43 can save a life!'

There was also a 3 X 5 piece of cardstock. Attached to it was a refrigerator magnet printed with an American flag. Hanging from the magnet was a little woven ring like a Native American dreamcatcher. Looking close, I could see that it was cleverly made, stamped out of plastic in such a way that it would look handmade to someone with poor eyesight. Attached to the dreamcatcher were three tiny roses. On the card it said, 'Your Gift...This dreamcatcher collects good spirits just for you, 24/7. It is a gift to you from the children saved by the Red Roses of Hope.'

On the back side of the brochure was yet another picture of a child, a little boy of about five with sandy blond hair and brilliant blue eyes. He wore dirty jeans and a T-shirt and was without shoes, his brown socks showing multiple holes. From his dirt-caked fingers dangled a necklace like the one Spot found on Fannette Island.

Underneath the photo, the copy said, 'Damien dreams of one day learning to play the piano. You can make that dream possible by sending $116.16, the cost of 6 month's worth of piano lessons at the orphanage where Damien lives. In return, Damien will send you a genuine, limited edition, Red Roses of Hope necklace. Save a child's life today!'

"This is obviously an effective direct mailer. But what about the electronic donations? Dory has a way for people to contribute online, right?"

"Yes. She has a website, and people can contribute in a number of ways. Paypal is the most popular. See on the brochure?" Kyle pointed to the corner where it had the website address.

"But as Dory always pointed out, a lot of charitable giving

comes from older people. She didn't like that because depositing checks is work compared to online payments. She would always say, 'Never forget that FMOs like to write checks.'" Kyle suddenly stopped himself. He looked uncomfortable and embarrassed.

"What was that you said?"

Kyle's voice was very low. "She called the check writers FMOs."

"What does FMO mean?"

"It stands for feeble-minded oldsters."

"The people who gave the most money," I said.

Kyle nodded. His face was pink.

"Why did Dory think they were feeble minded?"

Kyle's discomfort had blossomed to full, red-faced embarrassment.

I waited.

Eventually, he spoke in a small voice. "Because they succumbed to her mailer. Because her psychological approach worked on them."

"You're saying she had contempt for the very people who gave her the most money."

Kyle made an almost imperceptible nod.

"Kyle, you seem like a reasonable person, someone with a conscience. Did you ever express concern or regret over this phony charity?"

"Yes. Increasingly, as I got older. When I was fourteen years old and Dory inherited the business, I just thought, what a clever way to make money. But in the last couple of years, I began to see what it really was, a corrupt scam."

"Did you ever say anything to Dory about it?"

"Yeah. I made little comments here and there. And a month ago, I told her that it was all wrong. That she was a crook."

"What did she say?"

"She said that charitable giving in the U.S. is three hundred and sixty billion dollars a year. That works out to a billion dollars a day. She put real emphasis on that. Then she said that she was just trying to achieve the American Dream of getting ahead through hard work. I think she justified it by believing it was good that all of the money she collects gets put to use in other ways."

"A bank robber could think the same thing."

"Yeah, I thought of that, too."

I picked up the deposit book and flipped through it. Each slip had lines for about 30 checks. The names were written with the jerky printing of a teenaged boy, each with a first initial and a last name. To the right were the check amounts. A few were for $10, and an occasional check had been made for $50 or even $100. But as Kyle had said, the most common figure was $23.43. Flipping through the slips, I saw that some slips were comprised entirely of checks for $23.43.

At the bottom of each slip was a box for the total. The totals on most of the slips were in the $700 to $900 range. I counted the number of slips for each date.

"The dates on the slips show that most days produce about twelve slips," I said. "Does that seem right?"

"Yes," Kyle said. "Twelve is the average."

"Twelve times an average of eight hundred dollars is close to ten thousand dollars a day. I'm not a wizard with numbers, but I don't think that would add up to your estimate of six million a year that the Red Roses of Hope brings in."

Kyle shook his head. "No. It's only about three and a half million. The other two and a half million mostly comes from the online donations and from the occasional checks for much more."

I gestured with the deposit book. "Do those occasional checks end up in these deposit books?"

"Yeah, all the checks get written up on these deposit slips." Kyle took one of the books and flipped through. He stopped on one of the pages. "Here. A thousand dollars. We get one of those every few weeks."

"A rich Feeble-Minded Oldster?" I said, unable to keep a sneer out of my voice.

Kyle looked down. "Yes."

I looked at other names on the deposit slips. None of them looked familiar to me. But something seemed to repeat now and then. "This name. F Hanover. I've seen it a few times."

"Oh yeah. Frances Hanover," Kyle said. "She sends a check

every week. I've noticed that the checks are dated on Mondays. It's like that's how she begins her week."

"Twenty-three, forty-three. Fifty-two times a year. She thinks she's saving the lives of fifty-two children a year. That would be over a thousand dollars a year. Are there other people who send in checks on a regular basis?"

"Yeah. Some do it weekly, and some do it every month. One I remember is named Betty Rodriguez. She does it at the beginning of each month." He looked through the pages and showed one to me.

"This check is for one hundred dollars. Is that her regular amount?"

"Yeah."

"Twelve hundred per year," I said.

"Yeah."

"Probably pays part of the expense to heat the swimming pool," I said.

Kyle didn't respond.

"Do you have a way to look up their addresses?"

"Like I said, I photocopy them all for Dory before I deposit them. But I remember Betty's checks because they're pink with red flowers on them. She lives in Roseville."

"I want you to look through the photocopy sheets and find the names you recognize as regular donors. I'm interested in the ones that are closest to Sacramento. Tahoe, too, if there are any."

"Should I write down the names?" Kyle asked.

"Yes. Names and their regular donation amounts and their physical addresses. You can skip the ones that only show a post office box."

He reached into a drawer, pulled out a yellow pad and a stack of photocopies, and began going through the photocopies. He paused to write multiple names.

"I notice that all the names on the sheets are people who live in California," I said. "Any idea why there aren't any names from anywhere else?"

"I think the man who started Red Roses built his original mailing list from local sources. Dory talked about how her mailing list was local. She said that if she could expand to the entire country, the financial possibilities would be ten times as great."

"Her fraud could grow from six million a year to sixty million," I said.

Kyle took a breath, then went back to his photocopies. When he was done, he said, "These are all the sheets I have since she left. The ones before that are locked in her office." He handed me the pad. "I don't know about the amounts that come in from the online donations. Dory doesn't talk about the details. But I know it is a lot, and she loves it because she doesn't have to do anything. Paypal just puts the money in the bank account."

I looked at the names and addresses he'd written, all frequent contributors, all living in or close to the Sacramento area like Betty Rodriguez in Roseville, and one in Tahoe, a woman named Elena Turwin in Tahoe City.

I used my cell phone to Google the non-emergency number for the Marin County Sheriff's Office. There was a landline phone at Dory's kitchen desk. I picked it up and dialed the number that was on my screen. Kyle scowled. I don't think it was because I was calling the sheriff. I think it was because I didn't know how to call the number on my screen directly from my cell phone.

A man answered, "Marin County Sheriff's Office."

I began explaining what I'd learned, telling him much of what I'd previously said to Sergeant Bains of El Dorado County.

The man said they'd send someone over.

"In the meantime," I said to the man on the phone, "I have a recording of Kyle Spatt's statement. If you tell me the appropriate email address, I'll send it along."

The man on the phone gave me the address. I wrote it down on the pad. I thanked him and hung up.

TWENTY-TWO

I turned to Kyle.

"You saw that I recorded your statement. Can you tell me how to email it?"

Kyle's eyes got a little wider. "You know how to record on your phone and Google phone numbers, but you don't know how to email?"

"We learn to walk by taking baby steps first."

Kyle's alarmed look wasn't what he'd show if, say, his house was sliding down the hill in an earthquake. But it was alarm, nonetheless. He reached for my phone.

I pulled it away from him. "Nope. Just talk me through it." I didn't want him hitting delete on the recording.

So he explained, in halting steps, thinking his way through a process he had probably never verbalized.

I got the audio file attached and sent to the Marin County Sheriff's Office.

There was a chime from deep in the house.

"Doorbell?" I said.

Kyle nodded.

"Come with me." I took him to the front door and opened it. Two Marin County Sheriff's deputies stood there.

"Good evening, gentlemen. I'm Owen McKenna, and this is Kyle Spatt. Come on in. We have a lot to talk about."

After I left Kyle Spatt in the care of the Marin County uniforms, I hiked back down to Sausalito, calling Street while I walked.

"Everything okay?" I said.

"Yeah. Blondie and Spot are both sleeping. They've exhausted themselves playing. I haven't had any creepy sensations. Maybe that's because my father is lying low. Or maybe I'm just oblivious with the commotion of two dogs. But don't worry. I won't let down my guard. For a moment, I was tempted to run out to my car to get the book I'm reading, and I didn't want to wake the dogs to take them with me. I decided it could wait until morning."

"Thanks. Times of comfort are when vigilance is most needed."

"Is that, like, a thing?"

"Yeah, it's the McKenna comfort/vigilance thing," I said.

"Are you making any progress?" she asked.

"Yes. The address on Market Street was a maildrop. I followed the guy who picked up the Red Roses mail onto the ferry to Sausalito and found charity fraud headquarters. The Red Roses of Hope was owned and run by the woman who died on Fannette Island."

"Isadore?" Street said.

"Yup. Real name of Dory Spatt. She was taking in six million a year and using various accounting practices to transfer much of the money into a for-profit fundraising company that she also happens to own. Her errand boy was her brother Kyle, who acknowledges the scope of the fraud."

I was now down to the ferry dock. The outgoing boat was loading. I got in line.

"Wait," Street said. "If she was using legal accounting practices, then is it still fraud?"

"Maybe not technically. But ethically, yes. At this point, I don't have a clear answer to the legal question. Her brother said that, while Dory kept a lot of the details private, she openly admitted that virtually none of the incoming money went to children in need. Her brother also explained that she was in contact with other people in the charity business and that they too were running what they acknowledge among themselves are scams. He said they 'talk shop' about how to game the system and keep the vast majority of the money they raise, and, in cases like the Red Roses charity, give virtually none of it to the needy people they claim to help. Yes, the laws are set up in such a way that they have a lot of cover. It really looks like some of these charity people are human maggots eating off the good intentions of others who send off money thinking it goes to good causes.

Even for a guy like me who's seen a lot of underbelly over the years, it's shocking."

"What are you going to do?" Street asked.

"I've got her brother currently engaged in a tell-all with the Marin SO. He's hoping, based on what I said to him, that the more he blabbers, the less likely he is to go to prison."

"Is that true?"

"In some ways, yes. But, as always, a good law firm could bury the authorities with paperwork obstruction and maybe shut off any investigation. Fortunately, it seems like brother Kyle doesn't currently have access to the charity funds. Maybe Dory Spatt had a will giving her world to Kyle. Maybe not. But as long as some smart lawyer doesn't find a way to get Kyle access to the company funds, there won't be an easy way for him to hire legal firepower."

"What's next?"

The line was moving. I stepped onto the ferry.

"I'm heading back to my motel in the East Bay and will drive home tomorrow. Are you okay with His Largeness for the next day?"

"Sure. Call me tomorrow?"

"Will do."

We each said 'love you' at the same time and hung up.

When the ferry got back to The City, I found the stairs down into the underground depths, got on BART, and rode the train east under the bay toward Oakland and then on to Walnut Creek. I was in my motel room around midnight.

TWENTY-THREE

In the morning, I pulled up Google maps on my phone and looked up the location of Betty Rodriguez, one of the regular donors to the Red Roses of Hope. She was in Roseville, a suburb northeast of Sacramento. Just before I got to downtown Sac, I veered onto 80, cruised out toward the foothills and turned off in Roseville.

Multiple turns later, I pulled up at a row of eight modern townhouses, beige with brown trim. Around them were beds of white rocks interrupted by small shrubs where people used to have green lawns before the new water conservation rules began motivating developers and homeowners associations alike to trade in turf for stones. I parked and walked back through a passageway that led to a spacious courtyard with more white rock and several large maple trees that cast the entire courtyard in shade. On each of the four sides of the courtyard was another row of eight townhouses forming a large square. Each had a front door that faced the courtyard. The garages and smaller entry doors were on the outside of the square. Residents could come and go through their garages. Guests were funneled through the courtyard. If one loved conformity and regularity, it was an attractive way to construct a miniature village.

I found the townhouse with Betty's number and pressed the bell. A pleasant ding-dong sounded from within. In time, the door opened. A tiny woman wearing a white frock and over it a pink apron stood there holding a baker's rolling pin as if it were a club and she was ready to defend herself. Her hands were white with flour. The amazing aroma of baked goods – croissants maybe – washed over me. I felt like Spot probably does when he's hit with food smells. Try not to drool.

"My name is Owen McKenna. Are you Betty Rodriguez?"

She nodded without speaking. She had piercing blue eyes that were dramatic against her pale, pink skin and white hair. From the baking smells, it was obvious that she was an accomplished kitchen alchemist.

"I'm an investigator from Lake Tahoe." I showed her my license. "I'm looking into a charity called the Red Roses of Hope Charity for Children. I understand that you regularly donate."

I paused.

She didn't respond.

"May I ask you some questions about the charity?"

She nodded. "Would you like a croissant?"

"Yes, please."

She turned and walked into the kitchen. I shut the door and followed. On the counter was a bowl of dough and next to it pieces of dough that had been rolled out onto a sprinkling of flour and then cut into triangles.

On the stovetop sat another cookie sheet with a dozen or more baked croissants with golden exteriors that suggested a hint of crispiness. Betty opened a cupboard and pulled out a small thin, china plate with scalloped edges, a ceramic glazing with blue flowers, and a metallic gold line around the perimeter. On it she set a paper doily cut in a floral shape and on that set a croissant. Next, she set out a cup and saucer, both of the same delicate, gold-rimmed china. She poured coffee and transferred the coffee and croissant to the dining table on which was a narrow vase with a single yellow flower, a mum maybe. Or a daisy. She looked at me as if waiting for my reaction. She didn't move, just stood and leaned back against the kitchen counter.

So I sat down at the table, took a bite of croissant and truthfully told her, "This is the best croissant I've ever had."

She nodded and continued to wait.

I ate the rest of the croissant. "Really, the croissant is fantastic. You're an amazing baker." I drank the coffee. "Thank you so much. May I ask you a few questions?"

She didn't move from where she leaned against the counter, and she didn't speak.

So I said, "From the Red Roses of Hope records, it appears that you send them a check for one hundred dollars every month."

She didn't respond. Maybe because she realized that I wasn't asking a question.

"I'm curious about your motive for sending in a hundred dollars every month."

She frowned as if she didn't understand what I wanted. "I always pay my bills on time."

"Yes, of course you do. But every month you also send this charity money."

"They send me a bill."

"The charity sends you a bill."

"That's what I just said." She pointed to the end of the kitchen counter where there was a small bundle of envelopes. "I pay my bills on the first and the fifteenth."

"Is it possible I could see one of the bills from the Red Roses of Hope charity?"

Betty Rodriguez looked worried. "Are you suggesting that I'm doing something wrong? I've always tried to do the right thing."

"No. I'm not suggesting anything like that. I'm certain that you are a generous person who is making the world a better place. I'm just trying to answer some questions about this charity."

Betty thought about it. She walked over, took the rubber band off the bills, and looked through the envelopes. She pulled one out and brought it over to me.

The outside of the envelope had a small version of the picture I'd seen on the large marketing mailer Kyle Spatt had shown me. Even rendered very small, the poverty-stricken child tugged at the emotions. The envelope was open. I pulled out the contents. There was a return envelope and what looked like a standard bill. It said 'If you send us your payment of $100 by July 1st, we can save four more children. Thank you for your prompt attention to the needs of our children. Your funds are saving lives and transforming despair into hope.'

It wasn't a bill, and I didn't think that Betty Rodriguez actually thought of it as a bill that had to be paid. But it did have the subliminal urgency of a bill.

"Do you remember when you first learned about the Red Roses of Hope charity?" I asked.

"No. I think I got something in the mail."

"Do you get emails from them?"

"No. I don't like email."

"Do you send money to other charities?"

"Of course. Not a lot of money. But there are so many that need help. Children and disabled veterans and Native American kids trapped on reservations without any proper schools and Social Security and…"

"Wait, please. What about Social Security?"

"Well, they need help. Social Security is in danger. And so many people need it."

"Do you have an example of the Social Security charity?"

"It's not a charity. It's the government. They're fighting for the rights of old people who are less fortunate than me."

"I'd love to see what they send you."

Betty picked up the bundle of envelopes. She didn't find what she was looking for. She walked over to a pantry door, opened it, reached down to a cardboard file box, and slid it out. It made a scraping noise on the floor. She lifted the lid off the box and reached into a stack of papers. I was impressed by both the number of papers and the fact that she had kept them.

"Is that your charity box?" I asked.

"Yes," she said as she looked through its contents. "This box is how I know that I'm giving back to the world. After forty-four years as a grade school teacher, I retired. I took up baking. I've been baking for fifteen years. But my baking is a luxury. So many people don't have luxuries. So I help them where I can. I don't send lots of money to any single charity. One hundred dollars a month is my maximum."

I asked, "How many charities do you send one hundred dollars a month to?"

Betty frowned. "I haven't thought about the number. I suppose there are ten."

"A thousand dollars a month works out to twelve thousand dollars a year."

She nodded. "At least I'm fortunate enough that I can afford it. I have my California Teachers State Retirement pension. I live on that. When I sold the house my husband and I lived in for forty-one years, I bought this townhouse and used what was left over to buy an annuity. That gives me an extra thousand a month. That's what I use to help the charities." She pulled out some papers that she had stapled together. "Here's the info on the Social Security Safety Commission."

I looked at the sheets of paper. At the top of the envelope, it said, 'Official Communication from the Social Security Safety Commission.' Under that, it said, 'Protecting the Legacy of the United States of America.'

To the left side of the envelope, printed in red, it said 'This is a Priority Communication.'

I scanned the papers that Betty had stapled to the envelope. There were several slips of paper and one letter. In many places, copy was printed in red with italicized lettering. The overall tone was stern, and the presentation gave the impression that this so-called safety commission was a branch of the U.S. government, appointed and set up to safeguard what other branches of government were trying to dismantle. At the top of the letter, printed at an angle, were the words, 'Congress is trying to take away your Social Security. We need your help to save your income!'

It was, to me, a blatant and revolting attempt to misrepresent what was, at best, a lobbying group that wanted the Bettys of the world to send in money. At worst, it looked like another version of what Dory Spatt had been doing. But instead of scamming people by playing on their desire to save children from terrible fates, this one played on people's fears of losing what, for many, was their only source of reliable income in their old age.

I searched the pages for the address, but there was none that I could find.

"This Social Security Safety Commission," I said. "They provided an envelope for you to mail in your contribution?"

"Of course."

"Because I can't find any address on these pages."

"Well, they probably don't want to be easy to find. It could be that they want to avoid getting on the junk mail lists. They no doubt collect a lot of money. It would make sense that they keep a low profile so that scammers don't come after them."

Her statement seemed incredible. I didn't want to make her feel bad, but I couldn't resist responding. "Don't you think it's possible that they are scammers themselves?"

Betty didn't react. "Well, I suppose there are bad apples in every orchard, right? I've always thought that it was possible that some of the charities that I send money to might not give away as much as they should. But I wouldn't want to deny funds to the good charities because of the not-so-good ones."

"That is certainly a generous attitude," I said.

She showed no surprise. "If people aren't generous, the world would be in bad shape. I learned that teaching Kindergarteners. Some kids will always cheat. They're so young, they couldn't possibly have been trained to cheat. Yet they do. It's in their genes. But most kids don't cheat. So it's important not to judge all kids just because of the few cheaters."

It impressed me that Betty could feel good about sending money off to charities even though she thought some of them might be cheaters. If I'd sent money to a charity and then learned that it was a scam, I'd be very mad. Not mad enough to murder. But other people might be.

I thanked Betty for her time.

"Do you want another croissant for the road?"

"I've been trying to get up the courage to ask."

She put a croissant in a sandwich bag and handed it to me.

I left. After I'd shut the door behind me and walked into the center courtyard, a man approached from the street.

"I saw you leaving my mother's door," he said. "Is everything okay?"

"Yes." I introduced myself and explained that I was investigating charities. "Your name is…"

"Gray Rodriguez. I try to stop by every few days during my lunch break to see how mom's doing."

I nodded and held up the sandwich bag with the croissant. "And sample whatever she's baking? She gave me the best croissant I've ever had."

He smiled. "Yeah, that, too. I assume she was helpful with your charity questions. I've told her that they might be scams. I even offered to do some research on them online before she sends money. But she doesn't want that. She says she goes by her instincts." Gray's words had an edge to them. He clearly didn't like the idea that she might be sending money to scammers.

"It bothers you," I said.

"More than that," he said. "It drives me crazy. My mom is so kind and giving. Her whole life has been about helping others. From the little kids she taught to the teachers who worked with her. And now she sends money – lots of money – to charities. I've tried to tell her what I've read about charities paying their top executives a half million dollars or more in salary. Most of which comes from older women who live frugal lives all so they can send off twenty or a hundred dollars here and there. But apparently the joy she gets out of sending money would be lost if I found out that some of those charities were dishonest."

A bicyclist came through the courtyard at high speed. He swerved to go around us, but came too close for comfort. Both Gray and I took a fast step out of the way.

"Damn!" Gray said. "I hate that about bike riders! They drive me crazy the way they have no empathy for people on foot!"

He radiated anger as he stared off after the biker. His anger seemed out of proportion to the incident. But it was probably his anger at the scam charities that I was witnessing.

I pulled out my card and handed it to him. "May I call you if I have questions in the future?"

"Sure, although I don't know what I could help with." He took my card. "The bastards who prey on well-meaning people like my mom are parasites on society. They should all be thrown in prison or worse." Gray almost seemed to spit as he said it. He obviously harbored a deep resentment, and his anger was building as we spoke.

I still didn't know his phone number. "Do you have a card?"

"No. I'm just a worker bee, a bureaucrat with the parks and rec department. You can call the central number and ask for me. Maybe they'd put you through. Maybe not. They don't give cards to people like me. They barely even give me enough to live on." He sounded more resentful.

"I'm curious about one of the charities your mother donates to. It's called the Red Roses of Hope Charity for Children. Are you familiar with it?"

I watched as Gray's face grew pink and then red and then nearly purple.

"They're one of the ones that she gives a hundred dollars a month to. They send these mailers that are so obviously fraudulent, preying on people's natural empathy. Are you going to do something about it?"

"I'd like to. First, I need to get a sense of the scope of the problem. I was quite surprised to learn that your mother doesn't think they are obvious scams," I said.

"I know. I can't stand it. These crooks should be strung up."

I said, "Have you tracked down any of the charities to see if they are legitimate?"

"I don't have to. You can tell by looking at the mailers which ones make thoughtful presentations. Like, 'here's our situation, and here's what we're trying to do.' They print it out in regular type. They make their case in a basic essay format. It's a little bit like reading decent journalism. Then you get these disgusting come-ons with pictures of amputee veterans. The letters have lots of blue and red type and little balloons with exclamation points and arrows pointing to certain points. Sometimes the envelopes have windows that show coins or a check for a weird amount. All to try to get you to open the envelope and see the veteran without arms." Gray's eyes got wider, and I saw the bulge of his jaw muscles. "For only twenty-nine dollars and fifty cents this veteran will be saved. They're obviously deceptive, yet people like my mother fall for it. She actually says that the charities have to make excessive claims to get the attention of people who aren't as naturally generous as she is. It makes me nuts!"

"Have you ever thought about doing something to stop it?"

"Yeah, wouldn't you like to know! I want to find these people and tie a cement block to their feet and drop them in the Sacramento River!"

"I understand. But just to be sure that I'm getting this correct, you wouldn't really do that, right?"

Gray didn't back off. If anything, he turned redder. "Try me. Tempt me! If I could string these people up and send a message to the rest of them that we won't tolerate these scams, I might!"

I nodded, thanked Gray for his time, then left.

TWENTY-FOUR

An hour later, I'd come over Echo Summit and was driving down to South Lake Tahoe when my phone rang. "Hello?"

"Sergeant Santiago, here. You in the area?"

"I'm on the South Shore, in my Jeep, breaking the law talking to a law officer on my cell phone."

"I recently talked to Sergeant Bains of El Dorado County, and he said you were looking into the murder out on Fannette Island," Santiago said, ignoring my comment.

"Right."

"We've got another one in Kings Beach."

"Same MO? Hanging upside down?"

"Yeah. This time the victim is a man hanging from the top of the flagpole at the Kings Beach Post Office. Maybe you'd like to have a look."

"I can be there in an hour and a half, maybe less," I said. "If you could delay taking the body down, I could stop on the East Shore and get my dog. He found something interesting at Fannette Island. Maybe he can take a look or a sniff."

"That's why I called. We've already lowered the body. But maybe we can keep it here until you get here."

"Thanks. I'm on my way."

I clicked off.

I got Street on her cell phone. "Sorry to be abrupt, hon, but I just came down Echo Summit and got a call from Sergeant Santiago about another murder, this time on the North Shore. So I'm in a hurry to pick up Spot and get to the North Shore. Does that work for you?"

As always, Street didn't let her emotions get in the way of work, hers or mine. "I'm so sorry to hear that. We're at my lab. I'll be ready for you."

"Thanks."

I stopped at Street's lab fifteen minutes later. I was glad to see the little red alarm light blinking on the security system keypad. I made a polite rap on the door. Blondie barked from inside. Spot did not. I grinned at the peephole that Street had recently gotten installed. The door opened.

The dogs pushed out. Spot's nose was at my hand, pushing it around. I bent down to give Street a kiss.

"You're welcome to come with me, if you want."

"Thanks, but I better focus on my work."

"I'll call later." I kissed her.

Street nodded. "I'll be ready to move forward on the next installment of self-defense."

Spot and I left.

TWENTY-FIVE

I drove up the East Shore fast. When I pulled into Kings Beach, I saw multiple cop cars on both sides of the post office, which sits one street back from the main street and is visible from a distance. Drivers had slowed to a crawl, gawking at the cop cars. If I waited to crawl forward in my Jeep, it would take an hour. So I pulled off into a small shoulder area with a no-parking sign and parked. I let Spot out of the back.

"C'mon boy. Let's go and act like human death is no big deal."

I put my hand in his collar and we jogged forward.

When we got to the knot of cops and onlookers, there was a line of yellow crime scene tape wavering in the breeze. I walked up. A cop stepped forward.

"Sorry, sir, this is a crime scene."

"I'm Owen McKenna, here with my canine unit at Sergeant Santiago's request."

I heard a voice from over by the post office. "Hey, McKenna, come on over." It was Santiago. He held his hand up and said, "Let McKenna through."

Spot and I ducked under the tape and went over to Santiago. He was with two other officers. Next to him was a gurney with a body under the sheet.

I didn't look at Spot, and I tried to act normal. I knew Spot could smell the body as soon as we got close. But maybe I could telegraph a casualness about it.

"The man looked dead when we got here," Santiago said, "but we took him down as fast as possible in case he wasn't."

"Hanging upside down?"

"Yeah. His head and neck are swollen purple. Not pretty. You want your dog to look?"

"In a minute. He's death sensitive. So we're practicing how to chill around dead bodies."

"Got it."

"Do you or anyone else recognize the victim?" I asked.

"No. Some of the locals were here when we lowered the body, and they didn't recognize him, either. So it might be a tourist. But this kind of premeditated murder, you'd think it was someone the killer knew. And to pull off such a killing without being seen suggests a local with knowledge of the area."

"What's your sense of time of death?"

"The medical examiner was here, and he thought it had been maybe ten or twelve hours based on core temperature. That would also fit for how someone could get the victim raised up on the flagpole without being seen. Tourist season doesn't start until July. You hang out in Kings Beach at two in the morning in June, you might not see any vehicle for a long time."

"Who discovered the body?"

Santiago pointed toward a cafe over on the main street. "The woman who owns that restaurant was opening up this morning when she heard the line of the flagpole clinking in an unfamiliar way. You know how those things clink in the wind."

"Sure."

"Well, she said today it sounded different than normal. It made her look up. She said she could tell something was different about the flag. Like it was wrapping around something. But she couldn't tell what. So she waited for a bit and finally there was a little breeze that ruffled the flag. That's when she saw the body. Hanging upside down. The body was hanging by the same line that hoists the flag. It looks like the perpetrator lowered the flag, then tied the victim's feet to the line where it attaches to the top of the flag, then raised it up to the top of the pole. The thing is, it would take a very strong and heavy man to pull hard enough to lift that body up. Or maybe a few men. It took three of us just to lower it, reeling out the line, bit by bit, the rope cutting into our hands. If we'd let go, that body would have come crashing down."

"Anything in the victim's mouth?" I said.

Santiago raised his eyebrows.

"The victim on Fannette Island had roses in her mouth," I said.

"I see," Santiago said. "This guy has a tennis ball in his mouth. I don't see how the perpetrator got it in there. A tennis ball seems quite a bit bigger than a man's mouth. It's really crammed in. Probably dislocated the vic's jaw."

"May I have a look? And do you have a pair of gloves?"

"Help yourself." Santiago gestured, and one of his deputies reached out with a dispenser box of latex gloves.

I pulled on a pair, reached for the sheet, and pulled it down to expose the man's head.

The man was as described, with purple head and neck, swollen to half again its normal size. Protruding from the man's mouth was a bright yellow tennis ball, squeezed into an oblong shape by the confines of the man's mouth. As Santiago said, it would be hard to get a tennis ball into most people's mouths.

"Anything else of note about the body?" I said.

"Not that we noticed. I wrote down his descriptors. See if you think I'm guessing right." Santiago held up his clipboard and read off the form. "White male, about five ten, one hundred seventy-five pounds, brown eyes, forty-five to fifty years old. Thinning brown hair cut medium long, bald spot toward the back of his head. Hands soft like he'd never done physical labor in his life."

"Sounds accurate to me," I said. "Did the ME have an opinion on cause of death?"

"He said it could be any of several reasons, but exposure and the resulting hypothermia is sufficient to kill a person. Even though the weather has been a lot nicer since the woman died on Fannette Island, it still gets very cold at night. And hanging upside down for what could have been hours, that wouldn't be good for your brain, right?"

"Yeah. I'll have my dog take a sniff if that's okay with you."

"Go for it."

I turned to Spot. His ears were back, and his tail was down and motionless.

"Okay Spot!" I said with enthusiasm. "Find the scent!"

I pulled the sheet off and urged Spot forward. "C'mon, boy. See what you can find." I did the hand-drop gesture toward the body. "Find!"

Spot sniffed a bit, air scenting, his nostrils flexing. "Come, boy, let's walk around the body." I pulled on his collar. Spot came but with substantial reluctance. He never put his nose on the body. No doubt the scents in the air were plenty strong enough.

I walked Spot around the gurney. Spot seemed to pause just a bit at the man's head.

"What is it, Spot? What do you smell?"

I thought that if I let go of his collar, he would immediately walk away. So I held on, but I loosened my grip. I tried to sense any movement.

For a moment, Spot moved his nose toward the tennis ball, then pulled his head away.

I talked to Spot, encouraged him, acted like this was just a regular, everyday event that all people and dogs deal with. I brought Spot to the man's feet, around the bottom end of the gurney, then back up the other side.

Spot did nothing, alerted on nothing. His body language was lethargy and sadness.

"Not much," I mumbled.

"What exactly is it that you expect him to do?" Santiago asked.

"Find any unusual smells. He usually notices those things that stand out. It's like a kid picking up an unusual rock off the ground. If there is something he doesn't expect on a dead person, he will often pay attention."

"All I saw," Santiago said, "was that he kind of noticed the tennis ball. And that would make sense with what you said. Something he's not used to smelling on a body."

"Right. Can we take the tennis ball out of his mouth?"

"Sure. You think it would be easier for him to smell it that way?"

"Maybe," I said. "Plus, the tennis ball has a great chance of retaining some of the killer's DNA or other material that relates to the killer."

Santiago nodded. "I already thought about that. I figure, we can take an evidence bag, turn it inside out, then use it to grip the ball to pry it out of his mouth directly into the bag."

"Sounds good," I said.

Using a fresh pair of latex gloves, Santiago pulled a clear plastic bag from a box, turned it inside out, pulled it over his hand, and reached for the tennis ball. He got his thumb and forefinger into the corners of the victim's lips and pulled on the ball. It didn't move.

"This baby seems locked in place. Let me get my fingers in deeper." He pushed hard, pinched the ball, and tugged. It still didn't move. "I suppose we could puncture the ball to deflate it. But I hate to do anything that alters evidence. What do you think would be best, McKenna?"

"I had to say. We could wait and let the ME deal with it. But I would like to get the ball out and then have my dog take a sniff."

Santiago nodded. "Hey, Bonnard, pull on a pair of gloves and help me with this. You pull down on the victim's jaw while I push back on his forehead. Don't pull hard enough to fracture it, but just to open his mouth a bit more. That should make it easier to pop this thing out."

The deputy did as asked, Santiago pulled hard on the ball while he pushed back on the victim's forehead, and out came the ball.

Santiago held the ball out. "Your dog can sniff it now."

"It's not the ball I want him to smell. It's the man's mouth."

Santiago frowned.

"C'mon, Spot. Find." I tugged him toward the man's head. I knew that Spot's nose had already gotten used to the smell of the tennis ball. But I hoped that any other unusual smell would catch his curiosity.

Spot resisted my tug. "C'mon, boy! What do you smell?!"

Spot reached his nose over to the man's head, his nostrils flexing. His nose shifted to the man's mouth and gave it a sniff that some people wouldn't notice. But I saw it as an alert.

"Okay with you if I reach a finger in his mouth?"

Santiago looked a bit squeamish. "If you want to, help yourself."

I'd been holding Spot's collar with my right hand. My gloved left hand hadn't touched anything. I reached my left index finger into the man's mouth and swept it around. I found nothing near his tongue or in the main space between his tongue and palette. Then I felt inside his cheeks and hit an item. I pulled it out and held it up to the light.

"What is it?" Santiago said.

"Some kind of a little figure," I said. "A tennis player swinging a racket. It's got a type of paperclip shape on the back side so you could clip it onto something."

"A lapel clip?"

"Yes, I think that's what it is."

"And it looks like it's made of gold," Santiago said. "Makes me wonder why the killer didn't keep it."

I hefted the little figure and then rubbed at it with my gloved finger. "It's too lightweight to be metal. And in places, the gold is worn off and you can see white plastic. It reminds me of the necklace Spot found on Fannette Island. A cheap plastic trinket designed to look like metal. The kind of thing a charity might put in a mailer to ask for donations."

"A sports charity?" Santiago said.

"That would be my guess."

Santiago got out another evidence bag, opened it and held it out. I dropped the little tennis player into it.

"Sergeant Bains at El Dorado County told me about that necklace," Santiago said. "What's your take?"

"I was just in San Francisco, and I learned that the woman who was killed on Fannette Island ran a scam charity called the Red Roses of Hope Charity for Children."

"Now I get it," Santiago said. "There's a big mountain biking charity event going on in Tahoe. So we might logically think that this victim is involved in a scam charity relating to tennis."

"My thought exactly," I said.

"And," Santiago said, thinking, "these people are maybe being killed by a disgruntled money donor. A vigilante payback of some kind. And the killer is displaying the victims in a bold way. So maybe they're supposed to be warnings to other scammers?"

"We're thinking on the same track," I said.

"Your dog sure earned his steak today. I could see this corpse going through an autopsy and burial prep with no one ever finding that little figurine in his cheek."

I nodded as I pulled off the latex gloves. As I looked at Santiago, I noticed the group of people that still crowded on the other side of the crime scene tape, a mix of people similar to those who always congregate at crime scenes. Some are merely curious. Some have a fascination with death. Some are more interested in the emergency responders. Some have never seen a dead body, even one draped with a sheet. And, as cops know, once in awhile, the victim's murderer sometimes joins the crowd to get a perverse thrill out of the excitement he's caused.

I scanned the people more carefully. One of the faces seemed vaguely familiar. It wasn't someone I knew, but someone I felt like I'd met for a brief moment. A man, short, muscular build, with a flat-top haircut.

"Catch you later," I said to Santiago. "C'mon Spot, let's take a walk," I said in a low voice. Spot and I ambled toward the crowd, casual, slow, no sense of purpose to our movement. I ducked under the crime scene tape, then held it up so Spot could walk under. When I straightened up, the man was gone.

I trotted toward where he'd been standing, pushing through groups of people. When I got to a small open space, I turned around, scanning near and far. There were numerous places he could have disappeared to, between cars and buildings. He could have simply turned around to face a different way. The most distinctive thing about him was his haircut. I realized that if he'd simply put on a cap, I wouldn't recognize him.

Spot and I walked down a side street, came back a different way. We walked over to the beach and looked both ways, east and west, down the sand. Then back to the post office.

I tried to remember where I'd seen the man with the flat-top haircut. Then it came to me.

When I'd left Fairbanks at his condo, I talked to two men in the parking lot. A taller guy with a goatee who said his name was Kendall Martini. Martini was with a shorter guy with a flat-top haircut. I hadn't gotten his name. Martini said he worked at the Mountain Street Grill in Zephyr Cove. I'd stop there later.

TWENTY-SIX

S pot walked with a heavy gate back to the Jeep.
"You did a good job, Spot. We're figuring out this case
all based on what you found, at Emerald Bay and here in Kings
Beach. Good boy!" I rubbed the side of his chest. We got into the
Jeep, and he promptly lay down on the back seat, shut his eyes,
and appeared to go to sleep.

Before I drove away from my no-parking space in Kings
Beach, I got Douglas Fairbanks on the phone.

"I've learned more about Isadore. I'd like to talk to you."

Fairbanks inhaled as if he was afraid of what I might say. He
said, "Do you want to meet at my condo? I've had my walk, so
I'll be here the rest of the day."

"I'm on the North Shore. I'll stop by in ninety minutes."

"Bring Spot?"

"He'll insist on it."

When I got to Zephyr Cove, I pulled in and parked. The
Mountain Street Grill was a newer restaurant with a hip, modern
look of maple floors, beige walls, and black tables and chairs.
There were few customers. But a lot of activity indicated they were
gearing up for the dinner rush. I asked for Kendall Martini.

He came out a minute later. His goatee looked stiff as if it
had been waxed.

"You probably don't remember me," I said. "I'm…"

"Sure I do. You came by my condo building asking about
Isadore. Did you find her?"

If Martini didn't read the news, I didn't need to fill him
in. "No, I haven't seen her," I said. "But I recently saw your
companion from that day. A short, muscular man with a flat top.
Can you tell me his name?"

Martini shook his head. "I don't even know his name. I met
him at the Brewery that day I saw you. Just across the street from

the condo complex. We got talking about craft brews. He had a thing for IPAs. After awhile, I told him that I lived in a condo on the lake just across the road. He said he was looking at maybe buying property in Tahoe. So I invited him over to see the place. You showed up asking about Isadore when I was taking him out to see the beach."

"Did you get his number or where he lived?"

"No. Sorry, man. It was just a quick show-and-tell thing. You know, be friendly to the tourists and show them around."

I handed Martini my card. "If you see him, give me a call?"

"Sure. Good luck finding the lady. She's one sweet number. Hate to have her be lost."

Fairbanks opened the door as Spot and I approached. He hugged Spot, then pet his head. "You missed me, didn't you?"

Spot wagged, the first sign of happiness since we'd left Kings Beach. His moves and timing were so perfect, I might start charging for his services. But in this case, Fairbanks might charge me for cheering up Spot.

We sat in the same places, me in the chair, Fairbanks on the couch, Spot on the floor next to him.

I skipped the small talk. "Isadore's real name was Dory Spatt."

Fairbanks made a little jerk of surprise. "Dory Spatt?" Fairbanks sounded immediately deflated and disappointed. "So Dory was short for Isadore?"

"No. Dory's brother Kyle Spatt said that she adopted the name Isadore as a sophisticated affectation."

It took a bit for Fairbanks to recover. "Well, it fit with her theatrical nature. Jazz singing and performing."

"She was, in fact, a kind of actor who starred in what could be thought of as a type of play," I said.

Fairbanks looked confused, not sure where I was going.

"She ran a fake charity called the Red Roses of Hope Charity for Children."

"What do you mean, a fake charity?"

"She collected millions in donations each year under the guise of using it to help disadvantaged children. But she kept the money for herself, spending it on a lavish lifestyle, a fancy house and swimming pool overlooking Sausalito and the San Francisco Bay, a grand piano that sits in a room the size of your entire condo, fast cars, a condo in Hawaii, vacation travel."

Fairbanks widened his eyes as if I'd slapped him. He sat so still it was as if he'd suddenly become catatonic. He stared toward the opposite wall, his eyes unfocused. After a minute, he spoke.

"You're saying Isadore was a thief?"

"Yes. A thief who operated at a dramatic level. She had slick brochures and a charity address on Market Street in San Francisco that looked impressive but turned out to be just a maildrop. She would send her brother to collect the mail, which was heavy with checks, sometimes as many as one hundred per day."

"I don't understand," Fairbanks said. "There are lots of rules that prevent fake charities."

"Rules intended to prevent fake charities. But most of them are easily circumvented. In fact, Dory Spatt had colleagues in the fake charity business. And some of them are currently in Tahoe celebrating at the Tahoe Mountain Bike for Charity festival."

Fairbanks was speechless and seemed profoundly depressed. "Do you think she was killed for taking money that wasn't hers? Killed for punishment?"

"I don't know. But if I were to guess, probably yes."

"If it was about punishing her, why do you think a murderer would hang Isadore upside down? That's so excessive."

"My guess is that the killer wanted to display her body in a dramatic way so the world would notice."

Fairbanks looked confused. "You think that the killer wants to become famous? Like Jack the Ripper or something?"

"Maybe. Probably not."

"Then why?" Fairbanks paused. "Oh, maybe now I see. With all the charity people in Tahoe, some of them might also have fraudulent charities. So Isadore's death is putting them all on notice."

"That's what makes the most sense. The media has already picked it up. Papers and websites across the country are running stories and photos."

Fairbanks was quiet a moment. "With Isadore scamming

through her charity, do you think she was scamming me?"

"It could be a possibility. However, you said you offered money but she didn't take you up on it."

"True. But I…" Fairbanks stopped. His face turned red. "I'm embarrassed to say it. I gave her half of this condo."

I tried to hide my shock, but it probably showed on my face. "I thought your relationship wasn't that deep."

"Apparently, I was very stupid. She said she loved Tahoe, and that it was her dream to one day have a place here. I thought, you know, that if I signed over co-ownership in my condo, she would really love me for it. I feel like an idiot."

This time it took me a moment to process what he said. I said, "Now that she's dead, perhaps you'll have full ownership once again. Unless her share passes to her heirs."

"I put our names on the title as joint ownership with right of survivorship, so full ownership passes to the surviving owner. So it will all be mine again. I almost can't believe all of this. What a risk I took."

I realized that this new information gave Fairbanks motive in her death. His condo was worth a lot of money. If, after he signed over half the condo title to Isadore, he had discovered that she was a charity thief, he might have considered killing her to return full title to the condo back to him.

Spot was sitting next to Fairbanks, leaning against his leg. Fairbanks reached out and touched him softly. "When Isadore showed me attention and affection, I think I knew in my heart that it was partly false. But she was like a drug I couldn't resist. The little voice of reason in my head ran through all manner of disparaging thoughts. Like, how could a homely, middle-aged man like me lose his senses and act irrationally when confronted with a beautiful and much younger woman? Of course, I realized that men have succumbed to beauty from the beginning. I suppose knowing I wasn't the only one helped me rationalize it. Older men, touched by beautiful youth, so often lose control. I suppose older women do as well. But I don't know many women. Even if the older person realizes that they might not have been chosen for their physical or mental attractiveness, but for their bank accounts, they want to think that they are the exception.

My lover loves me for me, not for my money. Maybe it actually happens now and then. But how stupid and myopic is it to think that?"

Fairbanks still had his hands on Spot, leaning on him for support.

He said, "John Keats wrote about how beauty pulls the curtain off our dark spirits. Thus the attraction of beautiful people. I know all of these things intellectually. Yet I'm as foolish as any man there is. I see now that I was blind." His voice was monotone and not much louder than a whisper. "I saw attention and confused it with love. I saw beauty and confused it with value. I wanted meaning, but I thought it could only come if other people approved of me. I've made a complete mess of my life. I was vain and stupid, loving her attentions. I ignored the obvious. I ignored my own good sense."

I didn't respond. It is often characteristic of despondency that it is not only pointless to try to reassure, it often makes the person feel worse.

Fairbanks cleared his throat. "It makes me want to disappear. It reveals to myself what a fool I am."

Fairbanks looked over at the window. The light caught the brimming tears in his eyes. "I don't mind that others think I'm a fool. I've been dealing with that my entire life. When I was little, they picked on me for being the fat, clumsy kid. When I got older, they picked on me for being awkward and wearing the wrong clothes and always saying the wrong thing. When I was in high school, they picked on me for reading poetry instead of comic books. When I was in college, they picked on me because I never had a date. But I learned to live with all of that. I found some small comfort in accepting that it was okay to be different. I realized that I was unlike every person I'd ever met. I didn't think anything about me was great. But being just okay was enough. I worked hard, learned how to earn a living, became adjusted to having no friends. I even learned to cope with the fact that, when I asked my bride to tell me the truth about why we never consummated our relationship, she admitted that she preferred women to me. And when I asked why she didn't have the bravery to tell me before we got married, she said that it wasn't until she actually visualized going to bed with me that she realized she didn't want to."

"That would be very hard," I said.

"Harder still was coming to the realization that I would never attract a woman in the usual way, and that the wife I had was as good as I was going to get."

I thought about what Fairbanks said. "Maybe you've just been unlucky and have missed the beauty in older women."

Fairbanks looked confused.

"Here's a mental experiment," I said. "Imagine that instead of meeting Isadore, you'd met a woman your own age or older. Same place, same party. Maybe even the same exotic name. Also imagine that this older woman said the exact same words as Isadore said, looked into your eyes the same way, showed the same interest in your life." I paused, letting the thought soak in.

I continued, "If that had happened, would you have been touched by her manner and her caring and interest in you? Would you have seen that the older woman was wiser, had a better grasp of the world, knew more about those things that really matter? Would you have had more shared experience with the older woman, more to talk about, similar dreams?"

Fairbanks was silent. He frowned, his eyes searching. "I understand what you're getting at. Maybe I was blinded by Isadore's looks so that I couldn't even see where she might fall short. Maybe I might have noticed indications that she wasn't honest if only I'd been actually listening to and noticing her – the real inner person – not the model looks and the practiced gestures designed to show off beauty." He paused.

I didn't respond.

"I once asked her if she liked the romantic poets like Blake and Wordsworth and Byron. It was clear she didn't know what to say. She eventually said that, yes, she thought poetry was very romantic." Fairbanks put his hands to his temples and pushed in as if to keep his head from coming apart.

"I think you're right," he said. "If Isadore had been an older woman, if she'd said the same things, paid me attention the same way, I might have…" he trailed off, thinking, perhaps, of a world that might have been.

TWENTY-SEVEN

Fairbanks wiped his eyes with his sleeve. "In every basic manner of connecting to people on an emotional level, I'm a failure." He stood up, walked over to the kitchen, grabbed some tissues from a box, and blew his nose. "I misjudge. I always go overboard. I never see the world as it is, only as I'd like it to be."

"Sometimes," I said, speaking slowly, feeling my way through the words, "I think that when things are very tough, the best thing to do is to try to stop thinking about the big stuff that bothers you and just focus on what single task you should do next."

Fairbanks stared at the wall. "What, like don't think about how worthless I am, and just go and do the dishes?"

"Something like that, yeah. Then at least you'll be able to think, good, the dishes are done. Then you move on to another task. Gradually you'll feel less worthless."

"That's a very bleak life."

"You've already described your life as bleak."

"Point taken," Fairbanks said.

"So, for the sake of the process, what if you consider those activities that are a step up from doing the dishes? What do you think should be your next move?"

Fairbanks walked over to the window and looked out. Then, speaking to the glass, he said, "I had wanted to sign up to bike the Grand Tour, the final mountain bike event of the festival. But then Isadore disappeared, so I forgot about it. I suppose it's possible they are still taking late signups. They say that the entry fees go to charity. But after what you've said, I doubt that's the truth. But I should still maybe try it. No way can I imagine finding the energy and stamina to participate. But maybe I'll do it anyway. Prove to myself that I can do it. That my life isn't over."

"I think that's a good idea."

"Of course, I'd look like a cartoon in my day-glo road race uniform. The mountain bikers would laugh me off the mountain."

"There's still time to go out and get some mountain bike togs."

Fairbanks looked at his watch. He walked over to the little bowl on the kitchen counter and pulled out his car keys.

"What's the route?" I asked.

"It starts at Spooner Lake. We bike up the canyon to Marlette Lake. There's a loop route that we take up to around nine thousand feet by Marlette Peak. Then we come to the Flume Trail and take that to Tunnel Creek Road. From there it's back down toward Tahoe. There's a connector trail that heads over to Diamond Peak Ski Resort. I forget the total length. Something like thirty miles."

"That's a serious ride," I said. "I remember the views from the Flume Trail, looking down at Sand Harbor and across the lake to Squaw Valley. Mostly, I remember the ride along the edge of the mountain, nothing below you but water fifteen hundred feet down."

"And I have trouble with heights. But I'm not too proud to walk my bike if I get too freaked out."

"Do they run a shuttle from the finish back to Spooner Lake?"

"Actually, one shuttle runs from around the West and North Shores. And another runs from here on the South Shore. I can catch it right here outside my condo. They drop us off and pick us up when the race is over."

"Sounds like a good event. Good luck."

Fairbanks nodded. "Thanks for encouraging me. Maybe there will be life after Isadore."

We left the condo, and Fairbanks pet Spot before he got into his orange BMW.

I remembered that I still had Dory's pajama top. I waved at Fairbanks to stop, fetched the bag with the pajama top, and walked over to his car.

He rolled down the window.

"I forgot to mention, when we were out at the island, I scented Spot on this pajama top, and he found a little plastic necklace that depicted three roses. Does that sound familiar?"

Fairbanks shook his head. He looked worried and confused at once. "Do you think that's something Isadore... Dory brought with her to the island? Or something the killer brought?"

"I don't know. Spot also alerted on a little roll of paper that was floating in the water. It had a little three-line poem about red roses of deceit. Does that bring anything to mind?"

Again, Fairbanks looked stressed. "No. What did it say?"

"I forget the exact wording. Red roses of hope and false promises and wicked deceit."

"Do you think the killer left it there?"

"I don't know for sure, but it kind of fits. The poem was in haiku form."

"Do you mean the seventeen syllable aspect? Or did it have two images with a cutting word between them?"

"I was thinking more about the syllables. A line each with five, seven, and five syllables. Do you think the fact that the poem was in haiku form means anything?"

Fairbanks shook his head. "I'm sorry, but I really don't know anything about haiku. Of course, I studied Basho in college. And we spent some time on the kireji, the division that stops the stream of thought after one of the images. But modern haiku masters are changing it away from the rigorous metrics and away from the images of nature. If the killer was trying to communicate something with a haiku, I couldn't help you."

I thanked Fairbanks, and he drove off to go shopping.

TWENTY-EIGHT

Spot and I stopped by Street's condo, knocked on her door, and asked if she was available for a dinner date.

"Do you mean a romantic date?"

"Whatever suits you," I said. "Although I haven't yet been home to shower."

"And I have to get up early in the morning. So maybe we could just eat in. It's supposed to be a chilly evening. A fire in your wood stove would be nice."

"I always keep the essentials for when we get snowed in and lose power," I said.

"Essentials meaning Sierra Nevada Pale Ale, hotdogs, and charcoal," Street said.

"Of course," I said. "But you don't eat hotdogs."

"Right. We'll roast them for you and Spot and Blondie. I have a zucchini in my fridge. I can roast that."

"And eat it on a bun like a hotdog?"

"Do you have whole grain buns?" she asked.

"No, sorry."

"Then I'll eat it naked."

"That's not enough calories even for you," I said. I reached out and put my hands on her waist, appreciating her curves. "These hips are perfect, but it's not like you've got any extra padding. However, we could work on that. I've got a dozen donuts in the freezer."

"You think I'm too skinny?"

"You're not too skinny. You're just really thin, which allows you to eat donuts with impunity. And anyway, you could eat them on a bed of kale. Of course, you'd have to bring that, too."

"Zucchini and Sierra Nevada will do fine," she said. "I'm not driving, so I might drink a whole bottle."

I turned to Spot. "Look out, Largeness, we're in for a big night."

He wagged.

When we got up the mountain to my cabin, I built a fire in the wood stove using the political news section of the New York Times, with three big Jeffrey Pine cones, and three splits on top. Street went out on the deck with the dogs. They ran down the short stairs to the ground and raced around the cabin.

I opened two beers, carried them out, and set them on the railing near Street. Because it was close to the summer solstice, the sun was only just setting despite the late hour. We watched it lower into a few clouds near the Sierra Crest on the far side of the lake. The blue-black water was calm enough that we could see the wave patterns of individual squalls moving in different directions.

"Hard to reconcile this serene beauty with the violence that goes on among people," Street said. She picked up her beer and took a microsip.

"Indeed." I hadn't yet told Street about the murder in Kings Beach. I didn't want to bring more news of violence into her world when she was already grappling with the lurking threat of her father. But I also knew from experience that she very much disliked any sense that I was protecting her from reality. So I told her about the victim found hanging from the Kings Beach flagpole, a tennis ball in his mouth.

Street was silent for a moment. "That is so much like the murder of the woman who was hung from the Fannette Island tea house. One has to assume it's also connected to a bad charity."

"I think so." I drank beer. "When they removed the tennis ball, Spot alerted on the man's mouth. I found a type of lapel pin in the man's cheek. It was a miniature tennis player, gold in color but made of plastic."

"Like the necklace Spot found on Fannette Island."

"Right. I haven't had an opportunity to look up what kind of charity would have a tennis focus."

Street frowned. The golden light of the setting sun lit her face in a warm glow.

"Maybe it was also about children," she said. "It could be a charity focused on getting underprivileged kids out to play tennis.

They could provide funds to get kids with disabilities involved. Or, I should say, they could claim to provide funds."

"I bet you're right." I pointed at the sunset. "When the sun goes down, it gets chilly at seventy-two hundred feet. Wanna go in and sit by the fire?"

Street nodded.

When we were sitting, Blondie lay at Street's feet but had her head lifted up with her jawbone resting on Street's knee. Blondie gazed up at Street's face, her eyes intent and focused, aware of every tiny shift of Street's expression. I'd seen the same devotion in other rescue dogs. Even though dogs can't articulate their experiences, they have long memories. I'd once seen a rescue dog, safe in a new home for ten years, flinch when a friend of his owner came over to visit for the first time and casually picked up a newspaper and rolled it up into a tight, hard tube.

Unlike Spot, who'd never felt insecure in his life and thus took me and everything else for granted, Blondie seemed to sense that life was frangible, that she could count on nothing. To have Street save her from the emotional cliff was something she would be ever grateful for.

Street seemed somber, probably still thinking about her dangerous, wayward father. She said, "What did you mean the other day when you said that when someone assaults you, they have all of the advantages?"

"I just meant that they know they're coming for you. You don't. They know when they plan to take you down. You have no idea. They've planned which direction they're coming from. You're in the dark about that, too. Even if you've anticipated their attack, you have to consider all of the possibilities for how it might come about. Whereas, they only have to consider the one approach that appeals to them. So while they can exhaustively plan every aspect of that one approach, you have to spread your defensive planning over a wide range of variables."

"Give me a typical example?" Street said. Her voice was soft and higher pitched than normal. I could hear her fear.

I reached over and put my hand on her forearm. "Are you sure you're okay with this? We don't have to talk about this now."

She clenched her jaw. "I'm okay."

"But the downside of me talking about it is that you have to once again endure me reiterating that you and Blondie are welcome to stay with me and Spot. That I can drop you off at work and take you back home. That we'd be happy to move into your condo. And, of course, that you can keep Spot without me hanging around. I know you treasure your independence."

She nodded. "It isn't just that I treasure my independence as you say. It's that my independence is critical to my sense of self, my sense of worth. Growing up with no autonomy over any aspect of my life... I couldn't make my own decisions, I couldn't have any privacy, I had no sense of self. It was psychological torture on top of the physical torture. We never knew when he would explode, striking us, screaming at us, blaming us for everything wrong in his world."

Street sipped more beer. "So if I even think about not being in my own place, largely alone, I start to get shaky. I'm a mess in that way, always have been. But after I ran away at fourteen, I learned that when I live alone and have large blocks of time to myself, I do better. When I'm able to take a timeout like a little kid, taking deep breaths as often as I need, then I can put on my game face and make my presentation to the world, to my clients, to my very few friends, and mostly to you. Independence for me is my sustenance. Also, you can't always be there for me. I have to prepare. I have to be able to face the threat alone. Because whatever protection I have is something he can discern through observation, right? My father might be very twisted, but that doesn't make him stupid. He will watch and listen and figure out when are those moments when you look away. And that will be when he strikes. Am I right?"

"I think so, yes."

"And I know that Blondie, for all of her alertness and the way she makes the little warning bark at unusual sounds, is not going to deter any attacker. It's just not in her DNA. If someone broke in and grabbed me, I don't know if she would even bite him."

"Again, Spot isn't perfect, but he's a serious intimidation to anyone thinking of coming after you," I said. "I could still stay at my cabin, so we'd each have our own space."

"I've thought about that. You and I could keep our same

patterns, together often, but with me having the distance I need. I think that would work even if I had Spot. In a normal situation, he would stop any intruder. I've even imagined having Spot when I took a shower. I could prop the door open. If Spot was in the condo, I'd be safe from anyone unless they had – I don't know – a big weapon they were firing."

Street stared at the fire and drank some beer. Her frown was intense.

"But that's not the way I want to live, making sure I have a one hundred seventy pound guard dog protecting me at every moment. I think it's better to stay with my original plan. I operate on the assumption of the possibility that my father will come to exact vengeance for the testimony I gave at his trial. I practice all reasonable precautions. But I still try to lead a normal life." Street turned to look at me, her eyes imploring. "Does that seem crazy? Or is that something that makes sense?"

"I think it makes sense."

Street swallowed, then made a little nod. "Then let's go back to the lesson plan." Her voice sounded stronger. The scientist was back. Life experience, the entire world even, could be parsed into discrete components. Propositions. Hypotheses. Concepts that can be tested and verified and studied and analyzed for risk. And from that, reasonable courses of action can be planned.

"Okay," I said. "Let's start with time of day. You know he could come at any time, morning, noon, or night. The time we are normally the most asleep and hence most vulnerable is between three a.m. and five a.m. But maybe he plans to make his move just as you come home and reach into the trunk of the car to lift out your groceries. No matter how you analyze it, you won't know when an attack might come."

"What's the best way to deal with not knowing when he comes? If he comes at all."

"First, you vary your schedule. If he's a good planner, he'll watch you from a distance. He'll spend time out in the woods, noting what time you pull your blinds and when and in which rooms the lights go on and off behind the blinds. He'll park down the highway and see when you drive by and whether or not you have Blondie with you. He'll follow you. He'll take binoculars up into the forest behind your lab and find out when you arrive and when you leave for lunch and he'll note who comes to visit. He may attach a listening device to the outside of your bathroom window so that he can hear when you are running water and learn when you usually take a shower."

Street's frown deepened.

"Don't let this stress you. In fact, just knowing this makes you safer. Realizing what he can learn from a distance allows you to mess it up and confuse him."

"You mean I should fake stuff?"

"Yes. Plant false clues. You turn on the water in the shower. But while the water is running, you take Blondie out the front door. You sleep when the lights are on and move around and make noise when they're off. You head to work at different times each day, and you sometimes sleep over at your lab or here at my cabin. You figure out the times when you're most likely to be alone and then arrange to be seen with me at those times. You vary your driving routes, your walking routes, your sleep times, which grocery stores you shop at. As much as possible, you appear to have no regular schedule."

I paused, wondering about the line between useful information and too much information.

"Of course, you always make sure your doors are locked. In your car, at work, at home. If you are making multiple trips from car to condo, carrying groceries, you lock the door each time you go inside. Having someone assault you outside is obviously very dangerous. But having someone assault you inside is much worse."

Street said, "Because when I'm outside, I may have a chance to run. But when I'm inside, I'm trapped."

"Exactly. Last, always keep Blondie with you. Next to you. In your car. In your bedroom. In your bathroom. Think of Blondie as a new appendage on your body. You never go into a room at home or the storeroom at work and shut the door with Blondie on the other side. Bring her in with you. She goes into the bathroom with you and waits there when you shower. She goes in your car with you. And when you get out of the car, you hold the front door open so she can come out behind you. Never let her outside to run alone. Go with her on her walks. Remind yourself that the only time Blondie can be out of your sight is when you are with someone else. Even if she won't bite or attack, she's still a dog, she still barks, and she will still make a potential attacker worry about her response. At the very least, an attacker will wonder who else will hear her bark and come to your aid."

"Got it," Street said. "I've got the alarms at home and at work. I vary my schedule. I stay alert, and I keep Blondie with me twenty-four seven. But let's say someone gets to me anyway? Someone who disables Blondie. What then?"

"That's why we practice the self defense moves. I already mentioned the most important and most effective one."

"Right," Street said. "Run. Bolt like a sprinter. Be explosive in my reaction. Run fast and long. Calling nine one one, or reaching for a weapon, or screaming for help, all take second place to running away."

I nodded. "Few people can run as fast as you. Even fewer can run as long as you."

"And Blondie would have no trouble keeping up with me."

"Right."

"But," Street said, "what if an attacker keeps Blondie away from me? What if, as I get out of the car, he kicks the door shut, trapping her inside when I'm outside. I should still run, right?"

"Absolutely. Whenever possible, Blondie stays with you to help ward off trouble. But if the trouble comes to you anyway, you get out of there."

Street reached up and touched the lockett necklace hanging at her throat. "When they installed the alarm, they gave me this panic button. Just having it is discomforting, a constant reminder of danger."

"More self-defense practice will help," I said. "Shall we work on some moves now?"

"No. I think it's time to roast hotdogs."

"And a zucchini," I said, "which you will eat naked. Which makes me think things."

Street held my eyes for a bit. "We can figure out the naked part later."

I grinned.

TWENTY-NINE

The next morning, I had a fire going in the wood stove and coffee brewed, and the dogs had already gone out for their run and come back and passed out on the giant dog bed, when Street came out of my bedroom wearing one of my shirts. I poured a mug of coffee and handed it to her and kissed her forehead.

"Did you get some sleep?" I asked.

She nodded, looking a bit groggy. "Best in a long time. And yes, I'm noticing the circumstances that led to it."

I must have given her a look.

She said, "You in the bed next to me, and two dogs – one bigger than a mountain lion – in the room. What am I forgetting?"

"Sierra Nevada Pale Ale," I said. "An entire bottle. I made a check mark on my calendar."

Street sat in the rocker, stared at the fire, sipped coffee.

"That shirt you're wearing is like a very short mini-dress."

"Hmmm."

"The shirttails don't provide much coverage front and back, and the sides are open so that I can see all of your legs, right down to your perfect ankles."

"Your wardrobe doesn't give a girl much to choose from. Despite your excessive height, none of your shirts covers my ankles at all. And anyway, most guys, presented with this much bare leg, wouldn't focus on ankles."

"That's because most guys have never seen yours."

Street studied the fire, and I studied her legs, and she drank coffee. And after a long time, she said, "The person who killed Dory Spatt..." She trailed off as she thought. "Any kind of murder requires a great deal of motivation, right?"

"Sort of," I said. "Many murders come from great, sudden emotion. Your boyfriend beats you up one too many times, so you shoot him dead. Two drunken guys get in a brawl in a bar and one kills the other. A crazed driver on meth perceives some insult on the highway and kills someone in road rage. And of course, there is self-defense. Someone tries to rob you or attack you or your loved one, and you fight back, possibly killing the attacker. None of those are premeditated. They don't require any advance motivation. They're crimes of passion."

I walked over, opened the top on the wood stove, and dropped in two more splits. Then I went back into my kitchen nook, pulled out the coffee pot, and refilled my mug.

Street hadn't responded.

"Premeditated murders are special," I said. "The advance planning it takes to get a woman out to Fannette Island in Lake Tahoe and suspend her up by her ankles until she dies of exposure indicates a very high level of motivation. Such a murder probably involves greed or, to a lesser extent, revenge or anger."

"Why would revenge or anger be to a lesser extent?"

"Because emotional motives like revenge and anger tend to fuel crimes of passion, events without advance planning. Whereas murders that are carefully thought out in advance are usually about money. Even though revenge is not a common factor in premeditated homicide, it can be a motive. Especially if the murderer believes that someone destroyed their life. In that case, they may feel they have nothing to lose. They might go to great lengths to plan and carry out the ultimate punishment."

Street sipped her coffee. "Aside from Dory Spatt's scam charity, was there anything unusual about her?"

"Nothing I could find. Everything seemed to fit together in a clear way. She had a lousy, deprived childhood, a mother who, despite working two jobs, wasn't able to provide much and, worse, apparently taunted Dory for her desire to have money. So Dory ran away. She got involved in a scam charity as an employee and then later became a partner. He made her a joint owner, then he died in a boating accident. Dory was on the boat at the time but wasn't charged with any crime. Once she had taken full control of the charity, she managed to grow the business a great deal."

Street said, "Makes one wonder about the boating accident."

"Yes, it does," I said.

"It could be that someone close to the former owner plotted

her murder."

"Yes, it could."

Street said, "Which brings me back to Dory's life and the question of whether every aspect of it was normal, that is, normal for a person who perpetrates a massive fraud."

I nodded. "I've gone over what I learned about her and her brother Kyle. I've considered that everything he told me might be suspect, either fabrications or merely a simple spinning of his tale for one effect or another. I've revisited her house in my mind, walking through it by memory, looking for anything that stands out, anything different from other people's houses..." I stopped as a memory nagged at me.

"You pause on that thought," Street said.

"Well, it's just that I now remember an unusual framed print that Dory had hanging on the wall. It was a graphic depicting the Solar System, but it only showed the inner planets."

"Was she into astronomy?"

"Not according to her brother Kyle. He explained that the former manager of the Red Roses of Hope charity had a thing for certain places in outer space. Let me think of what they're called. Lagrangian points. They are apparently places where the gravity of two different planetary bodies cancels each other out or something like that. Other forces figure in there as well, if I'm remembering correctly."

"Are these points a real thing?" Street asked. "It sounds like something in a science fiction novel."

"I don't know. But Kyle made it sound like they are a real thing, and he said that the former manager saw them in some kind of metaphorical way that helped him build his business."

"Okay, now we're talking about my question about whether there was anything unusual in Dory Spatt's world. A framed picture of Lagrangian points certainly could qualify. I think you need to find out more about this."

"I think I do, too," I said.

Spot and I walked Street and Blondie down the mountain to her condo, a road trip that was a mile each way and was the equivalent of going from the top of a 100-story skyscraper to the bottom and back up. It was a gorgeous day with hot sun glistening on the snow-capped mountains. It was hard to imagine that just one week ago, a woman had been strung up on Fannette Island in a storm.

Back at my cabin, I searched Lagrangian points online and saw a short article about a scientist who was an expert on the subject. His name was Professor Giuseppe Calvarenna, a name that sounded familiar. The article was about what were billed as "Enrichment Lectures" that he gave on Pacific Cruise Lines ships.

So I searched on his name and saw why it was familiar. Calvarenna was kind of a local celebrity because he had a place in Tahoe and some years back had won a major prize for physics. I'd heard he was a recluse. I'd never met him, nor had I ever heard of anyone who knew him. But he was often talked about in the same way that people talk about the movie actors and rock stars and tech company CEOs who have houses in Tahoe.

I looked for contact information for Pacific Cruise Lines, the company where Professor Calvarenna was listed as giving enrichment talks, whatever those were. I found lots of photos that showed just how glamorous and exciting their cruises were, but the only contact information appeared to be sales offices.

Next, I searched for enrichment lectures and Giuseppe Calvarenna and I found something called Travel World Enrichment Speakers, a company that appeared to be a booking agency.

I dialed their number.

I got a recorded message featuring an enthusiastic woman's voice explaining that if I were an expert in my field and if I were a great public speaker, I could possibly be chosen by Travel World Enrichment Speakers to enjoy the amazing, exciting life of an enrichment speaker, traveling the globe, visiting exotic places, and meeting wonderful people from around the world. All I had to do was take the first step and mail them a DVD of one of my talks, and they would have their panel of world-class judges score it. If I became a Travel World Enrichment Associate, they would place me on any of dozens of exciting cruise ships, and the cost of the cruise would be discounted to only $100 per day of the cruise, thus saving me thousands of dollars. The message included the mailing address to which I should send my DVD. It repeated the address a second time, then disconnected.

I wondered how customers and speakers who'd already been accepted got through to an actual person.

I dialed again, and when the message began, I pressed zero.

"Good afternoon, you've reached Travel World Enrichment Speakers," said a young male voice. "How may I help you?"

"I'm calling about one of your speakers, a Professor Giuseppe Calvarenna."

"Oh, yes. He is one of our most popular enrichment speakers. In fact, he just finished a fourteen-day cruise with us to Alaska. Three lectures per week. The boat docked in San Francisco yesterday. And it heads out tomorrow. Unfortunately, he disembarked with the passengers. So if you're hoping to take a cruise that he will be on, it might be some time."

"I'd like to check on his next cruise, please."

"Let me check the schedule." I heard some sounds that might have been him moving and clicking a computer mouse. Or it might have been him clinking his coffee cup as he picked it up, drank, set it down, and nibbled on a cookie. "I'm sorry, we don't have him currently scheduled on any upcoming cruises."

"I'm wondering if you can forward a message to him?"

"Yes, I can do that. Oh. Actually, he's got the 'Okay to Release' box checked next to his email address. So I can give you that."

"Great."

I wrote as the man read off a Gmail address.

I thanked him and hung up.

I wrote an email.

'Dear Professor Calvarenna. I'm an investigator in Tahoe looking into a murder that took place on Fannette Island in Emerald Bay. Although it might seem far-fetched, it's possible that a clue to the crime involves Lagrangian points. I understand that you are an expert in this area, and I'm hoping I could have a few minutes of your time. Please let me know if there is a convenient moment when I could stop by. Thanks much, Owen McKenna.'

I hit Send and turned off my computer.

THIRTY

I called FBI Agent Ramos, told him I'd been hired to look for a missing woman who turned out to be the one who was murdered on Fannette Island, and asked if I could ask him some questions. He said he was available at lunch.

We met at an upscale cafe on South Shore's Ski Run Blvd. Ramos was outside pacing the sidewalk, talking on his phone as I drove up. I had to drive down a block to find a parking place for this popular restaurant. Spot was sleeping and didn't appear to notice as I got out and shut the door.

As I walked up, Ramos was still talking on his phone, using a soft voice, gesturing with his free hand. He had that unusual quality of being able to make his words commanding even though his speaking style was calm. His physical demeanor was like his voice, radiating precision and thoughtfulness. Despite his slight build, no one would ever think that Ramos wasn't powerful. And no one would ever underestimate him. He clicked off as I walked up.

"Mr. McKenna," he said. "It's been awhile." His tone made it sound as though I'd done something wrong. "Good to see you," he added, although I didn't think he actually felt that way. Agent Ramos was as self-contained as a man could get, in need of nothing and no one. His singular redeeming quality was that he was very good at putting bad guys away.

As always, Ramos telegraphed fastidious grooming. His pencil-line moustache was even thinner than normal and so black it looked like he might use a permanent marker to make it look more intense. Ramos's shirt collar was buttoned to the top. His black shoes shined like they were polished enamel. His trouser creases were sharp. He looked a lot like Clark Gable, and his style made him stand apart from the jeans-and-flannel Tahoe look the way Clark Gable would stand out among a group of coal miners.

"Sergeant Diamond Martinez told me you were hired in regard to the dead woman on Fannette Island. So it seems I should be asking you about these crimes rather than the other way around."

I ignored the apparent rebuke, attributing it to Ramos's style rather than an insufficiency on my part.

"Coffee?" a server asked after we'd seated ourselves at an outdoor table.

I asked for a black coffee. Ramos ordered an espresso mocha with a dash of cayenne pepper and a pinch of cinnamon. When she brought our drinks, Ramos held up his finger as if to signal to her that she should wait the way a sommelier waits for approval of a fine wine. Ramos picked up his little cup and took the tiniest sip, made a single nod of approval, and then said, "Good." The server hesitated a moment to be sure she understood that she was now being dismissed, then left. Ramos set down his cup, then looked at me.

"With yesterday's murder in Kings Beach," I said, "we now have two victims who were both strung up the same way."

"Yes, of course," he said, like I was wasting his time. "And they had items in their mouths."

I nodded. "The woman had roses, the man a tennis ball and a little tennis player lapel pin. My dog also found a necklace depicting roses on Fannette Island. Perhaps that had been in the woman's mouth as well."

"Then how did it get out of her mouth?"

"I don't know. It was down below where she was hanging. Maybe it fell out."

Ramos frowned and pursed his lips. "I heard that the woman ran a fraudulent charity," Ramos said, with no acknowledgment that I was the one who uncovered that information. Maybe he didn't know.

"Correct. I'm guessing we'll find out that the man ran a similar operation with a focus on tennis or sports."

"And so these murders probably have something to do with the charity festival here in Tahoe," Ramos said.

"Right."

"So how can I help you?" Ramos said.

"Because of the way the victims were displayed, it appears that the whole point was to get them noticed. The murders have gotten national media attention. Although this could be focused exclusively on the Tahoe area, I'm wondering if there might be other murders across the country where the victims may have been found hanging from their feet. The FBI has various databases like ViCAP and NCIC. Would they include that kind of crime scene information?"

Ramos took another sip of his espresso, tiny and delicate, the way Street savors mere drops of beer. "The Violent Criminal Apprehension Program and the National Crime Information Center are great sources of information, but they are far from comprehensive. In fact, they rely on information provided by local law enforcement across the country. But there's no requirement that they share that information. It's the same for the U.S. Marshals Service and the Bureau of Alcohol, Tobacco, and Firearms. They have a Violent Felon File. But that file comes from information gathered piece by piece from other law enforcement agencies. Even the CIRG is dependent on information provided by local law enforcement agencies."

"Critical..." I couldn't come up with the words.

"Critical Incident Response Group. The FBI unit that responds to bombings and plane crashes and hostage situations. Any kind of crisis that needs a rapid response. Significant events that involve loss of life, or potential loss of life."

"I remember now," I said. "Events that could be terrorism."

"That, too. The point I'm making is that national law enforcement agencies are not top-down organizations. They are bottom-up. They get nearly all of their information at the local level and feed it into the national level to formulate and coordinate an appropriate response. This is why I pay attention to murders that may seem to fall within the jurisdiction of states."

I drank coffee. "If a local sheriff's department thinks it's got information that the FBI might like, they can turn it over. But they don't have to."

Ramos nodded. "While investigating a crime or even a murder, they might see something that doesn't look important and not realize that it could be a useful reference point when looking at a bigger picture of crime across the country."

"But a victim hanging from his feet would be so dramatic, they would want to turn that over, right?"

"Maybe yes, maybe no. Sometimes local law enforcement is not always eager to help the FBI. Imagine that."

"Acknowledging that, could you still make some inquiries?" I said. "See if any other bodies have been found hanging upside down?"

Another nod, another sip of espresso. "Even though these victims were found displayed in an unusual manner here in the Tahoe area, our perpetrator could have been plying his trade elsewhere. I'll see if anything turns up." He seemed to think of something. "Your client was the murder victim's boyfriend, correct?"

"Yeah. Douglas Fairbanks from Vegas."

"There's a name. You're confident he isn't the murderer?"

"I don't think he is. But I'm not confident. He did have motive beyond the fact that she was playing him."

Ramos gave me a questioning look.

"In what must have been the throes of hopeful love, he gave her half interest in his Tahoe condo. If he decided she had manipulated him into making the gift, he might have been angry enough to kill her. Because he'd made their ownership a joint title with right of survivorship, he once again owns one hundred percent of his condo. I don't know the condo's value. But it could be half a million."

"Then why do you think he didn't kill her? You know the statistics about how many women are killed by their husbands and boyfriends."

I finished my coffee. "Gut instinct. He's a soft, lovelorn guy who's focused on poetry. I can't see him plotting to get her out to the island in a storm. I can't see him doing something so physically wicked as stringing her up by her feet. If he were a killer, I'd guess his weapon would be poison."

Ramos nodded. "You say he's focused on poetry. Didn't you also find a little poem out on Fannette Island?"

"Yes. When Street and I were paddling away, my dog alerted again, and we basically followed his nose back to the east shore of the island. We found a little roll of paper floating in the water. On it was written a haiku about roses and deceit. Sergeant Bains has it with the other evidence."

"Yet you don't think this implicates your poetry-loving client."

"Like I said, it's a visceral sense. Nevertheless, I asked him some questions about haikus, and his answers were focused on the art form. He didn't think he had any useful expertise."

"How does that contribute to his innocence?" Ramos asked.

"I'm not sure how to say it. If you have a question about a building where a murder victim was found, you'd assume the murderer is thinking about the building in relation to the murder. But if their comments were focused on the architectural aspects of the building, it would make you think that they weren't preoccupied with the dead person. When I mentioned the haiku, Fairbanks started talking about Basho, and then he segued into how modern haiku is moving away from traditional nature images."

Ramos said, "You're thinking that if he were the woman's killer, he'd talk about the haiku in terms of its subject rather than the haiku as an art form."

"Yes, you put it better than I did."

I picked up the tab. "Thanks very much for your help," I said.

Ramos made a little nod, stood up, and paused. "It might seem that I'm not that interested in the case," he said. "In fact, I'm quite intrigued. Please keep me informed."

It seemed a surprising thing for Ramos to say. He liked to keep his thoughts to himself. Rarely, did he ever reach out.

"Will do," I said.

We left.

Spot was still passed out in the Jeep, sprawled across the back seat from one door to the other. He lifted his head when I opened the front door. He sniffed the air as if searching for hints of leftovers in a doggie bag. From the speed with which he lowered his head and resumed snoring, I could tell how exciting it was to see me sans treats.

THIRTY-ONE

After leaving Agent Ramos, I stopped by my office. The phone rang as I bent down to pick up the mail. In with the bills was the newspaper. As with the last murder, the headline was bold.

Murder Victim Hung From Flagpole

I answered the phone.

"Owen McKenna," I said.

"I want to talk to the detective. Is that you?" A young man's voice. Garbled like he was talking through a thick scarf. Or maybe he'd put stones in his mouth to disguise his voice, Socrates-style.

"I'm the detective. What can I help you with?"

"I heard something about the, um, the woman who got killed. Then the man got killed. So I should tell you."

"I'm listening," I said.

"The thing is, I can't talk here. I gotta go."

"Wait, Mr.?"

"Matt..." he cut himself off mid-word. "I shouldn't say my name. Come to the pop-up charity party. I saw a pic of you, so I know you're real tall. I'll find you."

"What does that mean, a pop-up party?" I asked.

"A pop-up rave in a secret location. So the cops can't find it until it's over. They pick the place at the last moment. The last day of the festival is the Grand Tour race. After the Grand Tour, everyone goes home. So the pop-up party is the night before."

"Just so I'm sure, you're talking about the Tahoe Mountain Bike for Charity festival?"

"That's what I said."

"How will I find out where the party is?" I asked.

"Check the website. You must know some of the participants. Some of them will be getting email invitations at the last moment.

Just be ready to go. Nine o'clock is what I heard."

"Is this going to be in Tahoe?"

"Of course."

"North Shore, or South Shore, or...?"

"Probably the South Shore. I'll see you there." He hung up.

The phone rang again.

"Checking in," Diamond said when I answered.

"No doubt you know about the second victim," I said.

"Dude on the flagpole," Diamond said. "This killer is imaginative."

"And effective at public relations," I said. "He knows how to get press."

"No kidding. I saw a piece about it on national TV. The reporter mentioned a Great Dane that sniffed the body and focused on the victim's mouth, which led to the discovery of something revealing in the victim's cheek."

"It was a plastic lapel pin, depicting a tennis player. With the tennis ball and the similar MO to the Fannette Island killing, it suggested some kind of sports-related charity. But other issues have kept me from looking into it."

"Issues about..."

"I'm worried about Street," I said. "She may be in danger from her father."

"I know her father is a felon. But tell me again why the current worry?"

"Killer dad went AWOL from parole in Missouri, and Street's aunt believes he's coming to exact vengeance on Street for testifying against him twenty-some years ago. Add to that Street's memory of him threatening her when he was led out of the courtroom. She was fourteen at the time."

"Ouch. Has he been spotted in Tahoe?"

"No. But several times, she's been creeped out, feeling like she's being followed. With many people, I might just chalk that up to standard worry. But she's a scientist. She automatically discounts any data that comes from feelings. She always demands hard, observable evidence. So when she thinks someone might be following her, I give it a certain credibility."

"You could let her take your hound. That would put off any would-be attacker."

"I told her that. I also said she could live with me. But she says life isn't worth living if she lets a hypothetical threat put her day-to-day routine in lockdown. My wording, not hers."

"I can see that living with you would be hard."

"Funny guy."

"Like being a cop," Diamond said. "I've had several perps tell me they were going to fry my ass when they get out of the cage. Now they're out. I can't cover every aspect of my world all the time. I have to decide what's critical and prioritize accordingly. " He paused. "I'd give her space."

"Thanks. I'll think on that. I also have another bit of news. I just got a call from a stranger who would only identify himself as Matt. He said he has info for me, and he told me about a pop-up party that is supposed to happen on the last night of the charity festival."

"What's a pop-up party?" Diamond said.

"That was my question too." I explained it to Diamond. "Matt is planning to meet me there and tell me secrets about the murder victims."

"Sounds mysterious."

"I would feel better about it if you were there."

"I can't come if I don't know where the party is."

"You can hang with me near the appointed hour, then come with me when I find out where it is."

"How does one find out where the party is?" Diamond said.

"Matt said that some people will get email invitations and that maybe one of them would be willing to tell me when they get the email. I think Douglas Fairbanks might be on their list. So maybe I can find out from him."

"They probably announce it at the last minute so cops can't bust them," Diamond said.

"That's what Matt told me, yes."

"But if I'm alert and prepared, I could bust them anyway."

"I always knew you were a fearsome cop," I said.

After we hung up, I didn't want to pay bills, so I checked

email. There was a message from Giuseppe Calvarenna.

It read, 'Happy to talk. Call me.' It was followed by a phone number.

I wanted to refamiliarize myself with who he was before I called. I looked him up and found an article on him. The piece was titled, Parking Places in Space.

It began by explaining that Professor Calvarenna's main accomplishment was having solved an obscure theorem that had eluded mathematicians for two centuries and that the theorem solution was being used in space exploration, especially with regard to Lagrangian points, the so-called parking places in space. On a lesser level, Calvarenna was also an inventor who held numerous patents, the most significant of which was for developing a chemical process that is apparently used in the manufacture of computer chips.

I picked up the phone and dialed.

"This is Joseph," a man answered. By his rough voice, I guessed him to be in his 70s.

"This is Owen McKenna calling for Giuseppe Calvarenna."

"Speaking."

"I'm sorry, I thought you said Joseph."

"Giuseppe is the Italian form of Joseph."

"Oh, of course. Thanks for picking up. I'm the investigator who sent you the email. I assumed I'd have to fight my way through secretarial defenses."

He made a little chuckle. "I'm just a scientist. Nobody in the world is clamoring to speak to me. What can I do for you?"

"May I come by and talk with you about Lagrangian points?"

"I suppose. But I don't do drop ins. If we pick a time, I'll look for you."

"I'm open," I said.

"I'm about to have lunch. Would two o'clock work?"

"I'll be there if you're close enough for me to get there in two hours. Where do I go?"

"I live on Tahoe's North Shore. Are you familiar with Incline Village?"

"Yes."

"I'm off Ski Way, the road up to Diamond Peak Ski Resort. Do you have a pen? I'll give you the number."

"Ready."

He read it off. "My house is easy to drive past. Look for a stone arch and a portico over the front door."

At 1:45, I pulled off the street at an open arched gate set in a stone wall. Unlike many large houses designed to look imposing as you drive up, this house didn't present much of a facade to the street. It did have a substantial entry with an arched portico and a large front door. But most of the structure seemed to drop down the mountain on the lake side of the road. The lake was maybe a mile distant and 500 feet below the house.

I parked under a heavy tree canopy in front of a three-car garage on a stone parking area that wasn't large by large-house standards but was still big enough to handle five or six vehicles. The shade was complete, so Spot would be okay in the Jeep. I cracked the windows, and got out, and saw movement in my peripheral vision.

At a diagonal across the street was a double bungalow house, two side-by-side apartments. From a distance, I could see that it was run down, unusual for a building in upscale Incline Village. Each of the two units had its own small driveway. In the right driveway, I saw a woman leaning into the back of her old minivan, struggling to remove some kind of large, white, rectangular board and hold it with the same hand that held a couple of bags of supplies. She had crutches under both arms, and one of them seemed caught on the hydraulic support for the van's hatchback. I ran across the street.

"I saw you wrestling with your stuff. Can I help?"

She turned her head to try to see me but had trouble because she was very stiff as if her legs were locked up with spastic muscles.

"Sorry, I'm making things worse." I stepped farther forward so she could see me.

She was a small woman, maybe in her sixties, black as people come, with flawless skin and beautiful eyes.

"I'm just being foolish, trying to carry everything in one

trip," she said. "These legs keep getting worse, so I hate to make multiple trips. Going up the steps to my apartment is hard. Coming down is worse."

"Let me get this crutch untangled," I said. "The fabric pad cover caught on the hatch support when you leaned into the van." I separated cloth from a sharp edge of metal. "Now I'll get your things." I reached for her bags and picked up her board. It was lighter than I expected. The writing on the surface said Arches Watercolor Block. I remembered that they were special pads of heavy paper with the paper edges sealed on all four sides.

"I see you are a watercolor painter," I said. "My favorite is Mary Cassatt."

"You know watercolorists?"

"Not really. I like painting of all types. But Cassatt's paintings have always struck me."

"Well, you know enough to torture me by mentioning one of the watercolor goddesses. Every time I paint, I think, if only I could create that Cassatt charm."

The woman reached up and shut the minivan hatch. She started walking toward her front door. I followed her up a short series of steps to her duplex apartment. She went slowly, working her crutches with much effort, her stiff legs swinging awkwardly. She leaned her right crutch against the wall of the house, fished keys out of a shoulder purse, and unlocked the door.

"Once I get over the threshold without tripping, I'm good," she said.

"Looks to me like you manage well," I said, holding the door, following her inside.

"A lifetime of dealing with MS. Practice makes one good at anything."

Her living room was set up as an art studio. She had an easel designed for water colors. On it was another watercolor block, held in a horizontal position. There was a small table covered with tiny tubes of paint. To one side was a mixing palette, a white plastic tray with depressions holding dozens of dabs of paint that had been mixed into every color imaginable.

One wall was covered with dozens of watercolors pinned in place by push pins. The paintings were all landscapes. Several were obviously of Tahoe, but there were also images of other mountains and lakes as well as some urban settings.

"Wow, you are a serious artist," I said.

"If you mean that in the sense that I'm accomplished, the answer is no. If you mean that in the sense that I'm constantly focused on artistic qualities – shape, value, color, and beauty, power, pathos, emotion – then yes, I'm a serious artist."

I set her things down, then leaned over to look at some paintings up close. In the lower left corners, they were signed, 'Aubrey Blackwood.'

"Well, I never thought about what specifically makes an artist serious. But I can see that you don't need any Cassatt charm," I said. "You've got Blackwood Beauty."

"Oh, stop. I'm just a gimped-up woman living on a pension. So I have to find meaning in an activity that isn't too expensive and doesn't require me to move around much. When I heard from a friend that there was an apartment available on a long-term lease in Tahoe that I could afford, I thought, 'Aubrey, you've always wanted to paint landscapes, so get your butt up to landscape heaven and do it.' So I moved up from the East Bay. The MS keeps getting worse, and the spastic gait issues can overwhelm me at times, but I can do the scissors walk as well here as in the city."

"Looks to me like you made a good choice."

"How is it that you come to know about watercolorists?"

"Actually, I don't. I just like paintings, and I have some books on painters. Cassatt has always caught my eye. Recently, I've been admiring Sorolla. But I think he painted in oil."

Aubrey grinned. "Yes, he did, primarily. But he also did some wonderful gouache paintings, which is a type of opaque watercolor. You should check them out. They are scenes of New York." She glanced out the window. " I saw you come from across the road. Are you new in the neighborhood?"

"No. I'm just visiting your neighbor, Giuseppe Calvarenna. I'm an investigator working on a case, and we had a science question. His name came up as a science expert."

"Oh yes, Mr. G, the absent-minded science professor. I've barely met him. Don't tell him this, but I sometimes think he's got it worse than me. I struggle with body issues. He struggles with brain issues. I see him come and go from over here. He comes back from the grocery store, opens the trunk to get his groceries, then carries a bag inside and forgets the rest of the groceries sitting in the sun while the trunk of his car is open wide. I hobbled over there once and rang his bell to tell him. I also got his phone number so I can call him. Since then, I've called him about unattended groceries and mail that he left on the roof of his car. And another time when he left his front door standing wide open. The bears could have moved in, and he never would have noticed. And just yesterday, I saw him come home, unlock his front door, and then carefully shut the door behind him. But his keys were in the outside of the door lock when he went inside. Now that's security for you!"

Aubrey gestured toward her living room wall. "On that side of my house, there's an old barn back in the trees. Mr. G owns it. But one thing's for sure. He might be out to lunch, but he's one smart man. You should hear the way he talks."

"I guess I'll find out shortly." I turned to leave. "Good luck with your paintings,"

"Mister, you know my name, but I don't know yours." She handed me a card.

"I'm sorry. How rude of me." I exchanged cards with her. "I'm Owen McKenna. I live on the East Shore, and my office is on the South Shore. It was a pleasure to meet you, Aubrey Blackwood."

She reached out and shook my hand with a firm grip. "The pleasure is all mine, Mr. Owen McKenna."

She smiled, and her eyes crinkled in the most delightful way.

I said, "Maybe I can visit with you someday, and you can teach me about watercolor."

"Any time," she said.

THIRTY-TWO

I left Aubrey Blackwood and went back across the street. Spot was sprawled on the back seat, probably asleep. He didn't even notice my comings and goings.

The large front door had an alarm keypad and near that a doorbell button. I pressed it and waited.

After a minute came a voice. "Be there in a minute. But let your poor hound out of the car. He's welcome to join us if he doesn't mind a very particular, prima donna cat."

So I woke Spot up and let him out of the Jeep. He trotted around, nose to ground, investigating. I looked around for the video cameras that revealed Spot's and my presence, but I saw none.

It's an interesting dichotomy. If you have an ordinary abode, you make the cameras and the alarm components obvious, the better to ward off intruders. If you have a rich abode, you can hide the sensors because everyone knows they are there anyway. Most burglaries and other home invasions take place where regular folks live. Predators usually pass up the rich because they believe their chances of being caught are high.

The door opened. For some reason, I expected a secretary or a manservant to the mad scientist.

I got the mad scientist.

He was five-nine or five-ten and skinny as a telephone pole. He had a white walrus moustache and an untamed shock of equally white, Albert Einstein hair that lofted above his head. He looked to be in his late sixties.

Calvarenna's glasses had thick, black frames that had slid down and rested on the bulging knob of his nose. His left hand held a cane. In the crook of his right arm, held like a football, was a white, long-haired cat. It looked like the Persian cat that belonged to the Blofeld character in the James Bond movies.

"Mr. Calvarenna?" I said. "I'm Owen McKenna." Spot came

trotting up. "And this is Spot."

"My, what a sweetheart," Calvarenna said. He leaned his cane against the wall so he could pet Spot.

Spot was wary of the tiny cat in the man's other arm. The cat's expression didn't change as Spot approached. The cat yawned. Shut his eyes.

Spot reached forward slowly, sniffing, his movement tentative and informed by past memories. He knew that even if a cat was smaller than a decent lunch, never underestimate what it can do to your nose.

The cat ignored him, indicating that he'd had enough dog experience to know that it was the small dog breeds that were dangerous to felines.

"A beautiful fellow," Calvarenna said, one hand on my dog, the other holding his cat. "I've read a bit about dog olfaction," Calvarenna said. "Ten thousand times more sensitive than what we humans have. Our specialty is vision. As we evolved and developed sophisticated tools like bows and arrows, the information available in visual stimuli allowed us to hunt, which suited our relatively fast evolutionary development and led to our dominance of this tiny planet. Wolves, and their dog derivatives, didn't have tools that benefited from great vision. So their hunting consisted of chasing down their prey, often at night or in poor light conditions. For that, having a good nose on the ground was much more important than trying to see through the brush. Dogs have an olfactory that compares to ours as my computer compares to the slide rule I grew up with."

I said, "I've always been amazed when I really watch him explore his surroundings with his nose."

"I suffer a bit of anosmia, myself."

"Anosmia?" I said.

"Oh, sorry." He touched a fingertip to his nose. "The ol' sniffer doesn't do the job as well as it should. Unfortunately, they haven't yet developed the olfactory equivalent of eyeglasses or hearing aids. Perhaps one day an enterprising scientist will."

"Why do you suppose you have – what did you call it – smelling loss?"

"Anosmia? Age is the primary cause. A lifetime of insults to the nasal equipment takes its toll. We all get colds and the flu. Those viruses and others get into the gears and gum up the works. Viruses also get into our brains and damage the nerve cells that process how we smell. By the time people are eighty-five years old, the majority have significant olfactory decline. It is similar to age-related hearing and vision loss. I'm still a long way from my eighties, but I'm ahead of the normal curve on olfactory loss."

He rubbed the side of Spot's neck. "I'm sorry, I already forgot this guy's name."

"Spot. He also responds to His Largeness. Spot, say hello to Professor Calvarenna."

"Please call me Giuseppe. Or Joseph. Spot will like my deck. Come. We'll sit out there."

Giuseppe turned and walked inside. Spot and I followed. The entry had a small gurgling fountain with some mossy plants growing in it and sending plant tendrils dangling down over the side. Light came from skylights above.

Giuseppe went down a large spiral staircase with broad, varnished stone steps. It felt a little like descending into a cave. He moved at a slow pace, holding the spiral handrail with the same hand that held the cane. It looked awkward, but he was obviously practiced at holding the rail and cane while carrying the cat.

Giuseppe's wild white hair bobbed a bit with each of the man's steps. The skin of his scalp was blotchy, suggesting the man was in ill health.

After we'd made a single but complete spiral revolution, we came to a broad, wide room filled with tall tables like those that one would work at standing up. The far wall was all windows, and the view beyond was all lake with the mountains of the South Shore 25 miles distant.

"This is my workshop," Giuseppe said with a wave of his arm.

"This looks like a college classroom," I said as Spot wandered about the workbench tables, nose high, investigating a room that was unlike any he'd ever been in. There was a microscope, a white board with inscrutable math equations written across it, a paper cutter. On one counter was a Bunsen burner and a test tube rack. On a shelf at the back of the counter were beakers, vials of chemicals, liquids, and powders. Over by the door to a small deck stood a telescope.

"Some of this stuff I recognize," I said. I pointed. "Nice incubator."

"You know incubators? I'm surprised."

"I recognize it because it's similar to the one my entomologist girlfriend has." I gestured at the room. "You have stuff that doesn't normally go together. What exactly do you do here?"

He paused and gave me a long look. "You want the glossy magazine answer, or the truth? I think you'll want the truth. What I do here I think of as arbitrary and random accretion, then thoughtful destruction, then recombination of disparate elements. Of course, that sounds excessive. But it's actually quite an accurate description."

"I understand," I said even though I didn't at any serious level.

Giuseppe continued, "Of course, I'm speaking primarily of thought processes. However, my world of physical objects somewhat mirrors my thoughts."

"So this is the creative lab of a scientist who works in a variety of fields," I said.

"Yes, you could say that. Let's go down another level. We can talk out on the deck."

Spot and I followed the white puff clouds of human and feline hair down another spiral. There we came to a standard, large living room with a window wall like in the room above it. The floor was stone with several large, colored rugs that looked new. The fireplace was large with a fire laid of logs but no ash beneath the ash grate. There were artful groupings of furniture arranged for views of the fireplace and the landscape out the windows.

"Nice room," I said.

"I suppose," Giuseppe said, turning and looking at it as if he hadn't really considered it. "I walk through it carrying my coffee up to my workshop, but that's it. I hate the designer look. It's like they set it up as a showroom for a magazine shoot. The house used to be owned by a movie producer. Maybe he thought he would entertain clients or something. But as far as I can tell, he never used the room, either."

Giuseppe turned and walked through the living room toward a large kitchen. "The design of fancy living space," he muttered as he moved away from me, "creates spaces that are less artfulness and more artifice. Places where one doesn't really live." He was shaking his head as he walked. "Humans must be the only species...," he trailed off. He was still walking away from me, so I could barely hear him over the clicking of Spot's nails on the stone floor. "Animals create housing that is all about function, not look. But their plumage... Now there's something similar. I suppose a man's living room could be like a peacock's feathers, all part of the seduction routine."

I couldn't hear the rest of his words as he rounded a corner.

THIRTY-THREE

I followed Giuseppe as he walked through the kitchen and out a sliding door. Outside was a brick patio that was surrounded with bushes and trees. I followed him through an opening at the edge of the patio and stepped onto a brick path that curved through fir trees intermixed with clusters of aspen. The path went down a wide flight of steps made of the same brick, then traversed a short distance across the steep slope to another descent of stairs, and arrived at a wooden deck that was built out from the steep slope and overlooked the lake in the distance. The deck had a spectacular view. None of the neighboring houses was visible from the deck. To one side of the deck was a view of the steep, cliff-like bluff that was adjacent to Giuseppe's house. The cliff was mostly a vertical pile of boulders interrupted with outcroppings of Manzanita.

On the deck were two lounge chairs facing the lake. In one corner was an umbrella in a heavy stand. Still holding his cat, Giuseppe struggled with it, trying to raise the umbrella sleeve and open it up. I reached out to help, and the umbrella opened, the catch clicking into place. The lounge chair cushions were brilliant red, as was the umbrella, dramatic against the deep blue of the lake. Or maybe, as Giuseppe had said, it was just artifice.

He walked over to one of the chaise lounges, leaned on his cane, then, with some struggle, got one leg lifted over a cushioned seat, and slowly lowered himself down. The cat rode in his other arm like royalty.

Spot trotted the perimeter of the deck, which projected out over the steep slope. He came back, reached his nose toward the cat but stopped 18 inches away, sniffing, still wary, doing the doggie calculation of risk and reward.

I sat next to Giuseppe, both of us facing the lake.

"When I was trying to find you, I discovered that you were lecturing on a cruise ship. So I called the company, and they said you'd just gotten off a fourteen-day cruise yesterday. Is that a rewarding project, teaching people about, what, physics?"

"Rewarding? I don't know. It's kind of fun. I do it as an exercise in staying engaged with people. Scientists are basically introverts. We're happy to just be by ourselves, working on our projects."

I nodded. "I know what you mean."

"If we don't want to become shut-ins, we have to force ourselves to go out and mix it up. I made a little study of it. I listed all the activities one could utilize to engage with people. Then I scored them in terms of the type of people you'd meet. I considered book clubs and churches and service clubs and travel groups and all manner of boating groups. I decided to become a speaker on cruise ships because I do better when I have a role to play. I wouldn't be any good at standing around making small talk. The people running the lecture circuit told me that cruise passengers love learning about something new. So I decided that explaining about Lagrangian points might be fun. It's worked out quite well. As a result, I've met a few people with whom I've kept in touch. I suppose it's ego gratification. When you're known for something, people flatter you. They want to have a drink with you. Or maybe they just want to be able to go home and tell their friends they had a drink with you."

"It's the Lagrangian points that I want to talk to you about," I said.

"That's what you said in your email. I was, of course, somewhat astonished, so I agreed to meet with you."

"I'm a private investigator looking into the death of a woman named Dory Spatt. She ran a scam charity."

"Do you mean, a charity that was a fraud?"

"Yes."

"I've seen some charity marketing that looked suspicious. But I always hoped it was just my cynicism. I'm sorry to hear that charity fraud is real."

"Me too," I said. "My investigation took me to Dory's Sausalito home where I saw a framed poster of the inner solar system with Lagrangian points marked on it. When I asked Dory's brother about it, he said that her former charity partner believed that

Lagrangian points are a good business model."

"Goodness, what a concept. And an obscure clue," Giuseppe said.

"I understand you've done a lot of work on Lagrangian points. Does the idea that they could serve as a business model make any sense to you?"

Giuseppe shook his head. His wild hair wobbled. "Not at all."

"Maybe you could just tell me about your work on Lagrangian points," I said.

"All I'm doing is developing some new ways of analyzing them."

"What does that mean? Or is it too tedious to try to explain such things to a layman?"

"It's not that tedious."

"Just sort of tedious," I said.

"Yes. Sort of. I'll give you my lecture version. In seventeen seventy-two, my Italian namesake Giuseppe Lagrange, also known as Joseph Lagrange, discovered the solution to what was called the three-body problem for how objects move in space. That led to an understanding that there were various points of stability in space, what are now called Lagrangian points. They are parking places, if you will, where we can place satellites and have them stay put because there is an equilibrium of all of the forces acting on those points. In the case of Sun-Earth Lagrangian points, the gravity of the Sun and the Earth and the centrifugal force an object experiences as it goes around the Sun, all cancel each other out. In the case of Earth-Moon Lagrangian points, the same relationship exists but those would be for objects orbiting the Earth. Lagrange's mathematics predicted this. Many years later, they were demonstrated to exist."

"Parking places in space," I repeated.

He nodded. "They exist for any large body that orbits another body, places where a third object can park."

"You said seventeen seventy-two. So that was almost two hundred years before we were able to send up the first rocket ship into space."

"Such is the power of math," Giuseppe said. "Variational

calculus, to be specific. Newton figured out the basic laws of motion. Then guys like Giuseppe Lagrange came along and fine-tuned it. His math innovation is now called Lagrangian Mechanics."

"Does this high level math have any real-world applications?"

"Oh, yes, yes, yes!" Giuseppe said. "It is momentous. We now park multiple spacecraft at the Sun-Earth Lagrange points."

"I notice that you seem to use the words Lagrange and Lagrangian interchangeably."

"Yes. We use both words for the same concept."

I nodded.

Giuseppe continued. "We've used the Earth-Moon Lagrange points as well. We also turned our telescopes toward the Sun-Jupiter Lagrange points because we knew that because of Jupiter's large size, we would find natural objects suspended, so to speak, in space in those areas. It's similar to the way floating debris gets caught in the eddies of a stream. And do you know what we found in the Jupiter Lagrange points? Thousands of asteroids! We call them Jupiter Trojans."

"So Lagrangian points are something special," I said.

"Beyond special," Giuseppe said. His enthusiasm for such an unusual subject was infectious. "An eighteenth century mathematician, using abstract symbols on a blackboard, figured out that for every two big objects in space, like the sun and a planet, or a planet and one of its moons, there are five special points – moving points – where there is stability in space. Two of the points are especially stable. What Lagrange did was simply amazing."

"And so you've been figuring out something new about these parking places?"

"I have. Think of a merry-go-round. The different horses are the planets, orbiting around the sun at the center. If you set a marble on the floor of the merry-go-round, it flies off. But Lagrange points are like large, kidney bean-shaped bowls on a merry-go-round. Put a marble in one of the bowls, and it won't escape. But it will wobble around, this way and that as the big merry-go-round turns. I'm working on a set of principles for regulating spacecraft that have been parked in what we call the L-Four and L-Five points."

"Let me guess, your work would keep the spacecraft from wobbling around?"

"No. It's merely a type of prescriptive orbital mechanics, which leads to adaptive technologies."

Maybe Giuseppe could see my face go blank. He was so far over my head that I couldn't process what he was saying.

"Imagine one of the marbles in the kidney bean bowl," he said.

I nodded.

"Now imagine that it is a spacecraft with a powerful telescope trained on a distant galaxy."

"Oh, I get it," I interrupted. "If you know just how the spacecraft is wobbling around in the bowl, you can tell its computer how to adjust the telescope so the galaxy stays in focus."

Giuseppe beamed at me, his eyes intense and his wild puff of hair vibrating. "You should have been a mathematician!"

"Thanks, Giuseppe. But trust me, no, I should not have been a mathematician. Visualizing marbles in a bowl that sits on a merry-go-round is kind of fun. But just thinking about those little abstract symbols that you use to figure out the laws of the universe makes me want to get a beer and a bowl of popcorn and escape into a Hollywood movie."

Giuseppe seemed disappointed. He'd no doubt spent an entire life being entranced by higher math and its ability to discern the workings of the universe when other people were entranced by gossip magazines spewing the latest celebrity divorce scandal or cellulite reduction trick.

"This Lagrange math application," I said.

He nodded.

"Will it produce other real world benefits?"

"Oh, you can't imagine. As I said, we already use Lagrange points to park spacecraft for scientific study. But in the future, we'll use these points to build space communities and refueling stations for spacecraft heading off to other planets and, one day, other solar systems." Giuseppe's eyes were wide with excitement.

I said, "Kind of like when Columbus set off from Spain and found islands that became outposts for future explorations."

"Indeed."

"I'm awed. I'm a nuts-and-bolts guy. If I wanted to be innovative and invent something, I'd try to dream up a new kind of widget, a more efficient device for doing a household task. You are using math to unlock the scope of the universe. The nature of your mind exploration is amazing. This big-picture math stuff makes what most of us do seem insignificant."

Giuseppe reached out and put his hand on my forearm. "Mr. McKenna, in the big picture, we are all insignificant. Remember what Carl Sagan said when that spacecraft took the first picture looking back at us from far out in the Solar System? In the photograph, our planet was this unbelievably small blue dot of reflected light. Sagan described the Earth as a mote of dust suspended in a sunbeam. And the entire history of humanity has lived on that dust speck." Giuseppe squeezed my arm. "We are all insignificant," he said. "All I'm doing is trying to understand the nature of that insignificance. So I study these unusual places in space. Five special places for each pair of large bodies where one revolves around the other. Three of the five Lagrange points are somewhat unstable. The bowl on the merry-go-round is very flat, and sometimes the marble rolls out. But two of the five points are very stable, deeper bowls. I catalog how these places, each so simply numbered, climb toward instability. The math that describes these places helps NASA and its scientists plan their future space missions."

We sat in silence. Bird songs floated on the air. Boats tracked across the water. When the breeze paused, the high-altitude sun was burning hot. Spot lay down at the far end of the deck, legs splayed, jawbone stretched out on the boards. A hummingbird buzzed, floating in the air above our heads. He was as brightly colored as Douglas Fairbanks in his bicycling spandex. The bird shot over to a planter where flowers waved, the yellow and purple and lavender mixing with his red body. A distant sailboat came into view, its white triangle of sail brilliant against the indigo water.

After a moment, I said, "If you had to imagine a reason why

a charity scammer would see Lagrangian points as some kind of business model, what might it be?"

Giuseppe frowned. "I have no idea. I suppose it could be that if one could find places or concepts in the business world where the stresses and forces would cancel each other out, maybe such a businessman could make more money. Or, if a revenue source could be maneuvered into a stable place, the money would keep flowing? Does that sound crazy?"

I looked out at the lake as I pondered what he'd said. "You're saying that Lagrange points might only serve as a vague metaphor."

Giuseppe chuckled. "I don't really have a clue about what I'm saying. I'm reaching. Reaching for metaphorical Lagrangian points."

We sat for a bit, taking in the breeze and the view.

I gestured at the lake and the surrounding land. "An amazing place you have here."

"Yes, I've been very fortunate."

"Are you still working full time?"

"Of course. What else would I do? Oh, you're wondering if I would retire," he said as if surprised at the thought. "Perhaps if I were in a more ordinary line of work, I would. But what I do isn't something you retire from. Although recently, I've wondered if I'm starting to get some premature dementia. I have a new neighbor named Aubrey Blackwood. She lives in the duplex near my barn, so I see her when I walk over there. She's quite a good watercolorist. Anyway, she's taken to calling me when I leave my car doors open and such. I never paid much attention before. I'd just go outside, see my door open, and hope the battery hasn't run down too much. But now her concerned calls become a record of my lack of mindfulness, a catalog of my slow descent."

"I met her when I came here. Seems like a nice lady. This barn of yours... Do you keep horses or something?"

"Goodness, no. It came with the house. But I like to walk there and ponder what kind of life the barn builder might have had. Anyway, I'll keep working into the foreseeable future. Quitting would be like Aubrey giving up the easel and paints. For some, work is a means to an end. For others, it is the end.

Our raison d'être." He looked down at his cat, which was still balanced on his arm. "Quitting would be like Blofeld retiring from catching mice."

"His name is Blofeld? How fun. I thought of the James Bond movies when I first saw your cat."

"Yes, that's why I gave him the name. Even as a six-week-old kitten, he acted like Blofeld's cat."

"I should get going. I really appreciate your time."

Giuseppe nodded.

"If I have other questions, may I call?"

"Speaking of metaphors… Modern communication produces one of the great modern philosophical conundrums, very different from the days when we sent a letter by ship or train or Pony Express. Those letters were read and responded to at the recipient's leisure."

"I think I'm missing your meaning," I said.

"You mentioned calling me. I gave you my number, after all. But phone calls are all about the caller's convenience. The person generating the communication is, in effect, demanding to be attended to now. Email is all about the receiver's convenience. The modern version of a letter. It should be obvious that convenience belongs with the person who is asked the favor of communication, not the person who is doing the asking."

"Now I get it. So I won't call you," I said.

Giuseppe made a little grin. Maybe his whole statement was a bit of a joke.

"If I have a future question, I'll email you," I said.

The grin turned to a full smile. "I believe you have my email address as well."

As I drove away, I thought of Blofeld and his evil owner in the James Bond movies. I wondered if Professor Calvarenna could be stringing people up by their ankles, and if so, why. But I remembered that he had been out doing his cruise ship routine when Dory was killed.

THIRTY-FOUR

M y phone rang at 6:30 a.m. the next morning. "Owen McKenna," I said.

"Ramos, here."

"Wow, our tax dollars go to work early."

"I learned of a death from hanging by the ankles," he said, ignoring my comment. "Apparently, it was a house-painting accident. But I thought I should let you know."

"I appreciate that."

"The victim was an older gentleman, a retired doctor. He was up on an extension ladder painting the upper part of his house. He slipped and fell, and his foot caught in the rope that's used to raise the extension part of the ladder. The rope wrapped around the man's ankle, and he ended up hanging upside down, his head about five feet above the ground. The ME thought he'd probably hung for several hours before he suffered a hemorrhagic stroke and died. This happened in Ukiah. It's a small town about one hundred miles north of the Bay Area on one-oh-one."

"No sign of foul play?"

"No. His paint bucket was still hanging up on the ladder, he had paint on his clothes and hands, and the brush he'd been using was on the ground. It was clearly a nasty accident."

"How was the body discovered?"

"His neighbor was out walking her dogs on a path that goes behind the victim's property. The dogs barked and ran off the trail toward the man's house. The neighbor followed and found the dogs looking up at the body."

"When was this?"

"Five weeks ago. Early May. The neighbor said it was the first stretch of nice weather in some time. A good time for painting."

"What do we know about the accident victim?"

"Not much. Let me look at my notes." There was pause. "His name was Dr. Jack Smith, age seventy-two. He'd retired and moved to Ukiah from Southern California. The neighbor thought it had been about two years before."

"Did the dead man have family?"

"There was no mention of family in the report. You have many questions regarding an accidental death."

"Just trying to be thorough. Do you have an address?"

"Yes. Are you going down there based on the coincidence of hanging by the feet? You must be struggling to find out anything about these murders."

"Yes and yes," I said. "As you know, any homicide investigation is a struggle until it's not. This one is taking longer than usual to morph out of the struggle phase. I guess that's like most of our lives."

"Aren't you the philosopher," Ramos said.

Ramos read off the address, and I wrote it down.

"If you learn something interesting about the man's death, let me know."

"Of course," I said.

"One more thing," he said.

"What's that?"

"You had asked if I could find any serious crimes connected to charity scammers."

"Right," I said. "Any luck?"

"Maybe, although it is a weird one. Several months ago, a Hyundai that had been stolen from a Vegas hotel valet lot was found out in the desert. In the trunk was the body of an old man, shot twice through the chest. The bullets had exited the body and were not found. Neither were the shells or the firearm. There was no appreciable blood, so it appeared that the victim was shot at a different location then put in the trunk and driven out to where the car was left. There was a note, standard computer copy paper, nailed to victim's forehead with a sixteen penny nail. It said, 'Charity scammers who break up families and abuse children deserve to die.'

"That's intriguing," I said, remembering that Douglas Fairbanks was from Vegas. "ID?"

"The victim had no ID. We still don't know who he was. The car had been wiped clean. The car's VIN number showed that it was owned by a beauty salon owner from Houston. She and her friend had just checked into the hotel when the car was taken."

"What about the nail?" I asked.

"Old and rusted. Probably found on the ground somewhere. No hammer or anything else was found."

"How long had the victim been in the car?"

"The ME estimated three days, which fit with the time the car was stolen."

"Any idea how the perp left the area where the Hyundai was found?"

"No. But there are hard dirt trails that criss cross the area. It hadn't rained in some time, so there were no tracks. The perp could have walked three miles to a truck stop, or four miles to a shopping center, or even eleven miles to the Strip hotels."

"So it's a cold case," I said.

"Maybe not. After the murder was on the TV news, a journalist for the Vegas paper spent some time at the hotel where the car was stolen. The journalist made small talk with one of the hotel bartenders, asking if any customers ever mentioned charities. The bartender told the journalist a story, and the newspaper ran it."

"Which was?"

"The bartender said he'd had a man in several days before the murder, a serious drinker knocking back vodka martinis. The man paid for his drinks with cash, and the bartender only saw him that one time. The man seemed very sad. As he got drunk, he told a story of a woman who was married. The couple had two children, a boy and a girl. The family was poor. The woman fell for another man who had lots of money, a man who supposedly ran a fraudulent charity."

"Ah," I said. "Motivation for the husband and those children."

"Maybe. It gets worse. According to the customer's rambling account, after the charity scammer stole the mother's affections, the husband died from a heart attack. So the scammer got access to the children and abused the girl sexually."

"Now we have serious motivation for both the kids."

"Even worse, the bartender remembers the customer saying that the mother abandoned the children, and they were put in an orphanage. When they got older, they both left and disappeared."

"Very interesting. Did the bar's customer provide any time frame for these events?"

"No. The journalist who wrote the article thought that this may have taken place a long time ago, and that the bar's customer was possibly the son resurrecting painful memories under the vodka truth serum."

I said, "I assume you don't have the name of the customer."

"Correct," Ramos said. "We do have the names of the bartender and journalist. Local law enforcement has interviewed both several times with no new information."

"Did the drinker mention any names for the people involved?"

"In fact, the subject apparently came up," Ramos said. "The bartender said that he always tries to talk to his customers to make them feel comfortable. So he asked the customer if he knew the kids well."

"Did the man give an answer?" I asked.

"Yes, but who knows if it's true. The man said he couldn't even remember the kids names because they were interchangeable. The names were ones that get used for both boys and girls."

"Names that aren't gender specific," I said.

"Right," Ramos said. "Like Riley or Morgan."

I said, "Either the son or the daughter could have motivation to take out charity scammers. There seem to be lots of possibilities of payback, people upset with charities and pursuing some kind of vigilante justice."

"I agree," Ramos said.

"Quite the story," I said. "Was there any security cam near the bar? Any images of the customer?"

"No."

"I was thinking about Betty Rodriguez, the baker lady who gave money to lots of charities. Her son Gray was angry about it. "Gray is one of those names, right?"

"I think so," Ramos said.

We said goodbye and hung up.

THIRTY-FIVE

Agent Ramos had given me the address of the house where the retired doctor had slipped from his ladder, caught his foot in the ladder's extension rope, and hung upside down until he died. I thought I should pay a visit. I called Street and told her my plans. She assured me that she was comfortable with me leaving. But as she said it, she sounded tense and worried.

"Are you sure you're okay with it?"

"Yes."

I took Street at her word, printed a Google map of the area, and drove over Echo Summit and down to the Central Valley. I took the freeway north out of Sacramento, then took back roads around Clear Lake to 101, and drove north to Ukiah. My map led me to a small road and a turnoff to a smaller road.

As always in June, the Central Valley was hot. But when I got closer to the Pacific, lingering clouds swirled through the Mendocino National Forest. I rolled down the windows. The air was delightfully cool. Spot immediately stuck his head out. Clouds swirled so low that tendrils of fog wrapped the treetops.

Following the map, I drove past Ukiah and turned off on a narrow side road. The paint lines at the road edges and centerline were faded. There was no shoulder. The road was a motorcyclist's dream, made of continuous turns, left and right and left, over and over. Every third turn seemed to arc up over a hill and then plunge down into a little valley. The landscape was very green from a wet spring. There was an irregular patchwork of meadows, farm fields, and forest. I came upon picture book vineyards, the vines showing thick, healthy foliage. Over another hill was the sudden appearance of a turnoff. I couldn't see a sign. So I slowed to a stop and backed up.

When I got to the road, the sign was there after all, but largely hidden by the leaves of a tree. The road was the one Jack Smith had lived on, so I turned.

The new road was one lane wide. I went slowly around a sharp curve and over a steep hill. A pickup truck approached. We both had to slow to a crawl and put our outer tires into the dirt to pass. Every hundred yards or so, was a mailbox next to a dirt path that crawled back into the woods and meadows.

There were no house numbers visible for the simple reason that the houses were all back from the road. Instead, I looked for mailbox numbers. Eventually, I saw the shape of an old farmhouse back in a field at the edge of the forest. Soon, I came to a mailbox that stood at the end of a dirt drive. The number was the one Agent Ramos had given me for the dead man's address. I turned and followed a dirt path that meandered back through stands of fir and a meadow. The going was slow as the drive was bumpy.

The road went over a small rise. The air coming in the window made a sudden, startling change from cool and moist to warm and dry, no doubt a pocket of air that flowed from the sun-baked meadow. Then as we entered another stand of conifers, the air went cool again.

The dirt drive ended at the house I'd glimpsed from the main road. I got out of the Jeep and let Spot out of the back.

"Time to explore, Largeness," I said, giving Spot a rough pet. He ran off toward the house, then arced around it.

I knocked on the door. No one answered. Agent Ramos said the doctor had died five weeks earlier. Maybe no one else had lived with him.

I walked around the house, an old structure with walls that leaned a bit and a roof that sagged. It was once painted deep red as evidenced by flecks of rust red that still lingered in the weathered grain.

When I got to the other side, I saw that the top left side was bright red. The new paint came to a ragged, irregular edge. I realized that was what Smith had been painting when he fell.

I knocked and peered in the windows. I could see nothing.

There was a path into the woods. I called Spot, then explored farther down the path.

Spot ran past me as I walked. No doubt the low-elevation forest had scents much different from those of the pine and fir and bear and mountain lion at 7000-plus feet. He seemed eager and excited as he ran this way and that, with no apparent focus other than the joy of discovering a new world of smells.

The trail was narrow but well-used. A hundred yards into the woods, I saw a house in another meadow at the edge of the forest. Dogs began barking. The house door opened, and two dogs charged out. One looked like an Australian Shepherd, the other was a Boxer. Spot ran toward them. They, too, ran toward Spot as fast as dogs go, then slowed, then stopped, perhaps trying to comprehend that the animal running toward them was in fact a dog, despite its size. As Spot drew close, they burst forward, one to Spot's left, the other to his right. The standard dog ballet ensued, the three running around in frantic excitement. Few if any animals get such joy out of running.

The house I was approaching was more sway-backed and rundown than Dr. Smith's.

As I walked forward, I saw a woman in the doorway. When I got close, I called out to introduce myself. When I saw her eyes, I realized that she wasn't watching me, but was instead focused on the dogs, who were still racing around.

"Great Dane, huh?" she said. "Seen them before, but not this close. My God, he must eat a lot."

"Yup," I said. "I parked over at the old, red farmhouse. That's where Dr. Smith lived, right?"

"Yessir. I know you were coming," she said, an unusual use of the present tense. "I got a feeling for things. My friend Carol say, Judy, you're so psychic. I say it's my sixth sense."

"Hi, Judy," I said. "I'm Owen McKenna."

The woman shook my hand. She was around 80 years old, but she dressed like a forester half her age. She had on Dickies work boots below her Carhartt jeans, a red flannel shirt and a leather jacket that was 50 or 60 years old. It was a lot of clothes for June, but the woods were cool.

The woman's dogs came charging up. They sniffed me and wagged and jumped. The Australian Shepherd made whining sounds, then picked up a stick and dropped it at my feet. I knew where that would lead, so I let it lie there. The boxer jumped up as if to sniff my face, pawed my thigh, then ran off to rejoin

Spot.

"So innaway," the woman said, "the house is vacant and it's got holes with the animals coming and going. It's so run down, I know it will be torn down. But about two year ago, along come Dr. Smith who buy the place. I'm thinking, what's the deal with that? It's really just a pile of old lumber." She looked up at the sky, frowning, thinking. "What's that word I always call it? Rickety. That's what it look to me. Good for nothin'. But you know that one man's rickety is another man's mansion. At least, a crazy man's. So crazy Smith come up here from... A place near San Diego. Let me think. Oh yeah. Encinitas. Never been there myself. Probably get good tacos, name like that."

The Australian dropped a different stick on my shoe, then looked up at me with imploring eyes.

"Anyway, Smith starts working on that house. I think, give me a break, the place is good for firewood, nothin' more. And Smith's an old guy. Not old like me, but seventy or more. 'Course, my curiosity can't stand it. So one day, I go over there. I walk right up and say, what gives. And you know what Smith say?"

She looked at me.

"No, what did Smith say?"

"He say he gonna live there. With the owl and mouse and skunk and whatnot that call that place home." She was shaking her head at the thought.

"So I ask why he's not buying a nice house. And he just shrug his shoulders and say he like it. Not a real talkative one, that Smith. So then I ask if he's one of those hippy types what got some inheritance and is gonna start a nudie commune like the one north of town. He say no, he just like fixing up stuff."

The woman leaned toward me a bit and lowered her voice to a near whisper. "Then his cell phone ring. He walk away from me as he pull it out of his pocket. He go around the corner so I can't hear him. So I kind of walk real quiet toward him but stay where he can't see me. I listen real good. And I hear him saying something about he was only trying to do good with his money and that he didn't know it was a bad thing. His voice was all tense. And I get the feeling someone is pressuring him about what he do and how he spend. And I start to feel sorry for him, so I start bringing him my cookies. I'm probably the best cookie maker in the county. I have a secret ingredient. Want to know what that is? I'll give you a clue. It ain't weed like what everyone else 'round here use."

She stopped and looked at me, waiting.

"What's your secret ingredient?"

"Cinnamon. Just a tiny bit. You can use it in chocolate chip or peanut butter or oatmeal cookies. Make them all taste just a little bit like Christmas. Don't get me wrong. I love weed. But weed is for smoking. Cinnamon is for cookies."

She paused again as if waiting for me to say something.

"Did Dr. Smith have a family?"

"I ask him once and he doesn't answer real quick. Then he says not really. What's that about? Then it occur to me that maybe he has a wife who die. Or she divorce him. Whatever it is, my sixth sense tell me yes, he's got some kind of family. Then one day I'm walking the dogs on the trail near his place when he drive up. I go over to talk because he likes my dogs. He get out of the van, and he's holding his mail. The top envelope has a handwritten address in a real thin blue ink line. I can see it's a woman's writing. My sixth sense tells me it's from his daughter."

"Why would you think that?"

"Because it's not like the way a girlfriend would write, all attractive and such. It's more matter-of-fact writing. But still feminine. Handwriting is practically never used no more, right? What with everyone but me using computers. What else would it be? But a computer-type daughter maybe still write by hand if she sending a letter to daddy. Right?"

"Makes sense," I said. "Dr. Smith died, didn't he?"

She shrugged. "Yup. Some do it real natural like. Others do it like Smith. I'm the one what found him. Soon as I see him hanging upside down, I know what happen. He fall, catch his foot in the ladder rope, and dangle upside down until a little pipe burst in his brain. Then me and the dogs come along about ten in the morning and he already dead. Now even an old guy would probably survive hanging upside down that long unless something in his brain goes pop.

"'Course, I call it in, and the medics come out, and eventually a lady doctor come too, and I tell her what probably happen. She look at me like I'm a hillbilly who don't know anything beyond baking cookies. Later, the mailman tell me that he hear the man who die on the ladder has a stroke. That's what I say, right? A stroke is when a brain pipe blows its gasket. That ain't even my sixth sense talking. That's just common sense."

"When you found the body, was there anything that stood out as unusual? Something you didn't expect?"

"She shook her head. I've seen dead people before. He look like them, except his head is all swole up red and purple. But I know that's because of hanging by his feet."

"What happened to Dr. Smith's stuff? Did someone come to pick it up?"

"Yeah. Two, three week after he die, I'm out walking my dogs when two workmen come with a truck with a tilt flatbed. There's just a few things, mostly tools, that Smith has in the house. They take his stuff put it in his van. Then they winch the van up onto the flatbed.

"So I ask what gives them the right. They say their company is working for the man's daughter. And I think, there again I was right, just based on that envelope. So they haul everything away. Then two days later the daughter show up with a realtor, and the daughter look nothing like you'd expect."

"What would you expect?" I asked.

"Well a doctor's daughter ought to look refined, with city clothes, and have an educated manner. But this woman dress more like me, a real tough broad. The only doctor's-daughter aspect was her education."

"How could you tell that?"

"Well, I'm not shy, as you probably guess. So I walk up and ask for her bona fides. Like, just how do we know she his daughter. Of course, that get her hackles up some. But after a bit, she quiet down, and we get to talkin'. And it turn out she's some kind of Greek scholar, teaching about ancient philosophers at the university. She even quote them to me, like I could care."

"What was her name?"

"Glenn. I didn't think to ask the last name. I suppose it might have been Smith as she seemed a bit like me, not exactly the marrying type."

"Did you get her address?"

"No. Once I get that she's legit, I let her do her business with the realtor. There were some people looking a few days later. Pro'bly the place is sold by now."

"What did Glenn look like?"

"Aside from the woodsman dress, a regular girl. Maybe a bit skinny. About my height, five-six or so. Shoulder-length brown hair all stringy and messy."

"Eye color?"

"I don't know. Dark, I think. So I guess brown."

"Is there anything else you remember about her? Anything that stands out?"

"Not really. I liked her clothes. I liked her rough talk."

"How did that come out, her talking rough?"

"It was just something she was angry about. She had picked up her old man's mail, and in it was some mailer come-on for one of those do-gooder outfits. Send us your money. So Glenn waves this mailer in the air and say that her father got scammed by this outfit. She say he'd sent them thousands of dollars and then figured out it was all a cheat. Sorry, there's a name for those companies, but I can't remember it."

"Charities?"

"Yeah, that's it. Glenn was pretty hot under the collar when she saw that mailer. She said she blamed them for his death and that he probably only slipped off the ladder because he was preoccupied by how he'd gotten screwed."

"Do you remember what charity the mailer came from?"

Judy shook her head. "No, I wasn't that close. I could only see that it had a picture of a starving little boy and above it, a bunch of roses."

"Do you have any idea of how I'd find Glenn?"

"I'd start with the taco city. Encinitas. Maybe the daughter will be in there someplace. And that's no sixth sense. That's just common sense."

"Thanks Judy. You've been a big help."

The woman flashed me a big grin of crooked, stained teeth.

Spot and I went back to the Jeep.

THIRTY-SIX

After I let Spot into the back of the Jeep, I pulled out my phone and saw that I had no cell reception. So I drove back toward the town of Ukiah. When I found reception, I stopped in the parking lot of a supermarket.

I called Sergeant Bains of El Dorado County. I got his voicemail.

"Owen McKenna calling regarding the Fannette Island murder victim Dory Spatt. I've got a potential suspect name to check out. A woman named Glenn, spelling uncertain, last name uncertain but possibly Smith. She is the daughter of a Dr. Jack Smith who died in Ukiah in an accidental death that left him hanging by his ankles. His neighbor Judy met the daughter Glenn and learned that she was very angry about her father's donations to the Red Roses of Hope Charity for Children, Dory Spatt's scam charity. Agent Ramos has a little information on the doctor if you want to check in with him."

I next dialed Ramos, was put on hold, then put through.

"I'm in Ukiah where I've been talking to Dr. Jack Smith's neighbor. She told me he had a daughter named Glenn – last name uncertain – and that the daughter was angry about charities in general and the Red Roses of Hope charity specifically. I wondered if you can search your databases by the first name Glenn and see if anything turns up."

"Maybe. But you'll probably have more luck with the Bureau of Investigation."

"The California BI?" I said just to be sure I was clear on his meaning.

"Yes. The California Department of Justice has them tasked with financial fraud. They might even have someone who focuses on charity fraud."

"They're out of Los Angeles, right?" I said.

"Many of their resources, yes. Hold on and let me look in my computer."

So I waited for a long time in the Ukiah grocery store parking lot. Ramos came back on the line and said, "A woman named Jamie Johnsrud specializes in financial fraud. She's at the BI's Sacramento office. I'll give you the address and phone."

"Ready," I said.

Ramos gave me the numbers.

"Thanks much. I'll be in touch."

I hung up and dialed the phone number.

"Jamie Johnsrud," she answered in a British accent. No secretary. No voicemail. And this personal service from a bureaucrat. Impressive.

"Hi Jamie, my name is Owen McKenna. I'm a private investigator calling on a referral from FBI Agent Ramos up in Tahoe. We've had two murders that appear to be connected to scam charities. Agent Ramos said you and your department investigate these charities. I'm wondering if you would be available to talk."

"Will Agent Ramos vouch for you when I call him?"

"Like I said, it was his idea that I contact you."

"Then we can make an appointment," she said.

"The thing is, I'm driving from Ukiah to South Lake Tahoe. That will take me through Sacramento in a little over two hours. Any chance that could work for you today?"

"So you're talking about tea time, three o'clock. Sure, come on in. Let me give you a security code to give the desk guard. They are time sensitive, so you would only have a thirty-minute window. You'll also need your ID."

"Got it."

She read off some numbers and letters that looked like something a random number generator would produce. "Of course, the security code is dependent on my verification of your ID after we hang up. So if the guard doesn't let you in, it's because I called Ramos and he said or intimated that you were of questionable character."

"Got that, too. See you around three."

We hung up.

THIRTY-SEVEN

The office building that contained the BI Office was four blocks from the capitol dome in Sacramento. I parked in a ramp and left Spot in the Jeep. With the parking ramp shade and multiple floors of heat-absorbing concrete above him, he'd stay cool enough to snooze without panting.

The reception desk guard carefully entered my code in his computer, nodded as he saw the result, then let me pass.

I found Jamie's office number on the third floor down a narrow hallway with linoleum flooring that, despite regular sweeping with a janitor's dust mop and sweeping compound, probably hadn't been washed, waxed, or polished in 30 years. At least the bureaucrats weren't wasting tax dollars on excessive maintenance.

The door to the office I wanted was half-open, held in place by two big law books placed on each side of the door. I turned sideways and slipped through the narrow opening without bumping the door. On the other side of the door was a fan set on high and making a tremendous racket as it attempted to mitigate the high Central Valley heat that bakes Sacramento four months of the year.

"Hello," I said loudly enough to be heard above the fan. "I have an appointment with Jamie. Would that be you?"

"No harm in opening the door farther," a woman at a desk nearly shouted. She didn't look up from her laptop and the two-inch-thick pile of papers next to it. She telegraphed a weary intelligence, a look I'd seen many times on bureaucrats' faces after they'd put in ten or fifteen years at an often thankless job that they originally thought would come with psychological happiness from doing civic good.

The woman typed another sentence, then looked up at me and shouted. "If you turn the fan down to the low setting, we can possibly hear each other talking."

I reached over and flipped the switch down two notches.

"I've stopped asking maintenance to find a solution to the Attention Deficit Disorder that has afflicted our air conditioning," the woman said. "So I brought in my own fan, and I sip ice water all day. But I also keep my ski sweater and coffee mug close for those rare moments when the machinery kicks up for a brief spell and the air ducts kick out a fog of frost."

"Maybe the temperature fluctuations are designed to keep you alert." I said.

"Or to torture me." She stood up and reached out her hand. "I'm Jamie Johnsrud. You would be the man who called."

I shook her hand. "Owen McKenna. I'm a private investigator. I'm looking into the murder of a woman who appears to have been running a phony charity."

Her countenance changed from one of comfort to distaste.

"Which is the greater challenge?" I said. "Preventing burns and frostbite or watching over the state's charities?"

"No contest. I would likely mutate to grow my own fur coat or develop some kind of internal metabolic cooling system before I could remedy the legal theft that is our charity system."

"At least you haven't lost your sense of hyperbole," I said, grinning.

A severe look settled over the woman's face, pulling the inner points of her eyebrows down and compressing her lips into a tight, thin line. "There is no hyperbole in that statement," she said.

I pointed to a folding metal chair that leaned up against the wall. "May I?"

"Oh, of course. Sorry. You bring up the subject of charities and I lose all good grace. Sit down. And let me introduce you to a world that would turn Jesus, Santa Claus, and the Boy Scouts of America into the world's biggest cynics."

I opened the folding chair, set it in front of her desk, and sat. "The charity business model is not one that pleases an idealistic civil servant," I said.

"The charity business model is largely a scam that, even with some of the best charities, puts more money into the pockets of people who run the charities than the pockets of those whom the charities claim to help."

"Is your condemnation universal, or are there charities that buck the trend and actually do good work?"

"There are definitely some good ones. Although even most of them are businesses at their core, enriching the people who run them. And if you look closely at the numbers that these people publish to show how much they give to the needy, you usually find that their reporting is more creative than truthful."

"What about the big corporate approach?" I said. "Are the huge charities questionable, too?"

"I won't say that good large charities don't exist. But sometimes they seem rare. And if you apply any reasonable standard of measurement like, say, that a majority of money raised should go to charity work, then they are extremely rare. Mind you, most charities claim that a large part of their operating income goes to good charitable efforts. But the reality is that their so-called operating income is a small part of their total revenue. Most of their revenue is siphoned off through a range of fundraising and other expenses. And even though those expenses are substantial, they often report zero fundraising expenses on their Nine-Ninety forms. They hide them in with program costs. It's very shady. You mentioned investigating a woman who ran a phony charity."

"Yes," I said.

"Why do you call it phony?"

"According to the woman's brother and employee, the charity's revenue of six million a year didn't go to charity work. It went to her. She owned a for-profit fundraising company that she used to raise the money for the charity. Eighty-five percent of the money raised was paid to that company as a fee for the fundraising efforts. The remaining fifteen percent was what the charity had to work with. Yet the charity didn't even put that fifteen percent to good cause. It was nearly all spent on salaries, vehicles, and office expenses."

"Very common," Jamie said.

"I also found out that she used accounting tricks to inflate the supposed value of what the charity provided. So even though her charity had official non-profit status and a board of directors, it was still a complete scam."

Jamie was nodding. "What's the charity's name?"

"The Red Roses of Hope Charity for Children."

She typed on her keypad. Clicked her mouse. Stared at the screen. She looked bored as if she'd seen the same thing a thousand times. "You'll be glad to know that the Red Roses of Hope is officially in good standing with the state of California."

"Lovely," I said.

"Typically, charities like these use mailers and online come-ons that include things like photos of starving children, checks and cash enclosed, and they often have names and addresses designed to look like government mailers or designed to be easily confused with well-known, respected charities."

I nodded.

"They often use pictures of veterans with amputated limbs or old people with dementia. They also have warnings printed on the envelopes that say that interference with delivery of mail to the correct address is a federal crime." Jamie sighed. "These are the charity equivalent of supermarket check-out magazines, selling trash stories and sensationalism. Lowest-common-denominator stuff. They prey on people who are generous and trusting and really want to help the people in those and photographs. But nothing about it is earnest or sincere. Everything is about getting your money."

"Is this a common problem?" I asked. "Fraudulent charities?"

"Yes. What makes it worse is that this is a really big business. Conservative estimates put it at a billion dollars a day. What giving Americans don't realize is that these businesses are often not about charitable giving at all. People in the general public actually believe that charities are special, that they are all about helping the needy. As a result, the public gives enormous amounts, and charities bring in massive amounts of money."

"Aren't there watchdog groups? People watching out for good ethics in this business?" I asked.

Jamie made a loud guffaw. "Yes. But as with many areas of business, a lot of the charity watchdog groups are set up by charities."

"I don't understand. How could charities run the very

groups that are supposed to watch over them?" I felt like a naive schoolboy discovering vice and graft for the first time.

Jamie shook her head. "I'm sorry to burst your bubble. Charities get together and create supposed watchdog groups that are designed to rate charities on a wide range of qualities. They design their groups so that they look independent. They put up elaborate websites, and they promote journalistic articles that promulgate their desires. But in the end, the watchdog group ends up giving the highest ratings to the charities that run the watchdog group."

"That is the essence of unethical," I said.

"Welcome to the real world, Mr. McKenna. It's the same for organizations that rate car insurance, home builders and home repair companies, travel destinations, hospitals, doctors, and medical insurance. And, of course, the granddaddy of graft and dishonesty, politicians and political action committees. Most people know better than to take political news as fact-based. But charities? Many people out there still believe that when they receive an email that shows some poor soldier who was blown apart by a bomb in the Middle East, that if they send in a hundred bucks, they will make life better for that soldier. It could actually happen. But in my experience? More often than not, that hundred bucks goes toward a charity CEO's monthly wine bill."

"In your opinion, how much of charity money collected actually goes to help the needy?"

"I don't know the answer to that. But I'm always surprised at the gulf between what they raise and what they pay out on charitable activities. What's worse is that what gets reported as charitable giving is often inflated. And it's all mostly legal."

"How can that be?," I asked. "If I send money to some cancer charity, how can it be legal that the charity's owner could pocket my donation and not give it to cancer research or victims?"

"Because the law allows charities to hire a fundraising company and spend a great deal of money on that, maybe even most of the money they take in. The law allows the charity to claim salaries and benefits and a wide range of other expenses as necessary to their business. They then deduct all of these expenditures as a standard business expense and thus report only the small amount left over as Revenue Less Expenses on the Nine-Ninety form."

Jamie clicked her computer mouse and turned to face me.

"Viewed from the perspective of the Nine Ninety filing, it looks like charities use a large portion of their operating income for charity work. But that so-called operating income is often much less than the gross revenue the charity brings in. Even with the best charities, almost always the majority of their money gets spent on so-called business expenses. If members of the generous public knew how little of their money ends up going to charity work, they would be appalled."

"What about transparency? What about openness? Shouldn't a charity be required to tell donors exactly what portion of donated money goes to the needy?"

"We have some laws and some rules about charity reporting. The law says that charities are not allowed to distribute money for private gain. But the reality isn't that simple. Charities are allowed to spend their money on anything that can be claimed as an expense that supposedly helps the charity. So here's my challenge to you. Find me any charity with paid employees that doesn't spend most of its gross revenue on business expenses. Not net revenue. Not operating income. Gross. Pick the biggest, most famous charity names. Notice the claims on their brochures and websites. Then compare those numbers to their public Nine-Ninety filings. They often don't match up."

Jamie leaned back in her chair.

"The smaller charities simply funnel their revenue into for-profit fundraising companies. The large charities blatantly ignore the rules. They say they don't have any fundraising expenses, even though they hire telemarketers to bother you during dinner and direct mail companies to fill your mailbox with junk mail. Why the IRS treats them with soft gloves, we don't know. I suspect that bureaucrats actually believe that nearly all charities are doing such good work that they don't deserve scrutiny."

"In your work, you obviously get an insider's view of bad charities. But isn't the overall charity business ethical?"

"There are some good, ethical charities out there that actually appear to exist to serve the people they claim to serve. The most effective charity efforts seem to be small community efforts, local soup kitchens feeding the homeless, local service clubs buying holiday presents for the poor kids in town, hands-on school programs that get poor kids to and from the classrooms and feed them hot lunches, community programs to expand literacy. But after all the years I've worked in this job, I believe it is rare."

"Is there a way to tell the good from the bad?"

"In my opinion, yes," she said. "And the distinction is easy to verify. I believe the best charities are the ones completely run by volunteers. If no one is paid, and if the checking account requires two people to sign off on every expense, there is little graft. But as soon as a charity pays people to distribute money, you have the possibility of a different perspective among the employees. Those people see the money coming in and know it provides for their income. That can produce a shift in perspective that tempts them to consider ways in which more of the revenue could legally be routed into their personal accounts or the for-profit accounts of friends and associates running fundraising companies and other companies that provide business services to charities. The worst case situation is when a charity is run by just one or two people with little-to-no outside oversight. Those individuals are confronted by an enormous temptation when they realize that by utilizing certain techniques, they can legally keep most of the money the charity raises. The simple truth is that charities run by volunteers remain focused on the mission of charitable giving. Whereas for many charity employees who are paid, the charity is a business to make money, to earn an income."

"Like most other businesses," I said.

"Right. But when we give money, we like to think that the charity operates on a higher standard than the local sports bar or casino. The essence of a charity is getting people to donate their hard-earned money, and the charity does that by convincing them of their good work. But if you showed those donors pictures of the charity CEOs' houses and vacation homes and private airplanes, they would be outraged."

I said, "In addition to the murder of the Red Roses charity woman, we've had another murder in Tahoe. This victim was a man who may have also been involved in a charity. Is there some kind of charity database that provides information? Something a murderer might consult for information on charities and their owners?"

Jamie frowned, thinking. "First, I should say that charities don't have owners the way we usually think of it. Nonprofits belong to the public. The people who run them are managers or stakeholders. One of the easiest ways to get information on them is to contact one of the watchdog groups I mentioned. They won't usually be forthcoming except with positive portrayals of their member charities and negative portrayals of charities that are widely recognized as frauds."

"These are the organizations that you said are run by the very charities they purport to rate?"

"Yes."

"Who would you suggest I look up?"

"I'd start with a local group called Charity Lights Archive. Like other rating agencies, they are biased toward their charity investors. But a murderer might find them useful, as they provide information on many charities and then rate the best and the worst." Jamie opened a file drawer, pulled out some papers that were stapled together, and handed them to me. It was interesting that she had the papers preassembled.

"Thanks very much."

"Good luck," she said. "I'm sorry to say that you're going to need it. This business is one of the biggest there is. Bigger than most any industry." Jamie radiated frustration and even anger.

I stood up. "With a job like yours, I bet you can use frequent vacation getaways. Do you ever get up to Tahoe for a break?"

She immediately blushed. "I, uh…" She paused, thinking. "I was just up there last week."

"Not the best timing," I said. "The weather was chilly, and we had some snow, but hopefully that didn't cramp your visit."

I wondered why she blushed. Maybe she was like Douglas Fairbanks and met a romantic partner there. Or maybe she was up there to take out her frustrations on charity scammers…

"Yes, it was cold, but Tahoe's always enjoyable," she said.

I smiled, made a little nod, and left.

THIRTY-EIGHT

Spot was excited when I got back to the Jeep. I dialed the number that Jamie had given me for Charity Lights Archive.

A man answered. "Reese Rangeman at Charity Lights Archive where we answer all of your questions about charities."

"Hello, Mr. Rangeman. By name is Owen McKenna. I was just given your name by Jamie Johnsrud at the Bureau of Investigation. I have some questions I'd like to ask you about charities."

"I'm happy to oblige."

"May I come to your office?"

"Yes, of course. Any time you like."

"I'm in downtown Sac right now. Are you nearby? Maybe I could stop by this afternoon."

"We're out in Folsom. Rush hour is bad right now. But you can probably get here in forty minutes. I'll be here if that works for you. I'll give you the address."

"Great," I said. "See you soon."

Folsom is twenty-some miles east of downtown Sacramento. The small historic town near Folsom Lake still exists, but much of the area is now a continuation of the urban sprawl of Sacramento, a place of hotels and restaurants and shopping.

The rush hour was heavy, but people in Sac need only compare themselves to the Bay Area to feel that their highways are lonely places.

The Charity Lights Archive office was near the Highway 50 freeway in a large, four-story office building sheathed in glass that was nearly as shiny as mirrors. As I pulled into the parking lot, the wall of windows reflected the variegated green slopes of the foothills to the east, slopes that, because of the wet spring, were slow in turning the sunny warm-colored hues that the Golden

State is famous for.

I parked in the shade of two large trees, left Spot's window open, and got out. He stuck his head out. When I gave him a pet, he turned his head away from me, more interested in the local scents than the love and affection of his master. Although, as I had the thought, I realized that I was only Spot's master when I held food that he wanted. The rest of the time I was his driver.

As I walked to the building, I perused the sheets that the Bureau of Investigation woman had given me. I found the Charity Lights office on the third floor, down a hallway with thick carpet in forest green with swirls of maroon. Between the green and maroon were curving pinstripes of gold. The door was heavy oak, and the name Charity Lights Archive was emblazoned in raised gold letters.

It was the opposite of the government office of Jamie Johnsrud. One was all about making a fancy impression. Probably some were impressed, especially wealthy people who might donate large sums to charity. The other was all about getting a job done and being efficient with space and cost.

I opened the door and heard the swish as the door brushed carpet even thicker than that in the hall.

A distinguished-looking man sat behind a large mahogany desk. There was a green desk blotter and a green and brass banker's lamp and a brass pen and pencil holder. On one corner was a brass clock with a rounded top. It stood about ten inches high. Behind its glass front and back one could see gears turning, bit by bit.

The man wore a dark gray suit with a light gray pinstripe. His shirt was light gray, his tie dark gray. Peaking out of his suit pocket was a dark gray handkerchief. The man's hair was the same color as his shirt, and it was thick and brushed carefully to the side. He looked like a politician, someone who'd pick up babies and smile at them for photo-ops.

"Good afternoon," he said as he stood up. He smiled. His teeth were too perfect to be real. "You must be Owen McKenna. Reese Rangeman. Pleased to meet you." He reached out to shake my hand. On the cuff of his right sleeve flashed a gold cufflink. He gestured toward one of two leather chairs in front of his desk, then sat down.

"What can I help you with?" he asked.

"I'd like to know about scam charities."

Reese jerked as if he'd been slapped. "Well, let's get right to the point, eh?" He made a nervous chuckle.

"I'm investigating the murder of a woman who ran a scam charity. Something called the Red Roses of Hope Charity for Children. I'm here to ask you about it because I understand that your organization sorts out good charities from bad."

Reese gave me a kind, reassuring smile. "Well, Mr. McKenna, you've come to the right place. You are correct about our role in charity oversight. We investigate charity business practices and help to inform the public about charities such as the one you describe."

"How do you do that?"

Reese gave me an avuncular nod. "We look through public records, examine non-profit tax filings, do background checks on members of charity boards, things like that. Then we publish on our website a list of the fifty worst charities and another list of the fifty best charities."

"Is it possible that the Red Roses of Hope charity is on your list?"

"That's an easy question to answer. I'll pull it up and print it out."

He typed on his computer, clicked a couple of times, and I heard the whirring of a printer. Rangeman reached down, pulled some sheets of paper from a lower shelf, and scanned down them.

"Yes, indeed, look at that. The Red Roses of Hope Charity for Children." He tapped his fingertip on the papers, then handed them to me.

The listing was near the bottom of his 50 Worst Charities list. To the side of the name was the contact info, the Market Street address. Dory Spatt was listed as the CEO.

"You'll see by our list of bad charities that we are dedicated to protecting consumers from the questionable people who try to corrupt the good work of charities."

"Is this common?"

"Just enough to be a cancer on the charitable world. When people solicit money under the guise of doing good and then keep that money, those people should be punished. Severely punished. And not just because they give a bad name to what we do. Because they do evil."

Rangeman's antipathy was notable. It sounded like he took it personally when scam charities stole money. I wondered if he had also been in Tahoe when Dory was murdered.

"Is there anything else that Charity Lights Archive does beyond listing the best and worst charities?"

"Of course. One of our most important missions is to shine the light on how good charities work, and how there is a complex interaction among the various components of a well-functioning charity."

"Such as?"

Reese smiled. "For example, people always want to boil down complexities into bite-sized concepts. They often want a single metric for measuring the performance of a charity. Common desires are knowing the percentage of charitable contributions that get spent on charitable activities."

"You mean, if I give a hundred dollars to help feed poor kids, I'll want to know how many dollars actually go to buying food for kids."

"Exactly."

"What could be wrong with that?"

Another smile. "Just that it overlooks a more complex picture, such as what food is bought, how it is distributed, where it is distributed. Sometimes a charity that spends money on better distribution does more good than a charity that simply buys more food."

I said, "What you say makes sense, but the concept could possibly be used to justify charity expenditures outside of the stated goal of the charity."

"Technically, yes. That's why Charity Lights Archive pays so much attention to the inner workings of charities. We try to take a big-picture look at the charity system and find the good eggs as well as the bad eggs."

"Who runs your company?" I asked.

"You mean, the Charity Lights Archive?"

"Yes."

"Charity Lights is itself a non-profit. We have a board of directors, which has hired me as its Executive Director."

"But who runs it? Somebody has to set up a non-profit, right?"

"Yes, of course." Reese shifted in his chair, reached up and put his index finger behind the knot of his tie and gave a little tug to create more room. "We have multiple investors. They are people and companies who see the need for our services. They want the public to be informed. Charity Lights Archive is ultimately run by those investors."

"Can you give me some of their names?"

"Sure, but you wouldn't know them. Think of them as generous givers, people who feel it is important to fund activities that benefit society."

"Nevertheless, I'd like some names. Management records of corporations, for-profit or non-profit, are public. It would take some digging, but I can get the names. You can save me that trouble."

Reese again shifted in his chair. He pushed the chair back from his desk, crossed one foot over the other knee. His shoe looked Italian, polished leather, very expensive. "Our investors include companies like First Equality International, The Premise Foundation, Gift of Raptor Wings, Inc, Federal Amalgamated Veterans for Peace. All good companies spreading good will."

"And if you were to characterise the common ground of these businesses and organizations, what would that be?"

"Other than their positive community outreach, I couldn't characterise them. They are a diverse group who simply share a belief in what we're doing at Charity Lights Archive."

"Are these investors charities themselves?"

Reese seemed to think about his response. "Yes. But they are looking out for the good of the public at large."

"What exactly is your job?"

"I do the hands-on work of analyzing the charities we study. I also liaise with the legislators in Sacramento teaching them about the important concerns of legitimate charities."

"You mean, you're a lobbyist."

Reese made a little harumph and frowned. "Lobbyists are generally hustlers who are paid to go golfing and twist the arms of legislators who need campaign funds for their next election. I'm a consultant and educator."

I looked down at the pages that the Bureau of Investigation woman had given me. "Mr. Rangeman, is it true that your base salary is one hundred ninety-five thousand dollars?"

Reese frowned. "I'm sorry, but this is getting way too personal. I don't see how this could possibly impact on your investigation."

"You talk about the big picture of charity organizations. This is one more bit of information that I can get by myself. Why not save me the trouble and keep me from wondering what you are trying to hide?"

Reese looked flustered. "I'm not trying to hide anything." He took a deep breath. "Yes, that is my salary."

"Bonus? Health insurance? Unpaid sick leave? Other compensation?"

Reese's look seemed to progress from frustration to anger.

"Everything included, my entire compensation last year was two hundred forty nine thousand, which, I should add, is much less than what I'd earn in many other industries." He narrowed his eyes.

"One more question. Are any of your investor charities included on the list of the fifty best charities?"

It was a moment before Reese nodded. "Yes," he finally said.

"How many of them?"

"All of them. Now, I'd like to remind you that this is not a deposition. No one is suing me or Charity Lights Archive. This interview is through." He stood up and held his hand out, gesturing toward the door. "You may leave."

I stood, opened the door, and was leaving when I stopped and turned back.

"Mr. Rangeman, do you ever get up to Tahoe?"

"Of course. Doesn't everybody? I have a cabin there. What does that have to do with charity work?"

"Nothing. I was just curious. Thanks."

THIRTY-NINE

On my drive back to Tahoe, I thought about how the people had died, hanging by their ankles.

When I got up to my cabin, I made a call to Doc Lee, a friend who's an ER doc at the hospital. I left a message on his voicemail asking if we could talk.

Doc Lee called back and said his graveyard shift was going to stretch to late morning and would I be available to meet for breakfast at The Red Hut restaurant around 11 a.m. the next morning.

"Sounds good," I said.

I next called Agent Ramos and reported on what I'd learned about the Bureau of Investigation woman Jamie and the charity watchdog man Rangeman, who was actually a charity apologist whose bosses were the very charities he claimed to rate.

"Busy day," Ramos said. "Conclusions?"

"Charity laws need to be changed. No one should donate to any charity without doing a lot of research. And I'm not any closer to finding out what happened to Dory Spatt."

"Stay in touch," he said, and we hung up.

Next, I checked in with Street.

"Any more feelings you're being followed?" I asked.

"No. A good day in that regard."

"Want to have dinner?"

"Two nights in a row?" Street said. "Aren't you the serious boyfriend."

Street and I ate dinner at her condo. I showed her the 50 Worst Charities list that the charity apologist had given me.

Almost immediately, she spotted the Red Roses charity on the list. "Look, it's got Dory's real name listed. Do you suppose the murderer found her off this list?"

"I suppose it's possible."

"Then what about the victim who died with a tennis ball in his mouth. He could be connected to a charity on this list!"

"Maybe," I said again.

"Let me go over these." She started at the top, dragging her fingertip down the names. "Look." She sounded excited. "On the Fifty Worst list is something called, The Mountain Sporting Life Charity. The manager is listed as Nolan M. Avalon. Let me look that up on my computer."

She moved to her desk and started typing.

"Owen, this could be it. It says, 'The Mountain Sporting Life Charity gets people moving.'" She read off the screen. "'The key to a healthy life is movement, and nothing moves like sports. Moving benefits people's bodies and their brains. Moving prevents childhood obesity. Moving aids education. Moving helps self-esteem. Moving develops strong bones and muscles.' And then, in big letters, it says 'Moving Is Key To Success In Life and The Sporting Life Gets People Moving.'"

She tapped some more keys, then dragged her finger to scroll down. "Now look at this. On this page there are multiple photos of people playing tennis."

"That's revealing."

"And there's an online donation form with boxes you can click for different levels of donation. And next to each box is a little balloon with writing."

"How do you mean?"

"Look." Street turned her computer so we could both see the screen. She pointed. "See here? You can click boxes for ten dollars or twenty or, get this, twenty-seven dollars and thirty-six cents. Then the boxes go to fifty dollars, seventy-five dollars and one hundred dollars. Below that is a gold-colored box with a gold star next to it that says, 'Join the exclusive ranks of Golden Givers.' Next to the ten dollar box, it says, 'Get one hundred people moving.' Next to the twenty dollar box, it says, 'Get three hundred people moving.' And next to the box that says twenty-seven dollars and thirty-six cents, it says, 'Get five hundred people moving.' Then there's a red arrow that points to that box and in red caps it says, 'Check Here For Our Most Popular Option and Signal your Devotion to Health.'"

Street was doing an exaggerated shake of her head as she pointed at the screen. "Down below is a five-hundred-dollar box. It says, 'Join at the Gold Star level and become a Golden Giver. We'll rush you a signed, limited edition certificate of thanks along with the Gold Medallion commemorative necklace. This spectacular medallion comes with the Forever Feminine bar chain for women and the Go For Glory golden rope chain for men.'"

She turned to look at me, an expression of disbelief on her face. "You're not just choosing how much to give, you're selecting the most popular option. You're not just giving money, you're joining an exclusive club. They aren't just going to send you a plastic trinket, they're going to rush you a spectacular gold medallion necklace. This is designed to suck in the least discerning people who are desperate for someone to send them something that makes them feel like they're doing something valuable."

I said, "Can you imagine that this company actually gets anyone to move?"

"I don't know," Street said. "It sure looks sleazy. Let me look up the manager, Nolan M. Avalon." She typed. "Nothing comes up on Google."

"I'll give the name to Santiago. Agent Ramos, too. Maybe the guy's in one of their databases."

"You know what else this means," Street said.

"What?"

"It means that anyone connected to the organization that compiled this Fifty Worst Charity list could be a suspect in Dory's death and Nolan Avalon's death, if, that is, Nolan was the victim hanging from the flagpole."

"I was wondering that," I said, "because the charity watchdog guy who gave me this list seemed quite angry at the evil people who run scam charities. So I asked him if he ever comes up to Tahoe, and he said all the time. He has a cabin here."

Street raised her eyebrows.

"Also, the Bureau of Investigation woman who chases charity fraud for the California Department of Justice seems to have a permanent case of anger for all scammers. I casually asked her if she ever gets a break to come up to Tahoe. She hesitated, then said she was up here last week."

Street's eyebrows went higher.

Later, as Spot and I were about to go, Street said, "This private investigator stuff is exciting. Dead bodies from twisted murders and financial fraud and shady characters."

I looked at Spot. "Hear that, Largeness? What we do is exciting."

Spot yawned, long and wide.

Back at my cabin, I called Sergeant Santiago even though it was late. If he didn't want his phone to ring, he'd set it on voicemail.

He answered.

"Owen McKenna calling," I said. "Any ID yet on the body you took off the Kings Beach flagpole?"

"Nope."

"I have a name to consider. Nolan M. Avalon. He's listed on a Fifty Worst Charities compilation by a so-called charity watchdog group down in Folsom. His charity is called The Mountain Sporting Life Charity and their tag line is, 'We get people moving.' On the website are multiple pictures of people playing tennis."

"And this guy Avalon is on the list?"

"Yeah, he's listed as the CEO. I haven't found anything on him yet, but what's notable is that this Fifty Worst list is the first place I've seen the Red Roses Charity listed, and that listing also includes the Red Roses CEO, Dory Spatt."

"The woman who got strung up on the island in Emerald Bay."

"Right."

"Good lead," Santiago said. "Let's hope it goes somewhere. Hey, when you referred to the Fifty Worst list, you said it was by a so-called charity watchdog group. What does that mean, so-called?"

"It's called Charity Lights Archive, and it's really just a lobbying group that's owned by charities. It peddles biased information that the charities want to present as unbiased."

"Ah. And maybe some crank is using that list to track down bad charities and knock off their CEOs."

"Maybe," I said. "The person to contact at Charity Lights Archive is Reese Rangeman. Maybe he has more information on Nolan Avalon." I read him the number off the info sheets I'd gotten from the Bureau of Investigation.

"Will do. Thanks."

Late the next morning, Doc Lee pulled his little black sports car into The Red Hut parking lot just after me. He got out, took a look at Spot, whose head was out the window, and walked around the far side of his car to keep his distance. I'd never known Lee to be afraid of dogs. Maybe it was just giant dogs. Probably, he simply didn't want any shedding hair and dog slobber to end up on his clothes.

We shook hands. His graceful fingers and perfect manicure seemed designed for delicate surgery. A stranger might expect a precise, light grip. But he nearly crushed my knuckles.

We walked into the restaurant.

Like me, Lee wore jeans. But his were dark brown and fit just so and they didn't have any faded-color wear at the knees and butt. His shoes were tan suede and appeared designed for hiking, but there were no stains like Tahoe hikers get from stepping in snow and puddles and trudging through dirt. Lee's shirt was the same tan as his shoes, and it had a discreet logo patch sewn on the pocket flap. The sleeves were turned up in a careful fold revealing tan forearms, thin but muscular. His watch had a new band the same brown as his jeans.

"Table by the window?" he said to the host, who brought us over to an outside corner. The tables at The Red Hut are '50s diner design, with the classic salt and pepper shaker and napkin holder. Above our heads was a section of chairlift with two seats. It set the Tahoe-Laid-Back attitude.

We ordered without looking at menus. I got an omelette and coffee. Doc Lee got scrambled eggs and pancakes and side orders of hashbrowns and toast and sausage and milk and OJ and coffee.

"Hungry?" I said.

"We have these little bags of M&Ms in the ER. Six bags can get me through most any night. But I should probably have some other nutrients."

"Implying that M-and-Ms have nutrients?" I said.

"Sugar," he said as if I were missing the obvious. "One of the basic food groups for docs."

"I knew you were hyper concerned about nutrition, what with being a doc and all. But I must have missed the candy part."

"With sugar and strong coffee, you can face anything, even gunshot wounds and knife attacks."

"We have those in Tahoe?"

Doc Lee looked up at the chairlift, thinking. "Just last year I had a lady who was cutting up onions, and she sliced off the tip of her finger."

"And that qualifies as a knife attack."

He shrugged. "This is Tahoe."

A waiter brought our food. I had to scrunch my plate over to one side to make room for all of Doc Lee's plates.

The way he attacked his food made me think of the way Spot devours hotdogs

"You had a question about death," Lee said through a mouthful of pancakes.

"Yeah. You've probably heard about our recent murders. The victims were hung by their ankles and were found with items in their mouths. We haven't got the toxicology reports back yet. But I'm wondering if hanging upside down will normally kill a person."

"Here's the thing about death," Lee said as he stuffed sausage into his mouth, eating with gusto. "People are just another kind of animal. Like animals, some are fragile. Some are tough and resilient. You can't tell which in advance. You tie one person up by his feet, he will hang, fighting for life, for days. Another person anticipates that they're probably going to die, and they lose the fire and die of stress in a few hours. A third maybe has an undiagnosed aneurysm. In the brain. Or on the aortic arch." Doc Lee paused to work on his hash browns.

"You know about our circulatory system?" he said.

"Sort of. Our heart pumps the blood. Arteries carry our blood away from the heart. Veins return it to the heart."

"Right," Lee said, chewing, then swallowing. "The thing is, the heart produces enough blood pressure to drive the blood through the smallest vessels, our capillaries, where the blood delivers nutrients and oxygen and picks up the products of metabolism like carbon dioxide. But when the blood comes out of the capillaries and gathers in our veins, there's no more blood pressure to drive the blood back to our heart."

I figured out where he was going. "Which is why our blood spurts if we cut an artery and just oozes if we cut a vein."

"Yeah." Lee slurped more coffee. "So to aid in venous circulation, our veins have one-way valves in them. Especially in our legs. Those valves keep our blood from running back downhill. When you flex your legs and work your muscles and move and bend and do all the other stuff of an active life, those movements squeeze your veins here and there, squishing the blood inside. Because of the one-way valves, the blood can only squish one direction, back up toward your heart. But when you turn upside down, those valves don't do anything to prevent all the blood in your body from wanting to rush up your veins to your head. Even in the arteries, without all the one-way valves, the pressures and flows work when people are upright or horizontal or anywhere in between. When people are upside down, the arterial flow gets messed up, too."

"Stand on your head for very long," I said, "and you'll be very red faced when you get back up."

"To say the least. Now let's go back to the person who has a brain aneurysm. Turn him upside down, the increased pressure can cause that baby to rupture. The brain floods with blood, and the pressure on the brain shuts it down in minutes. In the case of an aortic aneurysm, a rupture causes the person to bleed out internally in less time than it takes to pound a beer." Lee slurped coffee, then shoveled a big forkful of syrup-soaked pancakes into his mouth.

"When you say bleed out, you mean all the blood that is normally in the arteries and veins comes out of them and collects inside the body cavities."

"Yeah," Doc Lee mumbled, chewing. "Depending on where the aneurysm is, that part of the body fills with blood. Could be the thoracic cavity or the abdominal cavity. But inverted suspension would create a greater stress on aneurysms that are higher in the body."

"Like the brain or the aortic arch," I said.

Lee nodded. "You have a good grasp of anatomy. You could be a doc."

"But would I want to?"

He looked at me as if my question made no sense.

"Let's say a person doesn't have an aneurysm," I said. "What if they're relatively healthy and have a strong constitution. How long would they typically last when hung upside down?"

"Hard to say," Lee mumbled. He was finishing off his sausages. Considering how vigorously he ate, I couldn't see how he remained so thin. Maybe it was the one-meal-a-day constraints of a 70-hour ER work week. "Could be days. More likely, one day. They didn't teach us this in school."

"I want you to play murderer for me. If you were going to kill someone, why would you choose to hang them upside down, considering that they might live a long time?"

Doc Lee chewed more pancakes. He swallowed and said, "I wouldn't try to kill someone by hanging them upside down. It wouldn't be painful in any major way, but it would still be a kind of torture."

"But what if you chose the hanging thing because it suited you for media purposes?"

"Then I'd kill them first so they didn't suffer."

FORTY

I thanked Doc Lee for his time and went to my office.

Doc Lee had me wondering about killers who want to punish their victims as opposed to merely wanting them dead. If a murder victim dies in a painless way, maybe the killer just wanted to collect an insurance benefit and didn't want the victim to suffer. But if a killer goes to the trouble of stringing his victim upside down and leaving them to die of exposure, then it would seem that the killer had a great deal of anger.

I remembered what Street had read about the Mountain Sporting Life Charity that gets kids moving. It made me wonder about how charities use sports to help disabled people. I also wondered how they find the disabled people they help. Or if you were disabled, how would you reach out to a charity that might help you.

I thought of Aubrey Blackwood, the watercolor painter with MS. She'd given me her card. I found it and dialed her number.

After I identified myself and we chatted a bit, I said, "I've an awkward question."

"I can probably give you an awkward answer," Aubrey said, sounding cheerful.

"I'm working on a case involving a charity whose purpose is to help people with disabilities. I'm wondering how they find the people they benefit. Or does it go the other way? Do the people getting benefits find the charity? So I thought I'd call you and ask if you've ever had dealings with charities. No doubt there are charities that provide benefits to people with MS."

"Well, now, you've just lifted up a rock with some nasty stuff underneath it."

"Your experience hasn't been great," I said.

"Let's just say that those of us in the disabled community trade stories now and then. The gist of those stories is that we don't see much help. When I lived in the Bay Area, I belonged to a poker club for disabled women. We called ourselves the Broken-Bod Girls. We met twice a month to play cards. And one of our running gags was that whenever we'd receive charity come-ons, we'd bring them to our meeting and make fun of them. It was always a riot reading them and mocking them."

I laughed. "It's obvious that you all love charities."

"Yeah. I've actually had no personal dealings with charities. None has ever contacted me about anything. When I was a kid, I once had a nurse who put together a list of needy kids who had Multiple Sclerosis. My name was on the list. The nurse sent it off to multiple charities that claimed to help children with difficult conditions. But from what the nurse said to me a year later, none of the kids on the list ever heard anything from any charity. I'm not saying that charities don't help the needy. Maybe they fund projects behind the scenes. Like maybe the nurse would never find out if a charity is paying for medical equipment at the hospital and such. But I never got any personal help."

"So you don't feel any animosity toward charities?"

"Oh, no. We just made fun of the goofy pleas they send out to get people to send in money. You've probably seen them. There'll be a picture of some little girl who can't stand up, and under the picture it says 'If you send us twenty-five dollars, we'll be able to buy crutches for this poor little girl and give her a new chance on life.' Well, I was that poor little girl who couldn't stand up, and my father had to buy my crutches with the money he made as a clerk in a department store shoe department. That man helped me in every way, carried me when my legs got too stiff, bought me clothes, and worked nights so he could take me to and from school in this old used wheelchair he found at a junkyard. He even encouraged me to go to college, and he put money in an account for that. That money eventually paid for two years of my tuition. I got my degree in accounting and spent my entire career working for Solano County. I've always said that if you want help with your disability, don't look to charity handouts, because they won't come through. Just find a father like mine."

"He must be very pleased that you are so appreciative."

"He would be, but he's been gone since my brother and I were in high school. I still miss him."

"Is your mother still around to enjoy your water colors?"

"Oh, no, she ran off before dad died. I never heard from her again."

"I guess I've brought up some uncomfortable subjects," I said. "I apologize."

"No worries. That's life."

"Thanks, Aubrey. You've helped me a lot."

After I hung up, I sat for a bit in silence. Thinking how even though it was a longshot that Aubrey Blackwood could be a killer, she fit what Agent Ramos had told me. He'd related what a murderous Vegas drinker had told the bartender about kids whose mother ran away with a rich charity scammer and whose father died not long after.

I thought about my previous case and a woman named Evan Rosen. When I uncovered evidence that implicated her in a murder, I did the ethical thing and turned it over to county law enforcement. They pursued it and arrested her for murder even though I didn't believe she was a killer.

Now Aubrey Blackwood had just told me something that might suggest taking a closer look at her. It wasn't evidence like I'd found in the case involving Evan Rosen. But, as with my previous case, I couldn't see Aubrey for a killer. If I passed the information about her childhood on to other law enforcement, she would have to endure lots of questioning at the minimum. I thought it through, and I realized that the information was much less damning than what I'd learned about Evan Rosen a few weeks earlier. So I decided to keep it to myself. If I later learned something significant, I could decide then to revisit the situation.

FORTY-ONE

My home phone rang at 8 p.m.

"Owen McKenna," I answered.

"You should know about a call that I just heard on the scanner." It was Diamond. "A body was found in Truckee. Hung from his ankles. I called Truckee PD and said they might want to contact you."

"You give them my number?"

"Yeah. Your home and office and cell."

"Then I better get off. Thanks."

The home phone rang a minute later.

"This is Sergeant Trummy from the Truckee Police calling," a man with a resonant voice said. "I understand you know Sergeant Diamond Martinez at the Douglas County Sheriff's Office?"

"Yes," I said.

"He told me that you've been investigating the murder victim that El Dorado County found out on Fannette Island and also the one that Placer County found at Kings Beach. I'm wondering if you and I could talk."

"Certainly."

"We have a murder victim in Truckee, a guy who was found tied up by his feet. A white male, maybe fifty years of age, about six-two, maybe one hundred eighty pounds. He's still tied up, hanging from his ankles. The lividity has his head swollen so much it's hard to tell much about him. The incident commander is an Amtrak Police Inspector. But you could probably help."

"Amtrak Police? Why?" I asked.

"The vic was tied to a train car. The railcar was on the back of an Amtrak train."

"Was the victim inside the car or outside?"

"Outside. The train the car was attached to is the California Zephyr on its way from San Francisco to Chicago. The engineer had stepped off the train to monitor the activities and the passengers. He said he walked down the platform to the end of the train, and that's when he saw the body hanging from the top of the rear car."

"The victim was already dead?"

"If not already, he was by the time the engineer got a step ladder and climbed up to the body. The engineer knew how to check for pulse and breathing, and there was neither. He also said that his first impulse was to cut the man down, but he didn't immediately know how, because the vic's feet were about fifteen feet up, and there is no easy way to get up to the top of the rail car. The victim's head looked like it could rupture at any moment. I've never seen anything like it. Can you come take a look?"

"I don't know if I can help. But I'll come. I'm on the East Shore. It'll take me an hour or so to get there."

"Look for us on the rail siding to the east of the train station."

"I'm on my way."

I hustled Spot out the cabin door.

I drove up the East Shore, went through Incline Village and then over the state line into California. When I got to Kings Beach, I turned north and went up and over Brockway Summit, then down across Martis Valley to Truckee.

The main street of the old railroad town was thick with patrol vehicles, parked in a scattershot pattern, light bars flashing blue and red. At one end of the vehicle group was a fire engine and rescue vehicle, lights off.

Some officers were directing traffic around the area. Others were taking photographs, making notes, talking on radios.

I parked, left Spot in the Jeep, and walked up to two men and a woman who were standing next to the train station.

"My name's Owen McKenna, here by the request of Sergeant Trummy."

"That's me," one of the men said. We shook hands. Although we were in the train station shadows, I could see that Trummy was dark brown like Diamond. The other man and woman were white. "Come with me," Trummy said.

He walked away from the others, and I joined him. We went past the east end of the train station and headed down the tracks.

"My name's actually Trummer," the cop said. "Sergeant Trummer. But the guys call me Trummy because I'm into swing-era jazz, and Trummy's the name of my favorite trombonist."

"Trummy Young," I said.

The man stopped, turned, and stared at me. "I don't believe it. You're the first person I've met since I left Chicago who knows Trummy Young. So you're a jazz cat?"

"Not really. I like the music, but I'm no expert. Didn't Trummy Young play with Parker and Dizzy?"

The cop gave me a big grin. "And Louie and Duke and Ella and Benny Goodman and Earl Fatha Hines. He really swung."

We were approaching a single rail car parked on a siding. There were several temporary floodlights set up on pole stands, illuminating the car, which was shiny silver and looked as if it had recently been washed and waxed. The car looked like an Art Deco design, which made it seem 60 or 70 years old. Yet, like a classic Airstream camp trailer, it still looked modern.

"This rail car doesn't sit here all the time, right?"

Trummy shook his head. "Just came in this afternoon."

"You said it was on the California Zephyr. That name sounds familiar."

Trummy nodded. "Yep. It's a famous train. Dates back to nineteen forty-nine."

"And where is that train now?" I asked.

Trummy pulled up his sleeve and looked at his watch. "It's ten o'clock, so that train is probably most of the way across Nevada on its way to Salt Lake City."

I looked at the big, silver rail car as we approached. "How is it that they left this car behind?"

"This is what's called a private rail car, getting pulled by the California Zephyr. When the engineer found the body, he called it in, and they sent out an APD inspector to process the crime scene. He's right over there, if you want to talk to him."

"APD…" I said.

"Amtrak Police Department. They have jurisdiction at train stations and on trains and on the tracks. Anything having to do with trains across the country."

"Who's the lead investigator?"

"It was me in the beginning. But when I talked to the APD on the phone, they asked that we not touch or alter the crime scene. When the APD inspector arrived, I handed the investigation over to him. I'll introduce you."

Sergeant Trummer walked over to a man who wore a very dark uniform and had a standard set of police gear on his body. The patch on his shoulder said police in large letters. Below it was the word Amtrak in smaller letters.

"Inspector," Trummer said. "This is Owen McKenna. I've asked him to help. He's maybe got information..." Trummer turned to me. "I guess you may as well explain."

I reached out my hand to shake his. "Owen McKenna, former Homicide Inspector with the SFPD, now a private cop in Tahoe. I'm working on two homicides where the victims were hung upside down by their feet. I've been asked to look at this case as potentially related."

"Inspector Howard Humboldt," the man said. "Good to meet you. With the Truckee PD helping, we've documented the scene, photographs and description. We've collected, inventoried, and bagged a few items we found that may be evidence but probably are not. We've found nothing that appears to connect to the killer. I've heard about those other cases, murder victims found upside down. Fannette Island in Emerald Bay and the flagpole victim in Kings Beach, right?"

"Right," I said. "How is it that a car from the California Zephyr can be disconnected from the train and the train sent on its way? Were there enough empty seats on the train to accommodate the passengers who were in this car?"

"This is a private car. We think there was only one passenger in this car, possibly the victim, so taking it off the train wasn't a problem. After we spoke to everyone on the train, we had the engineer pull the train forward and back this car onto this siding with the body still attached. Then the engineer disconnected this car, and the California Zephyr departed for Chicago."

"I don't understand what you mean about a private car."

"This car is probably owned by a corporation," Humboldt said. "Not too many private cars like it out there. Very luxurious.

Anyway, we think the victim may have been riding in that car."

As we came around the end of the car, Inspector Humboldt gestured toward the victim. The view was like something out of a Hitchcock movie. The victim dangled upside down in the bright flood lights. His head and neck were purple and dramatically swollen as his blood had pooled under the force of gravity. The blood had puffed out his face and neck enough that I doubted anyone could recognize him.

"ID?" I said.

"No. We got a warrant to search the railcar an hour ago. The preliminary search revealed nothing. Truckee PD officers are inside now, doing a full search. But as of now, we have nothing. No ID. No sign of distress in the car. No personal belongings such as wallet or cell phone or keys."

I looked up at the victim. "The line that goes from the victim's ankles up to the top of the train car looks like paracord."

"What's that?"

"Thin, strong, and smooth," I said. "It's the same cord that was used in the Fannette Island murder. Although the cord here looks brown. The paracord used in the first murder was green. The victim in the second murder was tied to the flagpole rope."

"Is paracord unusual?"

"It's common in sporting and camping and hunting activities. But many people are not familiar with it. Do you know what it's tied to?"

"It's looped through an antenna support bracket. The metal is smooth, and the cord is real thin. I can't imagine how the killer got the cord up there without a ladder when the train was stopped. Any number of people would have seen that."

I walked off to the side to see the bracket from a different angle. "One possibility is that the killer had a curved, stiff wire with the cord tied to the end. If he leaned out from one of the rear windows, he could have threaded it through the bracket. Do you think the railcar is connected to the victim?"

"Maybe," Inspector Humboldt said. "That would explain how the killer could have been in the railcar with the victim without anyone else on the train noticing. If the victim was in the car, maybe he heard a knock on the door. He let the killer in, and the killer locked the door behind him."

"Has the medical examiner determined cause of death?"

"The ME isn't here, yet. He was on a fishing vacation in Graeagle, north of here about sixty miles. That's why we haven't lowered the victim."

At that moment, a man emerged from the shadows. He was carrying a large, dark gray, plastic toolbox.

"I'm Doctor McCarthy, Medical Examiner. Sorry it took me a bit to get here." He had on his camping clothes, blue jeans and hiking boots and heavy green jacket with a half dozen zippered pockets. His baseball cap was red flannel.

Humboldt and I introduced ourselves. "The victim's around the back of this train car," Humboldt said.

We walked the doctor over into the floodlights. The ME was a small thin man, all jutting angles. McCarthy looked up at the body, his head tipped back so that the harsh floodlights lit up the baseball cap, the color as intense as fresh blood. McCarthy swallowed at the sight, his adam's apple protruding just enough to catch the floodlight as it bobbed in the glare.

"How long has it been since you arrived here?" the doctor said without turning.

The Amtrak inspector said, "I was down in the Central Valley when I got a call at about five to three. The engineer said he'd just found the body. That fit the schedule, because the Zephyr arrives in Truckee at two-forty. I left almost immediately and got up the mountain to Truckee in ninety minutes. After parking and walking over here, it was not quite five. Now, it's almost eleven p.m. So that's about eight hours from the time the engineer first found the body and called me."

The doctor gestured toward the body. "The lividity we see now, swollen head and neck, purple with pooled blood, how far had that progressed by the time you arrived?"

The inspector thought about it. "I would say the body looked very much like it does now. Maybe it's darker purple now."

"I was told that the engineer was certain the victim was dead when he found the body?" the doctor said.

"Yes. The engineer has had EMT training. He said the lividity made it obvious that the victim was dead. That's why he didn't attempt to climb up and cut the cord and get the body down to try resuscitation. How long does it normally take for a body's head to turn purple and swollen?"

The doctor paused. "Being dangled upside down would accelerate the pooling of blood in the head and neck. But the blood wouldn't begin to turn purple for some time."

Inspector Humboldt's eyes were wide in the floodlights. "Which means the victim was probably killed before the train pulled into the station."

The doctor nodded. "And because the lividity is in the head and neck, we know the body was hung upside down around the time of death."

Doctor McCarthy reached into his toolbox and pulled out latex gloves and pulled them on. Then he pulled out what looked like a rectal thermometer. He said, "Some people would likely survive many hours upside down. If a person is fit and has no vascular disease, being upside down would not, in itself, be a reliable cause of death. We won't know why the victim died until after the autopsy."

The doctor started up the ladder. He unhooked the victim's belt, unzipped his pants, then pulled at the victim's boxer shorts. He reached around and inserted the thermometer. "This victim has his hands bound behind his back. As the train turned and shook and the victim swung around, his bound hands would make it hard for him to cushion any blows to the head. His only defense against head injury would be to twist and turn his head to avoid blows against the side of the train. Suspension upside down might eventually have brought on unconsciousness. At that point, the head would sustain injuries from bouncing against the train. Combined with the increased fluid pressures in the head and brain, that might accelerate death."

The Amtrak cop said, "So it looks like the victim was strung upside down while the train was running. If the victim had been dead for an hour or more, then death occurred while the train was climbing up into the Sierra. If the victim had been hung up while the train was still in the populated areas near Sacramento, someone probably would have seen it and called it in. So the victim was likely strung up as the train drove into the mountains where there are fewer chances that someone would witness the murder. That almost guarantees that the killer was on this train car with the victim."

Doctor McCarthy made a small nod. He pulled a small flashlight out of his belt pack and was shining it at the shadowed areas that were unlit by the floodlights. "There are a variety of bruises on the body. The trauma indicates that they occurred while the victim was still alive. And they match up with this horizontal ridge near the train's windows. Post mortem tissue damage doesn't bruise the same way. That suggests that the victim received substantial bruising while he was still alive. That doesn't give us cause of death, but it allows for the possibility that the victim died of exposure, banging about the back of the train until the injuries and trauma from being upside down took their toll."

The doctor removed the thermometer and shined his flashlight on it. "The victim's core temperature is eighty-five degrees, which means the victim's temperature has cooled about thirteen and a half degrees. Using the Glaister equation, a victim of this size would probably lose one-point-five degrees fahrenheit per hour. That is very rough, as many factors influence how fast a body cools. Nevertheless, I'd estimate the victim died approximately nine hours ago. Which would be about two o'clock."

Inspector Humbolt said, "If that's accurate, that means he died about forty minutes before the train got to Truckee. That would suggest he was tied up as the train began to climb into the foothills east of Sacramento and before it crested Donner Pass. That's country where fewer people might see the body. I'll put the word out for anyone working near the tracks on the route. Maybe someone saw something unusual."

The Amtrak inspector paused, frowning, and looked at the doctor. "If the man was banging around and getting bruised up for an hour, would that be enough to kill him?"

"There are a lot of variables," Dr. McCarthy said. "But this man doesn't look especially out of shape. If I had to guess, I would think it would take longer than an hour to kill him. Now if I find signs of serious contusions under his hair, then brain trauma could certainly hasten death."

FORTY-TWO

While the doctor worked up on the ladder, turning the body, making notes about its condition, I turned to the Amtrak inspector. "Do the doors to the car lock?"

"Yes, Humboldt said. Several of them were locked. But we found the door to the inter-car passage unlocked. So it appears that the killer walked out of the car after stringing up the victim."

"You interviewed the passengers who were in the next car forward?"

"Yes. Two Truckee officers helped. We spoke to everyone on the passenger list. None of them reported seeing anything unusual or anyone who stood out. But the restrooms were at the rear of the car just in front of the private car, so there was a steady movement of people to and from the restrooms and hence, people near the entrance to the private car."

"How does it work, the private train car business?"

"They are uncommon, but the total number of them across the country is significant. They're generally owned by companies that want an exclusive way to hold meetings and conferences. And of course, in addition to exceptional meeting venues, they provide luxury travel for their clients. For a company, a private train car is like a yacht. Not as big as some yachts, but more unusual and thus more exclusive."

"But they use Amtrak trains to haul them around the country?"

"Yes. The scheduling is a bit tricky, but there are other companies whose only business is arranging those connections."

"It must be very expensive," I said.

"I don't know the details, but I assume so. I suppose that the travel cost is also like a yacht. And like yachts, companies usually outfit their private train cars to be very posh. Every kind of luxury that you can imagine can be found on a private train car."

"If you see a train while you're driving across the country, is there a way to tell if any of the cars are private?"

"There is no specific marking that a layman can look for. But if you see a railcar that appears to be lavish or one that is old but is obviously renovated, you're probably looking at a private railcar." He gestured up at where the body still hung. "This one, for example, has all the exterior indications of a private car. It is clearly an older style, with the bullet lounge and dome, and the entire exterior shines with polish. All of those little lights along the outside light up like the little running lights on a fancy limousine."

"Do you know who owns it?" I asked.

"No. But I texted in the reporting mark. I'll probably find out the owner at any moment."

"Is the reporting mark like a license plate number?"

"Yes. All rolling stock have them. Here, I'll show you." Inspector Humboldt walked around the side of the railcar and pointed up. "Those letters followed by the numbers," the Amtrak inspector said. "Those are unique for every railcar. The database will show the owner."

We walked back around to the rear of the car.

The doctor came back down the ladder. "I've got what I need. You can have the body removed to the morgue."

"Have you come to any conclusions?" Humboldt asked the doctor.

"No. I'll know more after the autopsy."

"Any chance you looked in the victim's mouth?" I asked the doctor.

"No. All the victim's cavities will be searched during the autopsy. Do you have a specific reason to wonder about his mouth?"

"In the other two murders where the victim was hung upside down, there were items in the mouth."

The doctor had peeled the latex gloves off his hands. He pulled out another pair and pulled them on. "I'll have a look," he said. He climbed back up the ladder, reached out with one hand to steady the body's swollen purple head, then reached his index finger into the victim's mouth. He angled one way, then the other, then appeared to move his finger around inside the victim's cheeks. He paused, moved his finger as if trying to pull out something slippery. His hand came out, pinching something shiny between his thumb and forefinger, then deposited the item in the palm of his other hand. He reached back into the victim's mouth and repeated the motion. Again, he pulled out something shiny and added it to his other hand. Once more, he fished around the victim's mouth, found one more object, then climbed down the ladder.

The doctor held his closed hand out so that it was in the bright flood lights. He opened his fingers. On his latex-covered palm were three small medallions.

One had a profile of George Washington against a purple, heart-shaped background. It was a Purple Heart, the medal awarded to members of the military who are wounded or killed in service to the country. The other two medals had a military look to them.

"This is a Purple Heart, right?" Inspector Humboldt said, pointing. "But I don't recognize the others."

"I don't either," I said. "Although they all look military." I turned to the doctor.

He shook his head. "I can't help here. I was never in the military. I can't imagine why the victim would have military medals in his mouth."

I pointed toward the large expanse of windows on the bullet lounge. "Do any of those windows open?" I said to Inspector Humboldt.

"Yes." He pointed. "That row, just above where the victim's head, they all open."

"So the killer could have waited until the victim was dead or nearly dead and then reached out and put the medals in the man's cheeks."

"What doesn't make sense," the doctor said, "is that if the man was unconscious, there would still be a good chance he would expel the medals from his mouth. And if the killer waited until the man was dead, that could have taken quite a long time. One would think that the killer would have left the train car as fast as possible after he strung the man up outside the window."

"Speaking of which," I said, "just stringing him up would be very difficult. The victim is a good-sized individual. The killer would have had to cuff the victim, gag him so he couldn't scream, and maybe tie him in place so he couldn't run. Then he would have had to reach out the window of a moving train, stand up on the sill so he could loop the rope through the antenna bracket on the top of the car, then come back into the car, tie the rope to the man's feet, and then hoist him out the window and up, pulling on the rope. The victim's weight combined with the friction of the rope going through and around the bracket would have required a tremendous pulling effort."

Inspector Humboldt nodded, then pulled out a plastic zip evidence bag and held it out near the doctor's hand. The doctor let the medals slide into the bag, then zipped it shut.

Humboldt and the doctor discussed the arrangements for the body and said goodbye.

"These other cases you're investigating," Humboldt said to me after the doctor had left. "Any suspects?" Humboldt asked.

"Some possibilities. But nothing solid."

The inspector turned and looked out at the night and the other cops waiting out of the glare of the lights. He called out. "Okay, guys, time to take the body to the morgue."

I said. "Have you had a canine unit take a look at the scene?"

"No. Do you think that would help?"

"It can't hurt."

Humboldt looked puzzled. "You think maybe this case involves drugs or something? We found nothing like that in the railcar."

"Dogs don't just look for drugs."

"Let's see if the Truckee PD has a dog," Humboldt said.

I walked over toward where Sergeant Trummer stood.

"Sergeant, any chance you have a canine in your department?"

"Officer Grayson is our canine handler. He's in Hawaii on vacation. He left Ranger, his Belgian Malinois, with a friend in Reno. You think there's something in particular a dog should look for?"

"My dog made the alert on the Kings Beach victim. That's how we found the lapel pin in the victim's mouth. Maybe I should have my dog take a look?"

Trummer said, "Did you bring him with you?"

"Yeah. I should let you know that he's not a professional police dog."

"What is it? A retriever?"

"No, a Great Dane."

Trummer still looked surprised. "I've never heard of a Great Dane doing a search. But what's the harm in having him look?" Trummer made a small grin. "And a Great Dane has a nose just like the professional dogs, right?"

"Right."

"Then bring your dog over and let him have a look. I mean, a smell."

"Give me ten minutes. He's in my Jeep, parked a few blocks over."

FORTY-THREE

I jogged across main street, down the block, and over to my Jeep. Spot was glad to see me, his tail thumping the seat and window before I could get the door unlocked and opened.

"Hey, Largeness, we need a favor."

He jumped out of the Jeep, trotted into the dark street, then circled around the Jeep and headed down the sidewalk a short distance. I let him explore a bit. Then I took hold of his collar, and we walked back to the train station. The cops near the line of yellow crime scene tape nodded at me as Spot and I ducked underneath.

I introduced Spot to Sergeant Trummer, Inspector Humboldt, and two other cops.

"Just give him a pet, and he'll be your pal," I said to the men.

Trummer and Humboldt went through the normal reaction at seeing Spot. "Yikes," Trummer said. "I've seen pictures of Great Danes. But in person, up close, whoa, he's a big guy." He reached out and gave Spot a little pet, then pulled his hand back to safety. Inspector Humboldt declined to take the risk of petting Spot.

"I'm going to walk Spot around and inspect the scene so he gets familiar with the local scents. He's friendly. So you can tell everyone not to worry if he comes close to them."

"Got it," Trummer said. He took his radio off his belt and spoke into it. "Men, Owen McKenna is the private cop taking a look at the scene at Inspector Humboldt's request. He has a big dog, emphasis on BIG. A Great Dane. But he's friendly."

From Trummer's radio came a single response. "Right on, sarge. Bring on the hound."

I turned to Spot, bent down, and pointed him toward the railcar. I said, "Spot, find the evidence! Find!" I gave him a smack on his rear.

Spot trotted away, his nose to the ground. He went forward,

turned left, moved into the darkness, then turned right. He seemed to have no purpose to his movements. He looked like he was simply sniffing out the past movements of chipmunks and other small creatures.

Trummer watched a moment, then said to me, "Does your dog know what the word 'evidence' means?"

"No. I could have said 'find the screwdriver' or 'find the ancient shipwreck.' There are some specific words he understands like 'suspect.' But in this case my tone just tells him to have a look around and see what stands out."

"What do you think he'll find?"

"I have no idea. Probably nothing."

Trummer glanced into the darkness, then turned toward me. "It sounds like you were about to say 'But.'"

"Dogs are not completely unlike a young kid. They look around at any environment they're in, and their eyes immediately go to the unusual thing that stands out from everything else. Put a kid in a room filled with normal stuff he's seen a thousand times and one unusual item he's never seen, the kid will always pick up the unusual item."

Amtrak Inspector Humboldt spoke up. "Only in the dog's case, it isn't seeing the unusual item, it's smelling it."

"Exactly," I said.

"This concept," Sergeant Trummer said, "of smelling out the unusual thing... A dog doesn't need professional search training to do that, right? Any dog could do it."

"Right. In fact, it's not just that any dog could do it. It's that any and every dog always does it."

"I think I see where you're going with this. The key is whether or not the owner learns to read their dog so to speak. If you know your dog's tendencies, then you could learn to notice when your dog finds the thing that's very unusual."

"Yes," I said.

The men had cut the body down from the railcar and had it on a gurney.

I said, "Now that my dog's got a sense of the territory, I'll bring him near the body." I called out toward Spot, who was in the darkness, down one of the rail sidings.

"Hey, boy. C'mon over, and let's do some work."

Humboldt and Trummer watched as my dog came forward into the shadows behind the railcar, his nose to the ground. Spot went around the railcar, then came out into the bright light of the floods. He got to the back end of the car, paused, lifted his nose from the ground, and looked over at the group of men and the body on the gurney. I could have predicted what would happen.

Spot air-scented a bit, his nose high. His tail, which had been held high with excitement, dropped down. He pulled his ears from forward attention and held them back. He took a half-step back, then another. The smell of another dead human was instantly depressing. He turned, walked slowly away from the train, out of the light and came toward me. He didn't stop as he went past me, but continued on into the dark. Eventually, he turned back around and gazed at the dead body from a distance.

"Sorry, boy. Yes, it's nasty work. But we need to focus. I need you to go through the scene and look for something unusual. Anything unusual." I rubbed the sides of his neck. I tried to put a casual sound in my voice. "We're just cruising the grounds, trying to find a murderer..." I pulled Spot forward, past the body and toward the station, like it was no big deal.

"Time to search, boy. Do your thing. See what you can discover."

Spot looked at me and didn't move.

"Spot, find the scent!" I shook his chest and patted him on his rear.

Spot took a step forward, then stopped.

I gave him a push.

Spot took another step forward, then walked over to the dead body, lifted his nose high, once again air scenting.

"Find the scent, boy!" I tried to radiate enthusiasm. "Find the scent."

Spot lowered his head and sniffed the victim's mouth. His sniffing showed no eagerness, and in fact, he seemed depressed and resigned. But it was a clear sniff, and it left me with no doubt that the only unusual smell in the whole crime scene was coming from the victim's mouth. I thought of checking it again myself, but I'd watched the ME do a thorough job.

"Okay, boy, good job!" I pet him as we walked away. "Time for you and me to go home and have a treat."

But Spot just hung his head and walked away with slow, heavy steps as if he was trudging through a stinky swamp.

When we got to Inspector Humboldt and Sergeant Trummer, I said, "Let's be sure that the pathologist who does the autopsy takes samples of what's in the victim's mouth."

"You think there's something significant about the mouth?" Trummer asked.

"I'm pretty sure, yeah."

"All because of your dog's reaction.

"Right," I said as I rubbed Spot's neck.

"Whatever was on the medals got into the man's mouth," Humboldt said.

"Possible. Or what's more likely is that whatever was in the man's mouth is now on the medals."

"Like poison?" Trummer said.

"Maybe," I said. "As the ME said, the victim could have died from hanging upside down long enough and bouncing his head against the outside of the train. But I'm guessing the killer wanted to make death more certain."

Humboldt's cell phone rang. He answered, listened, said thank you, and hung up. He turned to me.

"The private railcar belongs to a Los Angeles company called Southern Cal Dollar Logistics."

"Any other name on the record?"

Humboldt shook his head.

"Thanks much."

FORTY-FOUR

As I drove home, I thought about Southern Cal Dollar Logistics and wondered if it was a fundraising company. I also thought about the military medals in the railcar victim's mouth.

When I got home, I looked on the Charity Lights list of the 50 Worst Charities. I found one called Veteran Disability Saviors. I looked online and found a charity that looked very much like the Red Roses of Hope Charity for Children. Only instead of sad, starving children, this one had pictures of veterans in hospital beds, veterans with wounds dressed in blood-soaked bandages, veterans who were missing limbs. The website displayed all the pictures as floating on a background that looked like a waving American flag.

The next day, I called Doc Lee, left a message, and he called back.

"Remember our conversation about death by hanging upside down?" I said.

"Of course. People hanging upside down. Stuff in their mouths." It sounded like he was crunching M&Ms.

"Last night, we had another murder, this one in Truckee. A man hung upside down. He had military medallions in his cheeks. But after we pulled them out, Spot still alerted on the man's mouth. Can you think of why that would be? I can see that medallions might react with saliva and create a particular scent that a dog would notice. But the lapel pin in the Kings Beach victim was made of plastic. And Spot alerted on that man's mouth as well. I know he could still smell the items that had been in the victims' mouths. But I think he understands when the source of the scent is removed. So I'm thinking there's a good possibility he's smelling something else."

I heard more crunching sounds from Doc Lee. "Did your

dog pay attention to the first victim's mouth? The one that was found on Fannette Island?"

"He never saw that victim. It was these last two victims that produced a reaction from him. I spoke to the medical examiner last night. He didn't notice anything about the victim's mouth other than the medallions. Does my dog's reaction give you any ideas?"

"Remember how I said that I wouldn't kill someone by hanging them upside down? I'd kill them first?"

"Yes, I remember. You thought upside-down death would be like torture."

"And you described lividity in the head and neck, indicating that the victims were upside down when they died or right after they died."

"Right," I said.

"Then here's an idea." Doc Lee said sounding intrigued. "What if the murderer did in fact suspend the victims upside down first so that they would be helpless. But then, then he brought on their death by other means."

"Like?" I said.

"Maybe he added an accelerant of sorts to the stress-and-death process."

"You mean a death accelerant," I said. "What kind? A poison?"

"Yeah. If I were the killer, I'd introduce some kind of pulmonary interference."

"What would that be?"

"Anything that would gum up the lungs."

"Example?"

"A spray of some kind. You have your hanging victim. I assume his hands are tied behind his back, so he can't fight you. He still has to breathe, right? So when he inhales, you spray something into his mouth. Maybe you first cover his nose and mouth, get him to build up a big need to breathe. Then, when you release him and he takes a big, gasping breath, you have your pulmonary inhibitor spray ready."

"Can you speculate on just what this pulmonary inhibitor might be?" I asked.

"It could be almost anything that would attack the air sacs in the lungs. Spray paint. Oven cleaner. Although, those would be pretty obvious to anyone looking at the body. Heck, it could even be something that would just coat the air sacks, something as benign as olive oil. The stress it would cause from interfering with oxygen absorption, combined with the upside down stress, would be enough to switch off life in many or even most people. And post mortem examination might not notice a light presence of olive oil."

"Give me advance warning if I ever veer close to setting off any murderous impulse in you, okay?"

"Will do," Doc Lee said with no apparent sarcasm or levity.

We hung up.

I then left messages in turn for Sergeant Bains at El Dorado County, Sergeant Santiago at Placer County, and Amtrak Inspector Humboldt. "McKenna calling," I told each. "I just spoke to a doctor about the murder victims hanging upside down. I mentioned that my dog alerted on the mouths of the victims in Kings Beach and Truckee. He speculated that the killer could have hastened the deaths by spraying some kind of chemical into the vic's mouth. It could be something as benign as olive oil, which we might not notice. Yet it would still inhibit lung function. It could create death by asphyxiation. So I'm calling to suggest that you check with the medical examiners and see if they notice any coating inside the lungs."

FORTY-FIVE

The next day was the second to last day of the charity festival. Which meant the pop-up party was supposed to be that night. I called Diamond and reminded him. We agreed to meet for a beer before the party.

When I got off the phone, I walked out on my deck and leaned on the railing. A thousand feet below me was one of the most spectacular lakes on the planet. And the white mountain peaks of the Sierra Crest across the very blue plate of Tahoe water were a constant reminder to pause when dealing with the worst that people do to each other. The scenery seemed to demand that we take in its beauty along with the forest aromas and the bird sounds of spring in the mountains. A person can chase down bad guys, but a person can't fix all the problems that make those guys bad. When possible, you need to lose yourself in beauty.

Spot appeared at my side. He stared at the distant boats crisscrossing miles of water. Maybe he thought that they were white bugs of some kind, bugs that moved very slowly across the blue surface and left V-shaped tracks that slowly widened. From our distance above, it seemed those bugs were getting nowhere.

I felt like I, too, was making no progress.

I revisited what I knew.

Dory Spatt's brother Kyle had made it clear that donors to charity were very numerous, and they gave great amounts of money. After he gave me names of other donors, I'd spoken to Betty Rodriguez and learned she sent off large amounts of money to charities based on little more than the effectiveness of the mailers she'd received. She seemed to think that donating to a range of charities was the best way to help the world even if some of those charities were likely bad. It was as if she expected that some charities were frauds, and she was forgiving in advance.

When I spoke to the woman in Ukiah named Judy, she said her doctor neighbor gave large amounts to charities and that he too was as forgiving as he was generous. For these donors, it seemed like handing money to a homeless person. They accepted in advance the knowledge that the person might spend the money on wine and cigarettes. Yet they gave anyway.

But there was a group that seemed not so forgiving.

Relatives of donors.

Betty Rodriguez's son Gray made his outrage clear, almost suggesting that he might act on his anger about her donations to potential scammers. And when Ukiah Judy talked about the dead doctor's daughter, she said the woman burned with anger when she found the Red Roses of Hope mailer in the doctor's mail.

It seemed that vigilante murderers might more likely come from the ranks of donors' relatives than the donors themselves.

I remembered that one of the donors to Red Roses of Hope charity was a woman in Tahoe City. I went inside my cabin and paged through the notes that Dory's brother Kyle had written down. I found Elena Turwin's address.

Spot was still out on the deck, studying the slow-moving white bugs. I walked back out on the deck and pointed directly across the water.

"Tahoe City beckons, Largeness. Will you join me?"

He started doing the little bounce. He pushed past me, trotted to the front door, and waited for me to open it.

An hour and twenty minutes later, I located the address for Elena Turwin on the north side of Tahoe City in an old neighborhood of small, clapboard cabins. Her house was a mottled, sun-bleached, pinkish off-white, although I realized it had probably been painted a strong coral color 40 years ago. Likewise, the cracked, hard-vinyl window awnings which were a creamy pea soup tone, had probably started out life a deep forest green. Tahoe gets its share of serious, high-altitude sunshine, and building materials struggle under the assault. Next to the house was a narrow drive that went back to a tiny one-car garage that leaned a bit to the left.

I parked, and Spot and I got out. I held his collar, and he pranced next to me, ears focused forward, obviously interested in this unfamiliar neighborhood of classic old Tahoe cabins.

Elena Turwin's doorbell button was missing, revealing a dark hole between two long-abandoned screw holes in the cracked, wooden siding. I rapped my knuckles on the door.

Spot stood like a gentleman next to me, staring at the doorknob, no doubt anticipating the exact moment when it would turn. His tail was wagging for no apparent reason. The slow speed.

The door opened inward until it was stopped by the chain. A large woman in her sixties with salt-and-pepper hair cut very short and gray eyes that had lost the excitement of life long ago, looked at me with a doubtful expression.

"Hi. My name is Owen McKenna. I'm calling on behalf of the Red Roses of Hope Charity for Children. The charity told me that Elena Turwin is one of their valued contributors. Would that be you?"

"'Tis I," came the raspy voice of a woman who probably had run a lifetime of cigarette smoke over her vocal cords. She stared at Spot.

"Don't worry, he's friendly," I said.

"Of course he is," she said in her rasp. "A Great Dane with his tail wagging. Duh."

"May I come in and ask you some questions?"

She looked at me, hesitating. "You're not a missionary, are you? Because I've already been through that routine."

"No, not at all."

"Is this one of those marketing surveys? Or I suppose you could be working on scientific research. But you don't look like the business type or professor type. More like one of those cowboys who lead horse-packing trips into the mountains. Am I right?"

"Sorry, nothing that exciting. I'm a private investigator, and I'm working on a case that involves a charity scam."

She hesitated some more, then took the chain off the door. She turned and walked through the cramped entry toward a cramped living room. "Bring your dog in. He might keep my husband from biting you."

I still held Spot's collar. I shut the door behind us and paused at the entrance to the living room. Next to me was a door that opened to a small room, what most people would think of as a den. Only this room had been turned into a catchall storage room. There was a workbench and some pegboard above it for hanging tools. In one corner was some camping gear, what looked like a tent in a stuff sack, a Coleman lantern, and propane cookstove. A backpack with an aluminum frame leaned against the wall. Tied to its top was a rolled foam sleeping cushion. Hanging from hooks on the ceiling were a compound bow and a quiver of arrows. As I turned toward the living room, something on the workbench caught my attention. I looked back. There was a spool of paracord, similar to what was used on the Fannette Island and Truckee killings, although this was blue. I leaned into the room, looking for any green paracord like what had been used at the Fannette Island killing or the brown used on the railcar killing. I didn't see any. I remembered that the flagpole victim in Kings Beach had been hung up by the same line that hauled the flag.

I turned back to the woman in the living room. She lowered herself into a chair that was upholstered in nubby, blue fabric. She let herself flop down and back, sinking deep into the cushioned seat.

"I see you have a camper in the family," I said, gesturing toward the front room.

"Two of them. Hubby and son. Son is back east, playing guitar, mad and frustrated that the world hasn't recognized him as a significant country singer. Hubby is usually in the garage, emptying out beer cans so he can add to his recycling bin and, eventually, his recycling savings account, with which, he swears, he's going to invest in a stock he heard about. Going to make a million, he is. Show up all those people who flaunt their success with garage space for three SUVs instead of one, tiny, nineteen-sixty-one Corvair."

"The spool of paracord," I said. "What do they use that for?"

"Para what?"

"The thin blue cord on the workbench in your front room."

She shook her head. "I don't know what you're talking about."

The woman's chair was in the sun near a large window, which explained why the cool gray fabric of its upper edge was nothing like the intense dark blue at the bottom rear.

The woman wiggled a bit to get comfortable.

"What do you call him?" she said after she was situated. She was looking at Spot.

"Spot. Although sometimes, Hey You. And, of course, No, Don't Do That, and, quite often, Your Largeness."

Spot lifted his head up and around to look at me.

"Sorry, dude," I said. "I was just discussing nomenclature, and your name got in there."

He looked back at the woman.

"Dude is another name," she said.

"What? Oh, yeah, I guess so."

"Poor thing must have multiple personality disorder trying to deal with an owner who keeps calling him by different names."

"Maybe," I said. "But there's probably worse things than multiple names that he has to accommodate. Anyway, it keeps him sharp."

"So what's this about a charity scam?"

"Some charities aren't quite what they seem. The money they collect doesn't end up where the donors think."

"Well, well, Hubby will wish he was in here to chime in with you. He hates charities. And that's hate with a capital H. Says they're all phoney. And he hates that I send them money." She frowned. "How did you get my name again?"

"I've been researching a charity called, The Red Roses of Hope Charity for Children. You sent them fifty-six dollars. I wanted to ask you about that."

"Hold on." She stood up, stepped over to a desk, and pulled out a checkbook. She opened it and ran the tip of her index finger down the register.

"Here it is. The Red Roses of Hope. Yes, I sent them a check for fifty-six dollars last month. I remember now. They focus on children. That's how I sort charities. I give to the ones that support children. Other charities probably do valuable work. But I can't give to them all."

"Do you give to lots of charities?"

"No just six make my monthly list. The one I think is most important is the Girls Stay the Night In Charity. I send them sixty dollars, which is double-matched by a major corporation, and that provides a night's lodging and dinner for ten girls in trouble. Plus, all the girls who end up at Girls Stay the Night In get counseling to help them escape abusive boyfriends or pimps or whatever it is that has thrown them into a homeless life on the streets."

"Have you checked out that charity?"

"What do you mean? Their brochure makes it very clear how they provide for the safety of girls who might otherwise be on the street."

"Where is the lodging they provide?"

"I don't know. But when I read their material, it was clear they know what those girls need. I'm a good judge of these things because I went through a bad spell when I was very young. Why is it that you are investigating this?"

"You maybe heard about the murder of the woman on Fannette Island."

"Yes. What a horrible thing," she said.

I explained about Dory Spatt and the fake charity.

Elena listened without speaking. Her eyes showed more suspicion. I was pretty sure she thought I was the fake, not the Red Roses of Hope charity.

"Don't tell my husband," she finally said.

"Why?"

"Because it'd just be like throwing gasoline on a fire. He thinks I'm nuts to send off money when we have so little. He says I might as well send money to that ultimate scammer – what's his name – Bernie Madoff. But I'm the one who earned our money. It's my social security check we live on, not his."

"What's your husband's name?"

"George. But don't you go talking to him."

"Why do you say that?"

"Because…" Elena Turwin was shaking her head. "Because I don't know what he'd do. He's already threatened to take them out. That's his phrase. Take them out."

"The people who run charities," I said.

"Right."

"Do you think he could have had something to do with the

woman's murder on Fannette Island?"

"Oh, no. I don't doubt he could do it if he really wanted to. But he wouldn't. He's so afraid of the water, he could never go out on a boat."

"May I talk to your husband?"

She shook her head. "I'm not allowed to let anyone bother him. And he won't talk, anyway. He's what you call social shy. He's not afraid to speak his mind if he wants. But he doesn't talk to strangers. He says life is too short to waste it talking to people."

"This is helpful to me. I appreciate it."

"I've never met a true-life PI," she said. "So you interview people who have a connection to the murder victim. Then what?"

"I keep interviewing until I figure out who the murderer is."

"And then you lock him up. Or do you kick his butt first?"

"Mostly I focus on the lock part. But sometimes I do a bit of kicking first."

She grinned. "I'll tell Hubby that. It'll make him feel better."

"Thanks very much for your help, Elena. If I have any more questions, may I call you?"

"Yes." She told me the number, and I wrote it down.

After Spot and I left, we walked down the narrow drive to the garage. Peeking in through the window, I could see a very fine '61 Corvair. But the garage was dark, the doors closed, and no one appeared to be around.

FORTY-SIX

W hen I got home, I called Street at her lab. We chatted for a minute.

"Everything okay? No suspicious vehicles following you? Nothing's going bump in the night?"

"Well, it's daytime. But everything's okay," she said.

It was soon time for my beer appointment with Diamond. We met at a craft brewery at Heavenly Village on the South Shore. There was an outdoor seating area where dogs were allowed. I saw Diamond drive by in his ancient pickup, looking for a parking space. He continued until he was out of sight.

Ten minutes later, he walked up. He was wearing old jeans, an old tan flannel shirt, and over it an old brown leather jacket. Spot jumped up, wagging. Diamond pet him.

I reached out from where I was sitting, shook his hand, and said, "If you had ridden up on a horse, you'd look like a rancher from back in the days when California was part of Mexico."

Diamond made a little nod. "Just twenty-four sweet years between the time that Mexico got California from Spain and the time that the U.S. took it all away."

"I can't remember how that happened," I said.

Diamond was still standing, leaning on Spot's back. He hooked a boot heel onto the lower rung of a nearby chair, and struck a pose that I knew was half tongue-in-cheek professor and half Mexican machismo.

He said, "Modern-day California traces its roots to a country called the Republic of Texas, which was formed in eighteen thirty-six. But it's a convoluted story."

"Most are, right?"

Diamond made a little grin, happy for the moment to embrace the role of learned scholar. "Mexico achieved independence from Spain in eighteen twenty-one, and part of the territory that Spain had controlled was called Alta California."

"A big territory," I said.

"No kidding. What we now call California and Nevada and Utah and Arizona and New Mexico and Colorado and Texas."

He pulled out the chair and sat down.

We ordered beers, an IPA for me and a Porter for Diamond.

"I never got into the taste of Porter," I said.

"Dark beer for dark men," Diamond said.

I sipped my beer. "So how could modern-day California trace back to the Republic of Texas?"

"Back in the day, Texas, like California, was part of Spanish territory, which, after the Mexican independence, became Mexican territory. Problem was, a bunch of anglo settlers in Texas decided they didn't want to live under Mexican rule. They wanted to secede and create their own country. Mexican President Santa Anna tried to stop them. So he got together a band of soldiers and rode to Texas and fought the Texans with substantial success. Problem was, he went too far. During the battle at the Alamo Mission in San Antonio, Santa Anna's men killed a few hundred Texan men and even executed some of the Texans who had surrendered."

"Even in war, you can go too far," I said.

"Right. Of course, the Texans were outraged. They recruited many more soldiers and used the rallying cry, 'Remember the Alamo,' to motivate them. Over a series of battles, they eventually kicked Santa Anna's butt. In March of eighteen thirty-six, they declared independence from Mexico and called themselves the Republic of Texas, a brand new country. Just ten years later, the United States of America annexed this new country called the Republic of Texas. Because the anglo settlers migrated from America, they were okay with that. Unfortunately for my ancestors, Mexico still considered Texas to be theirs. So their hostility was now directed at America. Big mistake, that."

"Because that led to the Mexican American War, right?"

"Yeah. Ironically, at the same time that the Mexican American War got going, a bunch of anglo settlers in California followed in the footsteps of Texas. They too chafed under Mexican rule, the local headquarters of which was in Monterey. So, like those

Texans ten years before, they staged a revolt against Mexico. They fought Mexican General Castro, who was in charge at the time. They took the area of Sonoma, and created a new country called the California Republic, and they made their own flag with a bear and a star."

"That was the Bear Flag Revolt," I said.

"Sí. This new country, the California Republic, only lasted twenty-five days before an American military ship in Monterey Bay got a message about the war between America and Mexico and the word spread that Mexico's rule of the area was under assault. As soon as the U.S. military on the West Coast joined the war against Mexico, the so-called California Republic dissolved, and they decided it was okay to become part of the United States. But one of the long-term effects of the Bear Flag Revolt was that their flag became the basis for the current California State flag. So there's a clear connection between the state of California and the short-lived country called the Republic of Texas."

I drank beer. "America won the Mexican American War in short order, right?"

"Yeah. It lasted less than two years and ended when the Americans occupied Mexico City. The Mexicans surrendered."

"And America got California," I said.

"They got all of Alta California," Diamond said with emphasis. "The entire territory that comprised those states I previously mentioned, from California to Texas."

"A big chunk of Mexico," I said.

"Over half of Mexico. Almost as much land as all of Alaska."

"Wow. Big stuff happens when you make some wrong choices."

"No kidding."

"You do carry the nineteenth century look well."

"Not really," Diamond said, looking down at his clothes. "For that, I'd need buttons on my jeans instead of a zipper, and my pants would be made of wool instead of cotton, and my shirt wouldn't have a collar, and my jacket would be the length of a coat, and my hat would be wool or straw, and I would probably have scruffy facial hair instead of the clean-shaven, debonair look

I present today. And, perhaps the biggest difference is you'd smell me coming before you saw me."

"Indoor plumbing and showers and Old Spice hadn't arrived on the scene back then, eh?"

Diamond grinned. He took a swig of Porter, then licked the foam off his upper lip. "You said you were still concerned about Street?"

"Yeah. She's stressed and worried. I'm even more stressed and worried. My threat meter reading is very high, and I think the only sensible response would be for Spot and me to stay with her. Her place or mine. But she won't have it. She's fiercely independent."

"You mentioned that before? Diamond said. "Now you bring it up again. Has something changed?"

"She has twice wondered if someone was following her. I fear that I'm making a big mistake by not insisting on some kind of intervention."

"Like?"

"Like some version of living together. Some way that would keep Spot at her side."

Diamond made a thoughtful nod. "If you tried to insist on that, how would she respond?"

"I'm sure she would refuse. I'd be waiting for her to come home, and she'd take Blondie and go to whichever residence where I'm not so she could have her alone time."

"Some women find self-value in the men they attract. Some find it in the money they earn. Other women find self-value in their ability to function by themselves."

"That's a very good summation of Street. Do you think I'm stuck? If I push her to let me and/or Spot be closer, will that just push her away more?"

"Probably."

"This situation makes me wish for some kind of protective custody," I said.

"With no evidence of threat, and no cooperation on the part of the potential victim, it's not an option."

"I could hire off-duty cops to watch her," I said.

"Would she allow that?"

I shook my head. "No, she wouldn't give me permission. And

if I did it on the sly and she found out, she'd be outraged and consider it an unforgivable invasion of her autonomy."

"I'd agree with her," Diamond said. "Just ten years after the Mexican American War, John Stuart Mill wrote his seminal essay On Liberty. In it, he discusses when society has the right to interfere in the rights of men. Your situation is not that different. Basically, you have the right to interfere in Street's life against her wishes if you are preventing her from harming others. But you don't have the right to interfere against her wishes to prevent others from harming her."

"You're saying that, unless I can convince her to change her mind about accepting protection, I'm screwed. My only option would be to find the bad guy and take him out without ever forcing Street to accept more protection."

"Pretty much," Diamond said. "Just to be sure I'm clear on the situation, you still have no actual evidence that her father is in the area and planning to assault her."

"That's correct."

"Not much you can do," Diamond said.

We both drank beer.

"The pop-up charity party tonight. Have they chosen the time, yet?" Diamond asked.

"Not that I know of. The whole point is the hush-hush aspect until they announce it."

"And somebody named Matt is supposed to be at this pop-up party, watching for a tall guy – meaning you – and whistle-blow his heart out to you."

"That's my hope," I said.

"We just have to find out when and where the party is."

FORTY-SEVEN

"We have a new young deputy in the department," Diamond said. "Bradley Saunders is twenty three, so he automatically has some tech chops compared to you and me. Turns out Saunders has a software app on his phone. You put in search terms, and it monitors something like one hundred thousand websites that are most likely to have information like what you're looking for. If anything appears that's real close to your search terms, it sends you a text. I told Saunders to call when he hears something. Then you and I... Hold on, I've got incoming."

I waited. It was probably only a minute even though it seemed like I could have drunk another beer and ordered dinner while I waited.

Diamond listened, then hung up his phone and said, "Van Sickle Park. Nine o'clock."

"That's the new park behind Heavenly Village?"

"Yeah. With trails that crawl around the mountain. One even goes all the way up to Kingsbury Grade and the Tahoe Rim Trail."

"A big park," I said. "How do we find where the party is supposed to be?"

"I don't know. Probably, we just go there and follow the crowds."

"And if there aren't any crowds?"

Diamond paused a moment. "Then we fall back on the most reliable tracking approach and follow the smell of pot."

"I knew you were up on the latest law enforcement techniques," I said.

FORTY-EIGHT

Diamond and I ordered burgers and fries, then lingered over another beer. At 8:30 p.m., we left Spot in the Jeep in the far corner of the Harrah's parking lot. It didn't seem like Spot would help me blend into the party scene, if, in fact, there was a scene. I grabbed my flashlight and headlamp from the glovebox. I stuffed the headlamp in my pocket. Diamond looked at his phone as we walked.

"Someone posted the email that was sent out about the pop-up rave. I'll read what it says. 'Take the Rim Trail Connector trail up toward Heavenly. There will be an arrow sign directing you off the trail. Turn there, head upslope, and look for a bluff that rises high above. There will be a campfire at the base of the bluff. The fire will be out of direct view from the trail, but look for its light on the tall pines that grow in front of the bluff. You'll hear the DJ's tunes as you approach. Wear good hiking boots and pack your medicine and libation of choice.'"

"Like a country hoedown, twenty-first-century-Sierra-style," I said.

We walked down the back road from the Harrah's lot to the park entrance. The sun had set, and twilight was setting in. When we got to the entrance, the gate was closed. Probably the park hours were defined as daylight hours.

There were several groups of people walking toward the gate from the other side of the road. From the laughter and low-voiced jokes, it seemed everyone was already well into a party mood.

As we walked, Diamond said, "Do you suppose that this whistle-blower person called you just to get you away from Street?"

"That he's her dad or calling for her dad? I don't like that thought at all." The idea was disorienting.

"Sorry, just being a cop, I guess," Diamond said.

"As I think about it, the voice was clearly young, and his

words didn't sound practiced as if he'd been put up to the phone call. So, no, I don't think it was a ruse."

We walked in uncomfortable silence.

We turned and walked up the dark road behind the gate, knots of people in front of us and behind us.

Voices floated on the air. "I've been up here before," a young, male voice said. "Wait 'til you see this place. Awesome view. Awesome party spot. I drove up from the Bay Area, so I didn't have to worry about getting my bong and weed through TSA security. There's gonna be some fun tonight."

His voice was interrupted by a low grunt and then laughter and giggles.

Diamond muttered, "Feel like I live a boring life busting bad guys. Coulda been a charity scammer like these boys and have some real fun, huh?"

I said, "Outside of the view, this doesn't look like fun to me unless one compares it to living in his mother's basement."

"True." Diamond looked around at the people closest to us. "And unlike the activities of some of these guys, my fun fits all rational and necessary principles."

The road curved, and we followed the crowd.

"You're referring to what you said the other week?" I said. "Let me remember. The philosopher Kant described the Categorical Imperative as essential behavior that we should all adhere to?"

Diamond was silent for a moment. I almost could hear him grinning at my naivete. "Yeah. Something like that," he said. "It all gets down to good values."

"Which describes you, of course. So why did Kant call it Categorical Imperative? He could have just called it Good Principles."

"Right," Diamond said. "Could have and probably should have. But the smartest guys tend to be stuffed shirts."

We walked in silence for awhile. The groups of people became more numerous and dense.

"You carrying?" I asked.

"I might be a stuffed shirt, but I'm still a cop," Diamond said. "Got my backup, too. Why? You think something nasty is going to develop?"

"Someone keeps stringing up charity scammers. What if this psycho finds out an entire group of them is having a party? He might want to make it less fun."

The group of people ahead of us veered off the road and went into the forest. When we got to the same spot, I sensed a light-colored mark on the ground. I shined my light on it. A spray-painted arrow pointed the way. We turned and followed.

The trail was well-made, a gentle grade and easy to follow. We followed the group ahead of us, getting a bit closer, eavesdropping on their conversation. It was hard to make them out in the dark, but there were about five of them. By their voices, they all seemed to be men in their thirties and forties.

As it got darker, the group of people ahead of us turned on more lights. Flashlight beams bobbed around the ground. Somebody's voice came through the darkness.

"Have you heard about those murders? Three people killed and hung by their ankles. How psycho is that?"

"Yeah," another voice said. "All three were charity CEOs. That'll make a guy stop and think."

"All I can say is keep your eyes open and don't go anywhere alone."

The path rose up at a steeper angle. The view became grand, a sweeping vista across the lake and the Sierra Crest beyond. Although the sun had long since set, the sky glow still showed a clear silhouette of the distant mountains, and the remnants of wavering sunset colors of deep red and maroon reflected on the lake's surface.

We came over a rise and saw a campfire in the distance, a dance of yellow light in the trees. It was an illegal fire. But I didn't worry about forest fire because it had been a moist spring, we'd had the recent snow storm, and the fire was small and in a large open area.

Music grew in the air, a throbbing bass beat and chords on a synthesizer. An androgynous vocal track sang words I couldn't recognize to a melody that seemed to be the opposite of melodic. It was all about the rhythm and the monotony of pulsing sound. Take your drugs, feel the groove, and transport your senses to another world.

We came through a thick knot of trees and into view of the main group.

The backdrop to the group was a cliff of granite. The firelight lit its walls in a warm glow. In front of the rock walls was the DJ's setup. He was of indeterminate age and had a purple afro that quivered as he moved. He leaned over a table and speaker columns. On the table was a mixing board and a computer and an amplifier and a turntable on which he spun vinyl records. As an exercise in contrast, his tech gear and his workspace were all illuminated by five large candles in glass jars. The romantic light, combined with the insistent, loud music, created a surreal picture in the mountain forest. Heavenly resort and Monument Peak rose up 3000 feet behind him.

The crowd was about two hundred people, mostly standing around the fire. Either charity types were drawn to Tahoe for revelry, or those in the charity business had lots of friends and were good at convincing them to come to pop-up raves. They held cans of beer and smoked joints and moved to the music. There was some loud conversation and laughter and the occasional stand-out guffaw. A surprising number of people had their phones out, doing the thumb dance on the screens, playing whatever was the current game. Maybe they were texting messages to each other, embracing the new robotic, dysfunctional normal where people don't even make eye contact with their companions, but communicate with them through the electronic device in their hand. It is an inexplicable curiosity of humanity that people instinctively prefer communication through a screen interface more than spoken words and gestures and eye contact. How tedious to actually look at and speak to someone when it can be done through a computer that takes out the emotion.

Real emotion, those sudden surprising moments that make a person laugh or cry or become passionate about something, anything, will become a quaint notion experienced only by the shrinking group of old people who never substituted the screen interface for an actual conversation over the telephone or, in extreme circumstances, an actual conversation in person.

This group up on the mountain was a bridge from the past to the coming future. In this group, even as people stared at their screens as much as at the fire or the people next to them, they still exhibited the desire to be physically near other people. One could see, in that closeness, the self-focus that has made humans the lords of the planet. All they cared about was their communication with each other, even if it was done through their phones, even if it took place not in the forest but on a Facebook page that was more addictive than the alcohol and pot they were physically ingesting.

No one in the crowd seemed to notice the spectacular orange-red glow of fading twilight behind the Sierra Crest. No one looked up at the quarter moon or the emerging stars and planets. No one stepped into the dark woods to savor the crisp, high altitude air of the forest or put their nose to the bark of the Jeffrey pines to inhale the delicious butterscotch-vanilla scent. These people were oblivious to nature. And in that lack of appreciation for what the natural world offered, it was easy to see why we continued to treat the planet as a giant landfill, a place where the only conservation came because it was valued in a few circles, not because it was desired by the masses.

Diamond and I joined the group at a point equidistant between the fire and the DJ.

No doubt, some of the people ran honest charities that actually tried to help people. But I tried to see the group through the perspective of those who ran scam charities, business types who wrote creative stories about people in need and then set up false structures to take money from sympathetic donors. The scammer needed a special combination of the creative impulse and the criminal impulse. And, most important, the scammer had to believe that what he was doing was not morally wrong. He was merely a predator like any other, and his prey, like rabbits chased down by carnivores, was fair game.

Next to me, Diamond seemed to focus on those individuals who were physically the most boisterous. No doubt, that indicated to him where a physical altercation was most likely to break out.

I was lost in my negative reverie about the human species. I found myself thinking that people, who were so clever and so capable of amazing things, had a collective moral value below that of dogs. Rare was the dog who was intrinsically mean and self-serving above all other concerns. But it was common in people. Which was why people were the most successful predators.

As I scanned the people before me, imagining which ones were not in Tahoe to celebrate good charity work but were instead here to hang with fellow crooks, a person moved through my field of vision. He was on the other side of the campfire, not running, but moving with purpose. Something about him seemed familiar. I stared, squinting, trying to get a good glimpse of his face. I realized that he reminded me of the donor lady's son, Betty Rodriguez's son Gray. The man who had clearly stated his hatred of charity scammers.

Then he was gone.

A moment later, a murmur arose from a group on the other side of the campfire. Six or eight people had turned away from the fire, looking toward the dark forest. I heard a gasp. A cry. Then a collective exclamation of surprise and horror.

The words, "Oh, my God!" and "What's going on?!" and "I can't believe this!" rose from the group.

Other people heard and turned to look at some kind of movement in the dark. Something swung back and forth as if on a swing.

The vague shape swinging in the forest began to levitate. As it rose up above the crowd, it was lit by the campfire and also by the flashlights of several people in the crowd.

The gasp of horror grew as we realized what we were seeing.

It was a man, hanging from a rope looped around his ankles. The rope was lifting him up into the trees, a body, alive or maybe dead, being hoisted to the sky.

An amplified voice crackled through the night air. The voice was loud enough to be heard over the DJ's music. It was also garbled, like that of the young man Matt who had called me and told me to come to the party.

"You are all predators!" The voice seemed to come from everywhere at once. "Your crime is preying on the innocent and bleeding them dry. But you are not apex predators. I am the apex predator. And I am taking you down, one by one."

FORTY-NINE

Diamond was on his radio in a moment, calling in troops.

I considered whether or not there was a way to contain all the witnesses. But within seconds, they panicked, yelling and scattering into the forest as if running from a bomb. There would be no way to stop them. Our only hope was that if anyone had seen anything helpful, they might stay around and volunteer the information.

I pointed my light up toward the victim, but he was too high, and my beam was weak. Diamond got off his radio and pulled a flashlight from his pocket. He walked over below the victim and shined his light up. More people shined their lights. Eventually, there were enough combined beams to clearly light the hanging person, but there was little to see beyond the fact that there was no obvious movement. The victim was 80 or 100 feet above the ground, too far to reveal anything.

Diamond called out. "Hello to the person hanging in the trees! This is Sergeant Martinez, Douglas County Sheriff's Office. Can you hear me?"

There was no response.

"If you can hear me but can't talk, move your body."

Nothing.

We could see the rope from the victim's ankles rising above him, but it was obscured by tree branches.

Diamond called out again in a loud voice. "This is an announcement to everyone who can hear me. Your observations of what just happened are very important to us. We'd like to ask you questions about what you saw. Please stay here so that we can talk to you. We have more officers coming, and they'll be able to help speed the process so you won't have to wait too long."

From the standpoint of the perpetrator, it was a brilliant display of theater. Hoist a victim from the midst of a crowd in such a manner that we couldn't even see how it was done. Then, despite the presence of law enforcement on the scene, the perpetrator had little concern that anyone would identify him.

I looked around the dark forest, thinking about the process the perpetrator used.

If I had wanted to commit such a crime, I'd come out during the daylight and climb to the top of the bluff, which was 100 or 150 feet tall. From there, I'd toss a stone out and up into the tall pines. I'd have a long thin line tied to the stone. Something like paracord. If the line was forest green, even better. If the stone's trajectory didn't work, I'd toss more stones until I got it just right.

Once a stone and its line went where I wanted, I'd tie the end of the line off near the top of the bluff. Then I could climb down and secure the line near the tree trunk so that it would be ready when I wanted it.

Later, I'd have my heavy, beefy companions waiting up on the bluff. When I snared my victim, I'd give word over my cell phone, and my comrades would wrap the line over shoulder pads, loop it around their torso for grip, then lean into it and trot off across the top of the dark bluff, raising the victim who was tied to the other end.

As soon as I visualized the process, I realized a much better way to do it.

There are lightweight, low-voltage winches available for use on sailboats and, no doubt, many other applications. Instead of getting help from companions, the perpetrator could set up a winch, tied to a tree at the top of the bluff. A lightweight battery could be connected to the winch. The switch could be triggered electronically. I didn't know the details, but I'd learned about electronic actuators in a previous case. The winch might weigh 8 pounds and the battery another 8 pounds. Add a few pounds for miscellaneous gear, and the whole works would be less than 20 pounds. As soon as the perpetrator had snared the victim, he'd trigger the electronic remote. If he'd left no fingerprints on his equipment and there was no serial number on the equipment to identify where and when it had been purchased, the perpetrator would be very difficult to find.

Another possibility would be that while everyone else was still trying to understand what was happening, the perpetrator would already be climbing the bluff. Soon after the victim was up into the trees and the winch had turned itself off, triggered by a distance measurement or some other gadget, the perpetrator would be nearly to the winch. He'd take the line that stretched out into the tree branches and down to the victim, and he'd tie it off on something strong. The winch and battery would easily fit into a backpack with his megaphone, and he'd be gone.

The perpetrator knew from the lay of the land that no one would be able to reliably trace the activity and locations for hours and maybe even not until daylight. By then, even if the victim had still been alive when he was hoisted, he'd likely have died from the combined effects of cold temperature exposure, the stress of hanging upside down, and, if Doc Lee was right in his suspicions, the pulmonary impairment caused by some kind of spray in the victim's lungs.

The hitch in my concept was that the perpetrator wouldn't know about the pop-up party location and the bluff until it was announced by way of email that afternoon. Unless he had inside information from the pop-up rave organizers. However, the whole process could possibly be put in place in the time between the announcement of the location and the moment the victim was snared around his ankles.

The perpetrator might have no connection to the organizers.

As I pondered the possibilities, I realized that Diamond had been busy setting up a perimeter around the area below the hanging body. He'd recruited three young men to help.

I caught Diamond's attention. "You've got this area under control. Reinforcements will arrive shortly. I'm going to hike up the slope on the north side of the bluff and see if I can find the line that holds the victim. If there's any chance he's still alive, it would be critical to lower him down as fast as possible."

"Good idea," Diamond said. "When any of my men arrive, I'll send someone up to help you."

FIFTY

I wanted to go back to the parking lot and get Spot. There were few things better than him when dealing with a bad guy in the dark. But it would take me fifteen minutes to run down the trail, get him out of the Jeep, and return to the campfire site.

Meanwhile, there was a man hanging by his ankles up in the black treetops. If he was still alive, and if I had any chance of finding the rope that held him, I could possibly lower him to the ground.

I tried to run up through the trees toward the bluff. The woods weren't especially dense, but my light was small. The slope to the side of the bluff was very steep. As it got steeper still, my feet slipped in the loose duff that made up the top several inches of the soil. I remembered the headlamp in my pocket and put it on.

I used my hands as I went up. It was an imposing slope. I slipped continuously, dirt shooting out from under my shoes and hands. But with four traction points, I made progress.

I came to a wall of rock. Leaning back, shining the light left and right, I realized it was a house-sized boulder. It looked like I could get around it to the left.

With my hands digging into dirt and grasping at every little root fiber, I moved to the side of the rock face, then continued up. As I crested the top of the giant rock, the campfire from down below appeared in my peripheral vision. I was up high enough now that if I scanned into the trees, it was possible I'd see the man hanging from his feet. But I didn't dare look toward the fire. I didn't want to lose what night vision I had. It was more important to focus on what I believed I'd find at the top of the bluff. The perpetrator was probably long gone. But if I could get to the rope that held the victim, I could possibly lower the victim to the ground. Maybe he could be saved.

I continued to claw my way up the slope. Sirens sounded in the distance. The strong scents of moist soil filled the air as my fingers scraped dirt from the mountain side.

After several more minutes of climbing on all fours, I came to the top of the slope. Scanning with my light, left and right, I tried to sense where the perpetrator would likely run his rope from the trees to a winch and, probably, another tree that he would use to tie the rope off. Nothing was obvious. I turned toward the pine trees, but I couldn't see the victim among the thick branches.

I jogged along the top edge of the bluff, sweeping my little headlamp beam left and right, hoping to see a rope stretched taut from a tree or boulder, out into the dark space of the tree canopy above the rave's campfire.

The clifftop edge of the bluff was not obvious. I had to slow down to avoid tumbling off. I'd gone about 50 feet when I heard a noise to the side. Whether human or animal, I didn't know.

I turned, shined my light. I wasn't sure, but I thought I saw movement in the dark.

"Police!" I shouted. "Don't move, and you won't be hurt."

There was a rustle in the forest. Someone or something was running away from me.

"Stop!" I shouted.

I sprinted toward the movement, toward the dark. I tried to shine my light, tried to see the dark trees. My ankle caught on a branch, tripping me. I went down just as my ankle broke the branch with a loud snap. I tumbled face first into the darkness, hitting the ground hard with my shoulder and my left cheek. My hip ground across an abrasive rock. Something between my hip and the rock seemed to catch and jerk across the rough surface and then give way.

My first thought was that I was very fortunate that I hadn't knocked my teeth out.

My second thought was about the loud zipper sound as a broken line came out from under my hip and zinged through the trees, over branches, and down. The victim hanging upside down by his ankles dropped like a rock, head first, toward the ground 100 feet below.

FIFTY-ONE

I was stunned. There was no time to get up and run to the edge to shout out to the people below. There was no possibility of arranging a soft landing.

The sound of the racing line went dead. I heard a thudding sound followed by a collective gasp from unseen people below.

With a sickening sense of dread overwhelming me, I pushed myself up off the ground and stood up, listening to the woods back from the edge of the bluff.

Whoever or whatever animal had been in the trees was gone. Without a dog, I'd never find him.

I walked to the edge of the bluff, moving slowly as I got near the edge. I looked down.

While most of the crowd had disappeared, the campfire was still bright, now a lonely fire in the forest. To one side, I could see multiple people bent over a body.

I tried to gather my thoughts. My headlamp beam seemed more feeble than before. Or maybe it just looked dim in the forest compared to the klieg lights that were searing my mind space. I shined the flashlight here and there, but it was as if I was unable to register what I was seeing. I tried to find the place where the rope might have been tied. There were boulders and trees and shrubs throughout the black forest. But nowhere was there an obvious collection of synthetic fibers left by the paracord or whatever kind of rope the victim had been tied with.

After a minute, I realized the futility of standing in the dark at the top of a bluff on a mountainside where no one was going to arrive with searchlights anytime soon if ever.

I headed back down as more sirens sounded in the distance.

There seemed no familiar route down off the bluff. I looked for the slope to the side of the rocky cliff, the area where I'd climbed up. It seemed like entirely new territory. As it got steeper, I had to turn to face the slope, once again using both hands and feet to climb down without falling. It was very difficult to turn my head to shine the light behind me.

Mostly I descended blind, not noticing my surroundings, my mind occupied with the person I'd probably killed.

I knew that it was an accident.

But to be an agent of death was very difficult. At best, I was guilty of bad judgment. At worst, I'd made a terrific error of running where I should have been moving very cautiously.

Ten minutes later, I got to the bottom and walked out of the dark woods into the light of the fading fire.

There was still a perimeter set up. But this time it was officers in uniforms, Douglas County Sheriff's deputies. There was another officer talking to a small group of party-goers. One officer was stretching yellow crime-scene tape.

In the center of the perimeter, there was a group of people bent over the crumpled body on the ground. But for several flashlight beams, it was very dark, shadowed from the firelight by a rise in the ground and a large fallen log that lay on the ground nearby. In a surreal way, the officers vaguely looked like they were in a football huddle, plotting strategy.

At the center of the group was Diamond, obvious not by his face, but by the way he held himself. Diamond was a natural leader. He took charge the way a good ship's captain takes charge when the hull is ruptured on a reef.

I moved toward them tentatively.

"Sir, stay back!" one of the deputies shouted at me.

The rest of the men looked up.

"McKenna's okay," Diamond said. "Let him in."

I walked in toward the group. Two men and one woman were bent over the body. If they'd tried life-saving measures, they'd given up. The body was crumpled, head deformed and jammed down into the neck and chest in a manner from which no one would survive.

Next to the body was a stretcher.

"Okay," one of them said. "Roll over on three." It was a maneuver to save people with spine injuries from further injury, though unnecessary in the current context. But their efforts might help the medical examiner.

"One, two, three," the young man said.

They rolled the body over onto the stretcher. Diamond shined his light on the body's face. It was a young man in his late twenties, with curly, almost angelic brown hair that cupped his face.

One deputy said, "I sure don't get how the perp got a line tied around this guy's ankles without him yelling for help."

I was still dumbstruck by what had happened, breathing a fast pant, my heart pounding a rapid beat. You kill someone, even inadvertently, it still renders you useless. I tried to force myself to think and respond, but I couldn't come up with words.

One of the party-goers said, "The guy was really swinging when he was first raised up. I couldn't believe it! It's like he was lifted off the ground some distance away from the spot below the hanging point." A pause, then the person clarified, "Some distance away from where the body is now."

"Okay, guys," Diamond said. "The victim has no ID on him, nothing in his pockets. Search in circles, moving away from the body. Look for anything that doesn't belong in the forest."

Three deputies started searching, training their flashlights on the ground. Again, I thought of how much Spot could help. But I couldn't motivate myself to go get him. I could barely breathe.

"Hey, Sarge," the female deputy called out. "Found a wallet behind this Manzanita bush."

Diamond walked over and looked where the woman was shining her light. He had on his latex gloves. He reached down and picked up the wallet. "Put up an additional perimeter around this spot. Don't mar the ground. We want anything else, no matter how small. In the morning light, we'll search again."

Diamond walked back to the body. He opened the wallet, pulled out the driver's license, held it next to the victim's face. "It's him. Name is Matthew T. Woodvale."

"Matt," I said in a low voice. "That's the person who was looking for me."

"The guy who was going to give you information about the murders," Diamond said.

FIFTY-TWO

Two hours later, after multiple statements from people who had seen nothing and could provide no help, Spot and I got home to my cabin.

It was late, so I didn't check in with Street. With luck, she'd be asleep.

I tried to do the same, but I couldn't sleep with a dead man on my conscience. For two hours, I lay in bed, replaying in my mind what had happened. Eventually, I gave up. I got up, opened a beer, and turned on my laptop.

Spot knew something was wrong. He came over and stuck his cold wet nose on my hand.

"Don't worry, boy. I'll be back to normal in a year or three. You have to drop people on their head every now and then, just to show them who's boss. It's best to do it from a hundred feet up. Cave that head in good."

Spot lowered his head so that he could rest his jaw on my lap while he was still standing.

"And then, just for good measure, it's good to let a killer stalk your girlfriend. Don't send in any armed guards. Don't put up any extraordinary barriers. Don't demand that she sleep at your place with your hound at her side. Let her stay out in the wilderness alone. Because that's what she wants. Famous philosophers say that you have to keep your hands off. The imperative category principle is all that matters."

I Googled Matthew T. Woodvale. I found nothing. Which in itself was notable. Nearly everyone shows up in some manner on a Google search. It suggested that Matthew was a complete shut-in with no presence in modern life. Or he used a pseudonym for everything he did on the internet. Anyone who is so careful not to have any online presence – no Facebook use, no blog writing, no comments posted anywhere on the internet, no listing in an online phone or address service – those people have hidden everything else in their life. To find them, one needs a starting point. An address, the name of a school they attended, their occupation, a friend or acquaintance, a phone number.

But when someone calls you out of thin air, with no caller ID, and then hangs up…

All I knew about Matt was that he apparently knew something about the murders. It was a tantalizing notion. But it got me nowhere. My only hope was that Diamond would get a match on his fingerprints or, if he searched for it, his DNA. That might take many days.

However, there might be something to find at the crime scene come daylight.

I looked at the clock. I still had hours of darkness during which I could be miserable. Probably, Douglas Fairbanks could quote a poem about misery. Probably, a poem could put my misery in perspective, which would help me to focus on the fact that my misery was nothing compared to Matt's.

FIFTY-THREE

I went back to bed.

I lay in the dark, trying to focus on calm thoughts. But my attempt was useless. It would have been easy to anticipate that the line holding the victim would stretch from the tree where he hung into the forest at the top of the bluff. Any idiot could have thought to look for the line instead of just charging ahead like a stampeding bull. Yet I ran without thinking, and I went full speed into a disaster.

After another hour, I got up and made some tea. My brain was thick with self critique. My mood was black. What good is making an effort if the result is death?

I thought about my advice to Douglas Fairbanks when he was in despair over having been taken in by a thief who had hidden behind her beauty and charm.

Figure out your next, best task, and go do it. Get something done, and you will be better off for it.

So I turned my attention to other aspects of the case. In the past, I'd often found it useful to reconsider everything I knew about a case.

A doctor named Jack Smith had died while hanging from his ankles in Ukiah. I'd gone to Ukiah and met his neighbor Judy. She told me about the woman who showed up to sell the property, a woman Judy thought was the doctor's daughter. The daughter was named Glenn. But Judy had no idea about Glenn's last name. Maybe she used Smith.

So I once again went online and looked up Glenn Smith. There were hundreds or thousands. Same for doctors named Smith. A huge number were connected to Southern California. Because Jack is often a nickname for John, I also paid attention to any doctor named John Smith. I read through medical clinic websites. I looked over blogs that mentioned doctors named Smith. As I perused, I watched for any mention of a woman named Glenn.

If I could find a doctor Jack Smith mentioned in the same place as a woman named Glenn, I'd be onto something.

But the only Glenn I found in connection to a Smith was another doctor, an oncologist named Dr. Glenn Numesa. And after a bit more reading, I found out that Dr. Glenn Numesa was a man.

There seemed no easy way to learn about the man who'd died hanging from his ladder.

The next obvious source of information was public records of real estate ownership.

So I got on the website for Mendocino County and discovered that they had put much of the legal public information online. But I could find no recent transactions for a Dr. Jack Smith near Ukiah.

When morning came and I wasn't worried about waking people up, I called a prominent realty office in Ukiah. I explained my question and got transferred to two different people. A woman named Francine Sargent was very helpful and said she'd be happy to find me the perfect property for my dream home. When I told Francine that I was interested in the property owned by Dr. Smith that had been sold by his daughter after he died, Francine went silent.

After a long pause, she said, "I'm sure we can find many better properties for you."

"Any chance you know the purchaser of the doctor's property?"

"I have no idea."

"Perhaps you can direct me to the title company that handled the transfer of deed."

"I'm sure I wouldn't know that, either. I suppose you could try Fidelity Trust and Coastal Escrow," she said. "They pretty much have a lock on property transfers in our area."

"Thank you very much. I'll remember your help," I said.

"I'm sure you will," she said, her tone dry.

So I got the title company on the phone and after two more transfers, I learned that they had no idea about Dr. Smith. But they found that the property had been sold to a winery and vineyard outfit that was big in Coastal Pinot Noirs. Next, I called the winery, was transferred yet two more times, and was unable to learn anything about the dead doctor and his daughter who'd sold the property.

I realized I'd probably have to go to San Diego to track down the doctor and his daughter and establish their names, and that would be a big project.

In the meantime, I knew that Judy had said the daughter Glenn expressed outrage when she found in the mail a come-on from The Red Roses of Hope Charity for Children. Not much to go on in tracking down a murderer, but it was all I had. Not much more than being at a dead end.

Then I remembered the man I'd seen at the pop-up party, just before Matthew Woodvale was hoisted up into the treetops. The man had looked like Gray Rodriguez, son of Betty Rodriguez, world's greatest croissant baker.

I looked through my notes, found Betty's number, and dialed.

"Betty Rodriguez," she answered.

"Hi Betty. This is Owen McKenna calling. I'm the guy who…"

"Was asking about charities," she interrupted. "I remember. You liked my croissants."

"The best ever. I'm calling because I had a question for your son Gray."

"You know Gray? Well, what a surprise."

"Could you give me his phone number, please?"

"Of course." Betty said. "But you won't get him now. He went up to Tahoe, and he doesn't use a cell phone. I don't either. But I'm always here at my kitchen phone. He should have one for his job even if he has no social life."

"Do you know what he's doing or where he's staying in Tahoe?"

"No. I'm his mother not his pal. He doesn't keep me informed much about his activities."

"But you know he's in Tahoe," I said.

"Well, sure. He told me that much."

"Is he taking a vacation?"

"No. He just said he had something he had to do and he

didn't know how long it would take."

"Betty, let me ask you a different question, if I may. When I talked to Gray, he seemed unhappy that you donate to charities."

"Oh, don't get him going on charities."

"Why do you say that?"

Betty paused. "I suppose it's the resentment of a son who thinks his mother didn't give him an easy ride through life. After we adopted him, I made Gray earn everything. I wanted him to understand the value of hard work, the value of delayed gratification. And I think I pretty much succeeded at instilling those values in him. But whenever he sees me giving money to people he thinks are crooks, he turns red. I swear, if smoke could come out of a man's ears, Gray would be adding to our air pollution."

"Betty, do you have a photo of Gray you could email me?"

"I don't do that technology stuff, Mr. McKenna. But Gray showed me the Parks and Recreation website once. There's a photo of him planting trees on the American River Parkway. Maybe you could look at that."

"Thanks, Betty."

I found the Parks and Rec website, and poked around until I found the photo of Gray Rodriguez. It looked very much like the man I'd seen at the pop-up party. I copied the photo. Then I wrote a group email to all of the law enforcement people connected to the case. I explained what I'd learned, and I attached the photo of Gray.

I next called Elena Turwin, the woman in Tahoe City who focused her donations on charities that help children.

I reminded her who I was and that I recalled her saying that her husband didn't like charities.

"You got that right. Hubby isn't the mean and aggressive type. Truth be told, he's a pussycat. But charities for him are like a taunting mouse for a cat. He'd be happy to see those people strung up."

"Mrs. Turwin, remember the murder victims in Tahoe and

Truckee? People who were hung up by their ankles?"

"Oh, yes. I see why you would ask. But I just meant it as a figure of speech. Hubby wouldn't really do it."

"Mrs. Turwin, I need to ask you a question. It's just a pro-forma matter that investigators do. Can you vouch for the whereabouts of your husband at night for the last two weeks? Especially last night around ten p.m.?"

"I see where you're going with this line of thought. Unfortunately, the answer is no. Hubby keeps his own schedule, and I often don't know whether he's in his shop or out on a beer run. And I take half an Ambien when I go to bed. So I have no idea about anything until the next morning."

"May I ask his full name?"

"Harley Jasper Turwin, U.S. Army Reserve Captain, Retired."

"May I visit again and talk to him?" I asked.

"I wouldn't mind it. But I think I told you that Hubby doesn't speak to strangers, and he doesn't even engage with anyone but me. Maybe you thought I was just exaggerating. But it's the truth. Call it a combination hearing problem and social problem. You could haul him in on an arrest warrant, but he would just sit there stone-faced. It would be a waste of taxpayer resources."

"Is he currently at your house?"

"Like I already explained, unless he walks into my kitchen when I'm cooking, I have no idea where he is most times. We sleep in separate bedrooms. He comes and goes as he pleases. He always says that the Army Reserve spent decades telling him what to do and where to be. Now that he's retired, he treasures the fact that he doesn't have to answer to anyone. All I know is he's usually around for breakfast and dinner. But sometimes I find a note on the counter. 'Back tomorrow.' Things like that."

"Thanks, Elena. You've been very helpful."

"Welcome."

When I hung up the phone, it rang immediately.

"McKenna," I answered.

"Jack Santiago."

"Sergeant."

"I'm calling about the body on the Kings Beach flagpole. You said that your doctor friend thought we should look for some kind of chemical in the vic's lungs."

"Right."

"I just got a call from the medical examiner. Turns out the toxicology report shows the man had Prallethrin in his mouth and lungs."

"What's that?" I asked.

"It's an insecticide. Commonly found in wasp and hornet killer."

"That's a nasty thing to spray into someone's lungs," I said.

"Yeah, no kidding."

We hung up.

I called Diamond and left a message on his voicemail. I explained about the wasp killer and suggested the ME check the body that had fallen from the treetops. I next called Amtrak PD Inspector Humboldt. He answered, and I told him about Prallethrin. He said he'd contact the Truckee ME to check the body on the train. Then I did the same with Sergeant Bains regarding Dory's body.

Diamond called back and said, "The wasp killer must be how the killer at Van Sickle Park was able to get his victim tied around his ankles with no one noticing. He'd already killed Matt Woodvale with wasp spray, and he did it off in the dark where no one saw him. Then he tied the man's ankles with paracord and hoisted him up into the sky."

"Yeah, that description fits the evidence," I said.

"So you don't have to feel like your moves killed the victim. He was already dead."

I thought about it. "Thanks, Diamond."

FIFTY-FOUR

I looked up the charity website to see the details on the Tahoe Grand Tour bike ride that Fairbanks was participating in. It had the start times for the different groups, with Men 51 and over being the last group. It showed estimated finish times so that onlookers could be at the finish at the appropriate moments.

I thought it would be good for Fairbanks to see the support of a familiar face when he came down to the finish line. And it would probably be good for me to get out and see that life goes on.

I checked the time. The bikers riding the Grand Tour would be approaching the finish in another hour. It was time to leave.

Spot and I drove up to Incline Village. The road to the Grand Tour finish line seemed familiar, and then I recognized that it was the road that the scientist, Giuseppe Calvarenna, lived on. I wondered if his Lagrangian points could provide a metaphoric parking place for my emotions after the death of the young man. Maybe they could also be a model for Douglas Fairbanks.

I found a place to park not far from the Grand Tour finish line, which was on a road not far from the base of Diamond Peak ski resort. The event was a true grand tour. Even without a major focus on speed, the bicyclists would get a supreme workout.

After riding dozens of miles up and down the mountains, the race route brought them to the finish line up above Incline Village. Hopefully, there would be a large, cheering crowd.

I parked, and Spot and I walked over to where tables had been set up in the trees. On the tables were water coolers and stacks of energy bars that had been donated by a food company. There was a good crowd of people with cameras and smartphones out, ready for photos. The race organizers were busy with clipboards and lists, talking on phones and radios.

The first group was women up to the age of 30. When the first riders appeared, there was a lot of cheering and whoops and yells. The finish was close with multiple athletic young women flashing by at very high speed. Not much later, the next group began to come in, women 31-40. They also rode very fast. There were six women in the 41-50 group, and three 51 and over. When all four age groups of women were done, it was the men's turn, youngest to oldest.

When the 51-and-over men finally appeared, I counted sixteen riders. But they didn't include Fairbanks. I worried that he had crashed up on the mountain. I hadn't wanted to call Fairbanks before he left and spoil the surprise of showing up, so I had no way of knowing if he'd actually made it to the race start. But the organizers seemed to be waiting for more racers.

Spot and I waited, too.

After a long minute, another rider appeared up the trail, coming around a curve, leaning into the bank. It was a skinny, bald guy, older than me by a couple of decades, but riding faster than I ever would. When he shot through the finish line, the organizers continued to wait.

After another minute passed, we saw movement in the distance. Another rider came around the last banked turn. This one was chunky like Fairbanks. But he was wearing typical mountain bike gear, so I couldn't tell his identity from a distance.

A cheer went up as everyone realized that this was the last rider on the course.

When the rider got closer, I saw that it was indeed Fairbanks, his new gear helping him look like the other riders. His face was set in a grimace that looked like a combination of determination and fear. He was standing up on his pedals just as all the other riders had. His grip on the handlebars was firm. Too firm, I thought. And his elbows were too straight. It seemed to me that he was also going too fast, as if trying to make up for being last. Although I was no expert, I knew that riding a mountain bike at speed required a loose grip on the handlebars and bent elbows so that the violent vibrations from wheels bouncing on the trail weren't all transmitted into the racer's body, shaking everything, including his brain. But Fairbanks looked like he was squeezing the grips hard enough to crush them.

People yelled louder as he got closer.

When he was twenty yards out, his front wheel hit a protruding rock in the trail. The bike shimmied left and then right. Fairbanks's grip was so tense that he couldn't absorb the shimmy. He overreacted, first one way, then even more to the other. His bike began to skid. It was the kind of situation from which an athletic, experienced rider can often recover. And if he can't, the professional rider knows how to lay a bike down in the dirt at high speed with minimal chance of injury.

Fairbanks didn't have such skills. His front wheel folded back to the left, and the rear wheel lurched up into the air. Fairbanks launched over the handlebars. His facial expression turned to horror and shock. People gasped. A small scream rose in the still air. For a very brief moment Fairbanks was horizontal, arms out in front like Superman, flying through the air. Then he hit the ground in a belly flop, and skidded forward. He came to a stop near the finish line.

People rushed to him, bending over, kneeling next to him.

"Is he alive?"

"Yeah, I can feel his pulse."

"Should we call a doctor?"

"The poor man, I knew he was going too fast!"

A woman was shaking him. "Sir, are you okay?!"

As I got to him, we all heard him say, "I'm okay," in a tiny voice. "I don't need a doctor. I just need to catch my breath."

Several people were startled by Spot, and they jumped back. Holding Spot's collar, I knelt next to Fairbanks's head.

"I'm okay," he said again, still in the same belly-flop position, arms out in front of him, face in the dirt. It reminded me of my weapon hand training with Spot when I landed in the dirt in a similar position. But Fairbanks's collision was much worse.

I turned to the group of onlookers. "He's okay," I said louder. "This is my friend Douglas Fairbanks. It looks like he'll be fine. I'll stay with him."

Fairbanks didn't move. "I'm a failure," he said. His eyes were teary with the sting of falling or embarrassment or both. "I'm a complete failure at everything."

I ignored his comment as I helped him to his feet.

"I can drive you home," I said.

"No, I should take the bus. They're having a ceremony for us when the bus brings us to the South Shore. I'd like to be there for that. If you drive me, I'll just look even more like a loser."

"Losers don't ride dozens of miles on rugged mountain bike trails. That was quite an achievement. I've never ridden that far."

"I never should have, either," he said. "I always go overboard on everything I do. I never face my limitations. I never know how to stop myself."

We heard someone call out to the crowd. "Thanks to all of you for participating. The Grand Tour was truly a grand event. The South Shore ceremony is still on our schedule. However, there's been a slight delay with the shuttle bus. They had mechanical trouble, so they've sent another bus. Please be patient. The bus will be here eventually."

"We can wait in my Jeep," I said. "That'll be a bit more comfortable than sitting on the ground."

Fairbanks didn't protest. I picked up his bike. Although it was battered, it was still functional.

"If you want some support, you can hold onto Spot's collar."

Fairbanks took my suggestion. He leaned on Spot and moved with slow steps. Spot matched his pace.

I rolled the bike over to the Jeep and leaned it against the hood. I opened the passenger door. Fairbanks sat down in the passenger seat. Spot stood next to him at the open door. Fairbanks leaned his head back on the headrest and made a big sigh.

I got in the driver's side and sat with the door open.

The only significant sound was Fairbanks's breathing.

Eventually, he spoke. "When I was a kid, they called me Dougie Fatbanks. I was teased endlessly. I never had a girlfriend. I don't think any girl ever even noticed me. In college, I once asked a woman if she wanted to go on a date and get pizza, and she laughed at me."

"Really?" I said.

"Yeah. She made this choking sound. It took me a year to get up my guts to ask another woman out. That woman frowned and said, 'Are you serious? I'm sorry, I have standards.' Another time, I asked a girl I liked if she liked poetry. She looked at me like I smelled or something, and she said she liked football and jocks."

"People can be thoughtless," I said.

Fairbanks continued. "Then one day in college, a very business-like woman started paying me attention. I was so awestruck that I didn't even notice that she never once touched me, never once said anything affectionate. We never went out on a date. In hindsight, I think her marriage to me was just a way for her to escape her parents.

"Decades later, I took a kind of personal stock of my life, and I decided to change. I started walking to and from my office, four miles each way. In one year, I lost 100 pounds. I've still got more to lose, but that gave me confidence. Then I got a mountain bike and started bringing it to Tahoe. I told you how I met Isadore, a beautiful girl who paid me some attention. We went out to dinner together. We talked and drank wine at this romantic restaurant. It was amazing." He paused as if remembering.

"What about it was amazing?"

"Well, it was mostly just that I was going out to dinner with a woman. I'd never been on a real date before. I'd been married for decades but had never experienced a romantic evening." He paused. "But then it turns out that Isadore was really Dory Spatt, a charity scammer. A thief."

I didn't know what to say.

The race organizer again called out to the crowd. "People, we just got an update on the bus. It is currently going past Glenbrook. So the delay will be less than an hour. We're so sorry about this! To make it up to you, our race crew member William has gone to the market for a case of champagne along with cheese and crackers and other treats. So we'll have a free champagne party feast on the bus when it gets here."

There were a few whoops and hollers from the crowd.

"Do you still want to wait for the bus?" I said.

"Yeah. I should. I need to learn how to hang out with people." Fairbanks sounded pained. "I need to learn how to be normal."

He pushed himself out of the Jeep and stood up. "I think that while I wait I'll just walk my bike around the area roads, try to loosen up my muscles and get my brain in a better place."

"Okay. You've got my cell number."

Fairbanks nodded. He put his hand on his bike seat and

began to walk it away. Then he turned back.

"Hey, McKenna."

"Yeah?"

"That was awesome of you to come and show support."

"You're welcome."

I was about to drive off when my cell rang.

"Hello?"

"Bains calling."

"Yes, sergeant."

"First, I got your message about the wasp killer. I called the ME. They're confidant that Dory Spatt had no chemical in her mouth or lungs."

"Really," I said. "That's interesting."

"The other thing," Bains continued, "is that early this morning, we were called out to investigate a sunken boat that was spotted by a pilot who was flying over Emerald Bay. The boat was north of the entrance to Emerald Bay. We sent our boat patrol out there, and they found an aluminum runabout under twenty-five feet of water. In some ways, it's a surprise it took so long for someone to spot the wreckage because it was so visible from the surface. But it was in an underwater boulder field that boaters stay away from so they don't rip holes in their hulls."

"What was notable about the sunken boat?"

"Nothing about the boat itself. A sixteen foot runabout with a basic steering cockpit in the center. But there was a body attached to the boat. The body's right arm was trapped between the steering cable and the boat hull."

I was trying to visualize it. "Like maybe the person realized the boat was about to swamp, and he reached out to grab the edge of the boat for support but accidentally got his arm jammed in between the cable and the boat hull?"

"Right. Only the body was a she, not a he."

"That's unusual," I said. "Not too many women go out boating alone in bad weather."

"We found a wallet on the body. The ID said the victim's name was Glenn Smith. Sounds like the woman you told me about."

As soon as Bains said the name, I had a rushing cascade of thoughts.

"That's the woman who was at the doctor's house in Ukiah arranging for its sale, the daughter of the doctor who died hanging from his ankles. The neighbor lady said the doctor's daughter was really angry about the Red Roses of Hope charity."

Bains said, "That was the charity that you said the murder victim, Dory Spatt, ran?"

"Yeah. Which suggests that Glenn Smith could have been Dory's murderer."

"Right," Bains said. "In Glenn Smith's pocket was a brochure from the Red Roses charity.

"But if Glenn Smith strung Dory up on the Fannette Island tea house and then died when her boat swamped, then the subsequent murders by hanging don't make sense."

Bains didn't reply.

"Unless the other murders are copycat killings," I said. "That would explain why no one found any haiku at the other murders even though Spot found a haiku at the Emerald Bay murder."

"Right," Bains said. "We never publicized any info about the haiku. A copycat would have learned about the symbolic charity roses in the Fannette Island victim's mouth. That info was in the newspaper. But a copycat murderer wouldn't know to put a haiku on the scene."

We were both quiet a moment.

"We may have solved the Fannette Island murder," Bains said.

"Yeah."

"But we've made the murders at Kings Beach, Truckee, and last night at Van Sickle Park more of a puzzle," he said.

"However, we may have learned something valuable."

"What would that be?" he said.

"If we find any possible suspect who had an alibi for Dory Spatt's murder, that person can be considered once again."

"Good point," Bains said.

"Call me if you learn anything else?" I said.

"Likewise." Bains hung up.

FIFTY-FIVE

I sat in the Jeep, confused and surprised, trying to sort out the implications of a potential copycat killer. Because Glenn Smith was dead from a boating accident near Emerald Bay, everything I'd learned about her, especially her father's donations to the Red Roses charity, made the daughter a good suspect for Dory Spatt's murder.

Hanging her victim by the ankles might seem like a fitting punishment when her father had died that way. What didn't make sense was that the hanging by ankles seemed like a connection pointing toward Glenn Smith. It made her more likely to get caught.

I paused on that thought. Maybe, as happens with some murders, the killer wanted that connection. As if, in Glenn's anger, she found murder more satisfying when there was a faint clue that led back to her father's death in Ukiah, California. Certainly, the haiku made it very obvious that the motivation for the murder was the scam charity.

As I had that thought, a sudden realization startled me.

Haiku, spelled backward, was Ukiah.

I realized that could be a coincidence. However, it could also be a clever way to taunt law enforcement. I'd seen it before. Clues that, though somewhat obscure, were intentional. In my experience, it was almost a common component of very bright killers. It added the ego component. See how smart I am? I can give you a very clever clue. But you still can't catch me.

In this case, it seemed that Glenn was making her connection to the killing as obvious as possible without providing actual evidence. Unfortunately, for her, she likely died that same stormy night that she committed murder.

Spot and I still sat in the Jeep, Spot sound asleep.

In the distance, I saw Fairbanks plodding down the road, wheeling his bicycle. His head was lowered with obvious depression. He came to a T intersection, turned, and disappeared from my sight. I realized that he was heading down the road where the scientist lived.

My thoughts segued to the work of scientists. In Professor Calvarenna's case, the work was basically math. It must be an amazing life to earn your way through the world by conjuring up the laws of the universe using nothing more than math, and then applying those laws to things that no person had ever thought of before. Spending one's life studying Lagrangian points must be as esoteric a career as there is. Parking places in space. Concepts so dramatic that charity scammers use them for metaphorical business models.

Spot pushed himself up in the back seat where he was lying, standing with his back against the Jeep's headliner. I watched him in the rear view mirror. He looked at me with droopy eyes, turned a circle in the cramped space of the seat, and lay back down.

"Not sure turning a circle will give you a more comfortable parking place," I said.

Spot acted asleep. Maybe he was asleep. Maybe he wanted to spite me for not making barbecued cheeseburgers for lunch. Spot sighed, then rolled onto his side.

That would make his parking place more stable.

I remembered that Giuseppe had said that some Lagrangian points were more stable than others. A spacecraft could possibly fly out of the bowl at some Lagrangian points but would always stay inside the bowl at others. He said the astronomers had even found a small asteroid permanently trapped in one of Earth's Lagrangian points.

As I thought about Lagrangian points, a foggy thought nagged at me. My memory was not at all clear on the subject. But I thought Giuseppe had referred to the point numbers in a way that suggested that the lower-numbered points were less stable, and the higher-numbered points were more stable. But then I also thought he said that the numbers 'climbed toward instability.' Which would imply the opposite.

If the first three points were less stable, and the fourth and fifth points were more stable, the nomenclature didn't 'climb toward instability,' it climbed toward stability.

Did I hear it the wrong way? Or could Giuseppe have gotten it backward when he explained it to me? He was a classic scientist, focused almost exclusively on his work, absent minded as a result. There was no question that an absent-minded professor could forget where he parked his car, not remember the names of people he'd known for 25 years, and have trouble recalling the day of the week or month of the year.

But getting his basic science turned around?

That would be like forgetting how to tie one's shoes or how to spread peanut butter on toast.

I got out my phone and Googled Giuseppe Calvarenna. Up came several hundred hits. Winner of multiple prizes. Astrophysics professor emeritus. A feature on his patents in a magazine called Invention Journal. A Wikipedia bio. Author of numerous articles on cosmology and – surprise – philosophy. A New York Times feature about the professor speaking at a White House dinner. There was an article in The Times of London that described a conference where Giuseppe Calvarenna and Stephen Hawking made a joint presentation on the latest view of the Space-Time Continuum.

I clicked on the Wikipedia entry.

It detailed Giuseppe Calvarenna's long and illustrious career. There was a list of his substantial awards and a summation of his acclaim. There was even an entire section devoted to his groundbreaking work on Lagrangian points.

After I skimmed through the prose, I noticed the last paragraph, which told of his untimely death from heart failure a year ago.

I had almost missed it. The very-much-alive Giuseppe Calvarenna had supposedly died a year ago.

I hit the back button, which returned me to the Google page.

Below the Wikipedia link was a link to a blogpost by Giuseppe himself titled, "As With Mark Twain, The Reports of my Death are Greatly Exaggerated."

I clicked on that and came to a blog where Giuseppe wrote, 'I am still alive (to the great dismay of several people!) and I have no idea how the death of my poor namesake in Arkansas has been confused with me.'

I read through many details on how Giuseppe had been a victim of name confusion. It appeared that the primary reason was because the name Giuseppe Calvarenna was unusual. The person who inadvertantly spread the misinformation was a science writer at Cosmology Tech World. That writer had noticed the obituary of an Arkansas teacher with the same name, and the obit was in the same newspaper as an article on the scientist Giuseppe Calvarenna, and the writer had connected the two. The obit had also come just two weeks after a widely-reported heart valve scare that brought the famous Tahoe physicist to a Reno hospital.

As a result, Tahoe's number one scientist had been assumed to have died.

Yet, it got me thinking. I gripped the steering wheel, my hands squeezing the plastic as if I could generate insight through pressure alone.

Let's play the game of What If?

What if the brilliant physicist did in fact die from heart failure?

Then, what if someone well-versed in identity theft had been studying the man's reluctance to engage in the new world of Facebook and other such websites? A clever thief would realize that someone who has not embraced that new world is more easily manipulated by it. A clever thief might pay special attention to a wealthy scientist and inventor who had life-threatening heart disease.

What if the identity target, reclusive scientist Giuseppe Calvarenna didn't have close family? What if he wasn't enamored of uploading selfies of his every moment into cyberspace? That non-photographed person wouldn't be easy to identify. And without siblings or kids or neighbors who saw him often, a studious thief could see an amazing opportunity. When the scientist died, it might be relatively easy to adopt a similar hair style and color, wear the same frumpy clothes and simply move into Giuseppe's house and replace the dead man. If the real, dead Giuseppe hadn't been chummy with his neighbors, probably even the neighbors wouldn't notice the switch.

The biggest problem might be what to do about the dead body.

If the real Giuseppe had died at home, the new "replacement" Giuseppe would have to convince the authorities that the dead body had belonged to an imposter or an acquaintance who looked like him. If the real Giuseppe had died while out of his house, shopping or traveling, the process might be easier. The new Giuseppe could simply claim that there had been a terrible mistake. Once the new Giuseppe had moved into Giuseppe's home, his presence there would help him telegraph a sense of legitimacy.

I thought about how society handles death.

When a person with a previously identified health problem like heart disease eventually dies, the people closest to the deceased simply report the death. If there is no close family member or roommate, perhaps the caretaker or gardener makes the discovery and calls it in.

The mortuary would come to take away the body from wherever it was found. When there is no surprise about the cause of death, there is no substantial inquiry into what happened. A doctor would establish cause but would probably do so without the thoroughness he or she would apply to a known victim of murder. With an anticipated death and no questions about identity, the doctor rarely has reason to check fingerprints or dental records or DNA.

As a result, if a person who was known to be at risk of death had died, it would be relatively easy to later claim that the deceased wasn't the person they thought it was. And if the deceased was cremated, there wouldn't be a body to exhume to run tests.

If the scientist didn't have a lock-down grip on his house and finances, nothing could keep his replacement from pursuing the ultimate identity switch, adopting all aspects of the scientist's life, intercepting the mail, paying the real estate taxes, looking into Giuseppe's files to get the Social Security and bank account numbers and learn how the real Giuseppe Calvarenna signed his papers. Like many people, Giuseppe probably kept a piece of paper that listed his various computer passwords.

If the imposter had acted fast, then possibly few authorities or institutions had been notified of Giuseppe's death. If necessary, the identity thief could file various papers and forms saying that the dead person believed to be the scientist had been misidentified.

A letter from an aggressive lawyer claiming that the personal items found on the dead body were stolen would probably get them released. Those items might include a driver's license and credit cards.

Afterward, the authorities would be puzzled about who the dead body really was. The confusion would cause a minor fuss. But without anyone coming forward and asking about their missing relative or friend whose description matched that of the deceased, nothing would happen.

The new imposter scientist would go on with his life, and the authorities would wonder just who it was they'd put into the graveyard or the crematorium.

As I thought about it, I realized that the whole concept was a wild flight of my imagination. Every aspect of it seemed outlandish. But that didn't make it impossible. I couldn't reject the possibility. The reward of substantial money and life in a gorgeous house could easily motivate an identity thief.

While I had outlined an outrageous possibility, I had no evidence. From an article that said that Giuseppe had died, I had conjured up a huge, complicated scenario. And any imagined premise would go nowhere without hard evidence. The only way to get evidence was to go and shake the tree of Giuseppe Calvarenna and see what fell from it.

FIFTY-SIX

I started the Jeep and drove down to the intersection where I'd seen Fairbanks walk his bicycle. I turned where he had turned. Nothing seemed familiar until I saw the double bungalow where the watercolorist lived. It took me a moment to remember her name, Aubrey Blackwood. Across the street was an open area that appeared to come to an abrupt end as if there were a dropoff below. In the distance was a great view of Lake Tahoe. The open area also seemed unfamiliar. I realized that the last time I was on the street, I'd come from the other direction. The position of the trees near Calvarenna's house had given me a different view toward the lake than I had coming from this direction. Now I realized why Aubrey had said that she lived in a perfect place for painting landscapes. She had a gorgeous view of the lake and the mountains.

As I drove by, I saw that her van was gone. Looking into the drive with the van out of the way, I could see a barn behind Aubrey's house. I remembered that it belonged to Giuseppe Calvarenna.

I pulled into Giuseppe's drive and parked in front of the big garage.

Spot and I got out. Spot seemed excited to be back at the inventor's house. He always remembered people who doted on him.

I rang the doorbell. Waited. Rang it again. Waited. Knocked loudly. Knocked very loudly. Because the garage was shut, I couldn't tell if anyone was home. I didn't know what kind of vehicle Giuseppe drove.

The only windows on the drive side of the house were made of glass blocks. I wasn't going to see anything through those. When I visited Giuseppe earlier, he had made it clear that he wasn't easy to contact. He wasn't inclined to answer his phone. I could, of course, send him an email with my phone. But how many hours or days would it take to get a response?

The garage doors were shut. So I couldn't tell if there were vehicles inside. Garage doors are easy to jimmy, but causing property damage left me with few options. If I broke in, maybe I'd find evidence that the Giuseppe I'd met wasn't the real Giuseppe. Knowing if that was true would be nice. But without a search warrant, the evidence would be inadmissible in court. I would also risk being caught and convicted of burglary. From my last visit, I already knew that Giuseppe had a good security system that included hidden cameras. A jury wouldn't grant me any leeway if they saw me on video, smashing windows and crawling in.

Another option would be to stake out the house and wait for Giuseppe to come home. But he might be on a long trip hanging out with Stephen Hawking and his physicist colleagues in Britain.

Or maybe he had walked back to the barn he owned, the one behind Aubrey Blackwood's house.

FIFTY-SEVEN

I took Spot's collar, and we walked up the street and back toward the open grassy area. When we got to the grass, I veered toward the edge just to see the view. The ground dropped abruptly away toward big boulders sixty or eighty feet below. The lake was in the distance. It was a spectacular view very much like the one from Giuseppe's deck. Spot and I turned back toward the street.

Across and down a bit was the watercolorist's bungalow. I mumbled her name. "Aubrey Blackwood."

Spot looked up at me, curious about why I was speaking when no one was around.

"I think Aubrey is most commonly a female name," I said to no one. "But it is also given to boys." I kept walking. Thinking. Talking to myself. "Agent Ramos described a Vegas bar customer who talked about a woman who left her poor husband and kids to run off with a rich charity scammer. The customer seemed especially focused on the kids. But when asked their names, he said that he couldn't remember them, but said that they had the kind of names that were used for both boys and girls."

Spot seemed fine with me talking to myself. He'd be the perfect dog for someone whose dementia led them to announcing baseball games to no one.

"It would be highly unlikely that the story of the bar drinker from Vegas could link up to a Tahoe watercolorist with the somewhat-androgynous name of Aubrey," I said.

Normally, I would dismiss such thoughts about Aubrey Blackwood. But for one recollection.

When I first went to help Aubrey carry her supplies, it was because she used crutches. As we talked, she referred to being skillful at living independently because she'd been dealing with MS all of her life, a challenge that was possibly extra difficult because her mother had abandoned her when she and her brother were young.

It wasn't much, a woman who could loosely fit the description given by a bar customer who described children with unisex names, children whose mother had run off with a charity scammer. But it made me reconsider my conversation with Aubrey. I looked for any other possible connection to the killings, the victims. Then I remembered something even more obvious.

When I'd asked Aubrey if she had any experience with charities that helped people with MS, she'd said that a nurse had once put together a list of needy kids who had multiple sclerosis. Aubrey's name was on that list. The nurse sent that list to charities asking for help. But none of the kids on the list ever heard anything from any charity.

Was it possible that Aubrey felt burned by being ignored by charities that purported to help kids like her? When her mother ran off, could it have been with a rich charity scammer? When I asked her about charities, it sounded like she dismissed them as largely worthless.

To imagine Aubrey as a killer, I had to consider how she would function with her crutches. It would certainly be difficult. But that didn't make it impossible.

Just past Aubrey's empty driveway was the trail to the barn back in the woods. Spot and I headed up the trail.

The trail went through a stand of trees and came to the old barn. I guessed the barn to be built in the 1940s. But modern windows and a stone chimney suggested that it had been renovated into a lodge of sorts 30 years later. I knocked on the door.

After some wait, Giuseppe opened it. He was leaning on his cane, looking more unsteady than Aubrey did with her crutches. When he saw Spot, he grinned widely.

"Oh, hello! What a nice surprise. And my favorite Great Dane, Mr. Spot!" He leaned toward me and spoke softly as if he didn't want Spot to hear him. "Actually, he's the only Great Dane I know."

He rubbed Spot with enthusiasm. Spot wagged.

"Where's Blofeld the cat?" I asked.

"Oh, he refuses to leave the house. If I even pick up my car keys, he runs and hides. Plus, he does that feline sleep marathon in the afternoon. How any animal can sleep so much, I don't comprehend. Although, I've read that male lions sleep seventeen hours a day."

Giuseppe turned away from us and started moving back into the barn. "Did you go to my house? I have to say I'm glad you stopped here at my barn, because I'm excited to show somebody my discovery about iron pyrite. So you'll be my test audience. Come over to my workbench and have a look."

He led the way through stacks of boxes. The spaces between the piles were dark, and Giuseppe placed his cane carefully. I followed, watching him move. He had a quality of minimizing his cane movements as if he were hiding significant pain and discomfort. Spot wandered elsewhere.

"Perhaps you're familiar with fluorescence?" Giuseppe said over his shoulder. "The absorption of short-wavelength light energy – wavelengths invisible to us – and re-emission of that energy at longer, visible wavelengths. Many materials exhibit it. Some living creatures fluoresce, too. Anyway, I've been experimenting with different wavelengths of light. Sometimes the simplest investigations provide the biggest reward."

The barn was dimly lit with natural light coming in through windows on either side of the door and either side of a large stone fireplace. Apparently someone had decided to turn the barn into a ski lodge-type place that still had the rustic characteristics of a barn but with the addition of modern conveniences.

Along one wall was a long workbench, obviously old but with a row of modern fluorescent light fixtures above it. The workbench held a large vise and a chop saw with dust vac and a set of what looked like rock hammers and another set of chisels. To one side of the bench leaned a variety of thin pieces of wood, each about eight feet long. Some looked like dark, tropical wood. Some were light-colored. One appeared to be balsa. Another bamboo. They looked old, and several of them were substantially warped. Giuseppe saw me looking at them.

"You probably think that science moves forward with the aid of complex electronics and super precise measuring devices and reams of paper filled with inscrutable math equations and computers running complex software."

"Yes, actually, that is the way science seems to me."

Giuseppe gestured toward the various kinds of wood. "Well, behold basic science. If you undertake to study the most basic things, you can add to man's knowledge base." He pointed to the bent bamboo pole. "For example, do you know that by some measures, the lowly bamboo pole has a greater strength-to-weight ratio than all other woods? Greater, even, than steel?"

"I didn't know that, but I believe it," I said. "Tough stuff, bamboo. And it weighs almost nothing."

Giuseppe turned to the workbench. "Anyway, this fluorescing phenomenon was a two-part discovery," he said. "I know that what scientists think is terribly important often seems like nothing to the layman. But this is pretty cool, so maybe you'll think so, too. First, take a look at this big chunk of fool's gold."

He picked up a sizable rock, hefting it in his hand. It was clearly heavy. The rock sparkled under the workbench lights just like gold, although perhaps more greenish than real gold.

"You've probably seen this stuff before. Iron pyrite has often been confused with real gold. Now watch what happens when I turn on this light fixture, which has light-emitting-diodes that produce a particular wavelength of light."

Giuseppe reached across the workbench toward the LED cord. On it was one of those little rotating switches. It was just out of his reach. He shifted his cane, leaned on it, and reached over the bench again. He missed it again.

"Here, I can reach it." I took a step to the bench, reached out, and flicked on the light.

In my peripheral vision, it seemed that Giuseppe reached a different direction, toward the bamboo pole.

At Giuseppe's touch, the bamboo pole snapped straight as though it had been under great tension. I sensed the snaking zip of a line I hadn't seen. A snare of thin rope encircled my legs at knee level. I tried to leap away, but the snare was already tightening around my legs. At the same moment, some kind of lasso loop dropped over my head. Giuseppe had stepped behind me. The lasso jerked tight around my torso, pinning my elbows to my side.

I yelled, "Spot! Find the suspect. Take him down!"

But Spot was exploring over by the fireplace. The takedown command requires me to be next to him, vibrate his body, and drop my arm next to his head to point toward the suspect.

Spot looked at me, wagged, and trotted over as the whine of a winch filled the room, and the rope around my calves jerked my feet so close together it was difficult to stand. I struggled to stay balanced and vertical. That was a mistake because it gave him a moment to work some type of ratchet device that tightened the line around my chest to the point that it was hard to breathe.

Next, Giuseppe shoved me hard, which knocked me off balance. I fell over, my shoulder bouncing off the floor.

"Spot, take him down!" I said again, knowing it was futile. We like to think that dogs understand our words. But words are just part of a command, and they need body language and hand motions to be understood.

"Hey, boy," Giuseppe said to Spot in a cheery voice. "Look at Owen. He's having so much fun!"

He reached out and rubbed Spot.

The line tightened on my legs. The winch continued to reel in the line. The paracord drew tightly around my ankles, lifted them into the air, and I was hoisted up toward the roof of the barn.

FIFTY-EIGHT

The line was thin and bit into my ankles like a wire. The workbench where I'd gotten trapped by his snare was along one side of the barn. The paracord hoisting me extended up to one of the timber frame roof trusses, one that was in the center of the barn. As soon as the lifting motion brought me clear of the floor and the stacks of boxes, it caused me to swing wildly across the room in a big looping oscillation.

Despite my upside-down vision, Giuseppe suddenly looked more athletic. He set his cane aside and rubbed Spot. "Hey, boy, look at your master. It's like the Cirque du Soleil." The words were mocking, but the voice had the weariness of years of pain.

"I hadn't wanted it to come to this, McKenna," he said. "But you are too tenacious and I can't have that. But unlike the scammers, your body will never be found."

Spot seemed to lean into Giuseppe, gaining comfort from him while his owner was performing dangerous tricks in the air.

The winch kept hoisting me up. When my head was eight feet above the floor, the winch stopped. As my swinging traced a big ellipse above the barn floor, I could see that Giuseppe was no longer bent but now stood up straight without the aid of his cane. He looked strong and agile. Earlier, I'd thought he was in his late 60s. Now he looked closer to my age, mid-40s. I now realized that his wild, white hair and the skin problem on his scalp that I'd noticed when we first met were probably both part of a wig. Take it off, he would look even younger.

There was nothing I could do to command Spot to help. Dogs are as reasonable as people. They take everything in context. You can't tell them to believe something dramatically different from what they know. It would take highly specialized training to use a voice command from a distance to get a dog to decide that a person formerly thought to be a friend was now a foe.

Spot knew this man was a good guy. This was the second time

he'd met the man, and both times the man had been affectionate. And the way I'd acted on both occasions made it clear that we were friends. The only way I could tell him otherwise was if I could be down on the floor next to Spot, talking to him, giving him a certain tone and using physical motion as I spoke about the man. I had to think of another approach.

I called out as I swung through the air, "My guess is that you aren't Professor Giuseppe Calvarenna, but Lynn, the man Dory called Larcenous Larry. You and the man she called Hustler Harry started the Red Roses of Hope charity, right? Harry died on the sailboat with Dory, so that leaves you, the man who was entranced by Lagrangian points."

I felt sick, hanging upside down, swinging wildly across the open interior of the barn. I focused on talking.

"Your mother left your father to take up with a charity scammer. Your father died of a heart attack, a literal broken heart. Then the scammer molested your sister. You wanted to lash out at the world. Anyone could understand that. So you and your equally larcenous pal Harry started the Red Roses charity."

The man was silent. I wanted to provoke him. "The Vegas bartender said you mentioned kids with noises names. You'd probably been waiting a long time to tell that story."

When the man spoke, his voice was a hiss of anger. "We'd been in the orphanage less than a year when my sister Kelly killed herself. I've been planning to punish that bastard slime ever since. I finally tracked him down. Now he has a nail through his head and a bullet through his heart."

I said, "The charity guys you hung from the flagpole and train didn't hurt you."

"First, I avenged the crimes against Kelly and me. After Dory was killed, I realized how easy it was to find other scammers and avenge their crimes the same way that Dory was killed. Dory showed how the charity scam could be perfected. I admit that. So I'm rebuilding her charity to beat the scammers at their own game, and I'm using their deaths as warnings to the other scammers. It's easy to find them. They're listed on charity websites."

"Doesn't that make you as bad as them?"

"You get old enough, you realize that Darwin was right. Life is survival of the fittest, not survival of the ethically pure. As I eliminate more scammers, I make the world a better place." The man was petting Spot, watching me with a look of contempt.

I realized that even though I was hanging upside down, I could influence my swing by how I flexed my body. Because my legs were tied, I couldn't swing my legs like a kid on a swingset. But I could swing my head and chest. That realization did me no good unless I could find a useful purpose in swinging one direction or another. I got myself turned around, facing another direction, but with no control. However, I now saw the tall black spray can on a shelf above the workbench.

Wasp killer.

When someone is about to kill you, the rule is always to fight back. If you can't fight back, try to stall the killer. "Dory's brother told me about how Dory was into Lagrangian points, scientific curiosities that could also be a metaphor for aspects of business."

By doing a slight crunching motion, I'd increased my amount of swing. Now I just needed to learn how to change direction.

I continued. "So it was your interest in Lagrangian points that caused you to look up the professor and read about him. You learned that he was a loner with a heart problem. So you hatched a wild idea."

My swinging ellipse had rotated so that I was now arcing almost directly over Lynn. If he noticed my change of direction, he either didn't care, or he thought it was just the result of randomness.

"Probably you really wanted to be a scientist when you were young. You were smart, but you didn't have that level of mental power. You were a dilettante, a wannabe. You knew enough science to pull off the substitution of yourself for Professor Calvarenna. That was an inspired fraud, stepping into Giuseppe Calvarenna's shoes, taking on his identity. And it was especially bold moving into his house."

Lynn boosted himself up and sat on the workbench. "Rewards come to those who take risks," he said. "I didn't know whether the professor knew any of his neighbors well. His closest neighbor was the old water-color lady who lives in the little bungalow. But she accepted me in his place. So either she never met him up close, or she's a demented old fool."

I continued, "What perfect timing that Dory got killed while you were off playing the lecturing scientist on a cruise ship. You had an alibi, so you could embark on copycat killings and be out of suspicion."

My head was throbbing with blood pressure from hanging upside down. But I wanted to keep the man distracted from his plan for me. As I looped around the barn, looking at my surroundings upside down, I searched for any possible way out of my situation. I'd managed to change my path so I didn't come as close to him. I didn't want him reaching up and striking me with one of those sticks of wood.

I kept up my chatter, thinking that it couldn't hurt and could possibly help. And if I angered him, maybe he'd make a mistake.

"I get that you feel it's okay to kill charity scammers. But why the kid Matt? He seemed too young to be a scammer."

"He was a thief, and probably on his way to getting into the business. I hired him to do computer work for me. Then I came home and found him copying my files onto a memory stick."

My brain felt about to rupture. I had to make a mental map of everything in the barn that was at my level. I had to find some way to cut myself down.

"So you took care of that with your boldest killing yet. Killing him at the charity party sent a powerful message of hate aimed at scammers."

Lynn made a dismissive snort. "You spin a story," he said. "But now we're done." He picked up the remote from the workbench and pressed a button. The winch started lowering me. With his other hand, he lifted the can of wasp killer off the shelf.

I was desperate, unable to think clearly.

A tense, deadweight of dread knotted my insides as I swung back and forth, hanging from my ankles. I'd made every possible mistake. I'd fallen for every possible trap. The man had complete control over me and Spot, and he'd outsmarted me in ways I never should have let happen.

I started a gentle bucking, bending at the waist, trying to

twist, using my limited movement in an attempt to keep myself gyrating and be hard to grasp.

But my arms were tied. It wouldn't be hard for him to grab me and give me a lungful of wasp killer.

I took several deep breaths to calm myself and give myself more oxygen to aid in holding my breath, if it came to that.

When the winch lowered me so that my head was five feet off the floor, Lynn pressed another button and the winch stopped.

He picked up the bamboo pole and used it to poke into me and stop my swinging. He held out the wasp killer.

"This can go easy," he said. "I tape your mouth shut. Then I pinch your nose shut. You'll make it easy on yourself if you take a big breath when I release your nostrils and direct the spray into your nose. Trust me, it works very fast. If you try to resist, you'll just make it so you experience agonizing torture before you die. There's no glory in that."

I tensed my stomach muscles to prepare. As he reached for me, I contracted my abdomen, bending forward at the waist in an explosive movement. My upper body came up and forward in a fast arc. I tilted my head forward as well.

I heard the hiss of wasp spray in the air as he panicked and tried to back away. But he wasn't fast enough.

My forehead struck him a hard blow on his upper lip and nose. I felt teeth crack and heard nose bones splinter. The wasp can flew through the air as Lynn was slammed backward.

He tried to take a step back to stop his fall. But he was staggered by the blow and moved with no coordination. His foot caught on something, and he went over backward. The back of his head struck the edge of the workbench. He went down and collapsed on the floor in a messy heap, blood oozing from mouth and nose. He moaned loudly, the sound seeming to twist in my ears as I swung back and forth.

Spot sniffed at the motionless man, no doubt confused, possibly sad.

Now came the hard part. The thin paracord around my ankles was like wire, cutting into me just as it had with the other victims. The only difference was that I hadn't been forced to inhale wasp killer. But I would still likely die, as I had no way to cut myself down. My head felt so much pressure, it seemed certain that I would rupture major blood vessels. My heart thumped audibly in my ears. My vision blurred.

I had to focus and put aside the stress of knowing that Lynn could come to at any moment and finish the job he'd started. I turned to take in the rest of the room.

I looked for the remote. If it was close enough to grab, I could lower myself. I swiveled and rotated, trying to see where it went. There. On the floor.

Could I reach one of the pieces of wood? Use that to get the remote? As soon as I thought of it, I realized there was no way I could grab a piece of wood or pick up the remote.

What else could I grab with my arms bound at my sides?

I pictured an ellipse, a path I could swing through the room. What was near that path?

Nothing that would do me any good.

I thought about trying to yell for help. But the closest house was Aubrey's bungalow apartment, and even that was too far to expect anyone to be able to hear me. And she wasn't home.

I re-examined those portions of the barn that were within the distance that I could swing. There was nothing except two wall sconce light fixtures on either side of the fireplace and two more on each of two other walls, a total of six in all. They had bases made of brass and frosted glass chimneys. The ones on the walls were far enough from me that, even if I could swing over to them, the arc of my motion would bring me too high to reach them. But it appeared that I could possibly reach the sconces near the stone fireplace.

So I did the hula hoop swivel, gyrating this way and that until I got a sense of what made me swing. Sometimes I just contracted my abdomen, lifting my head up to stare, momentarily, at the ceiling. Other times, I made a full twist with an accompanying shimmy. In time, I had myself swinging in a loop like a comet on a very long and lopsided orbit around the sun.

As I arced around, I did more of the hula gyrations to alter my swinging orbit. My head pounded with pain from hitting Lynn's face. My feet were numb.

As I swung around, I contracted my abdomen to intensify my

movement. My orbit gradually shifted and gradually elongated.

My arms tingled. My left hand seemed to light up with jolts of nerve pain. The pressure of hanging upside down threatened to blow a pipe in my brain.

As I gyrated and hula-hooped, I gradually changed my orbit about the room. I was soon swinging over Spot and the prostrate man, increasing my amplitude so that I approached the fireplace wall with the sconces.

Spot watched me, confused, worried.

I swung farther. Two more trips back and forth and I could possibly grab one of the sconces.

I went out and back, abdomen flexing, a cramp building in my muscles. Out and back again.

At the top of my next arcing swing, I gyrated so that my right side was facing the sconce. Although the cord around my chest bit severely into my elbows, I stretched my right hand out from my side. I tried to grab the glass chimney of the wall sconce.

My fingers touched glass and then slipped off as I swung away.

I swung back out, flexed my abdomen to increase my swing, then arced back.

This time my fingertips got over the top edge of the glass chimney.

I held on as I swung away. Glass shattered in a sharp loud crack. Pieces fell away. But I felt the reassurance of a shard in my fingers.

I concentrated on gripping the shard, trying not to shift my fingers, which might cause me to drop it. I tried to turn the broken glass in my grip so I could angle it toward the cord around my chest. I felt a sharp point poke hard into my palm. Maybe it cut me, maybe not. I couldn't tell.

The cord around my chest burned my elbow as I bent my arm to bring the shard of broken glass against the paracord at my chest. I sawed one edge against the paracord, back and forth, over and over. I was still swinging in a large arc. The swinging made it hard to concentrate on how I was using my glass shard. My sawing motion felt like it did nothing. I had no sense that the edge of the glass was cutting the cord. There wasn't enough light to see. I might have been sawing at my shirt and into my chest. I couldn't even tell if I was trying to cut the cord with a broken edge of the glass or the smooth edge that had originally been at the top of the chimney.

Complicating the situation was the fact that my hands were numb from the constriction of the cord. And the pressure in my head was growing worse.

I kept sawing. Sawing and swinging.

I heard the man groan. I strained to look down at him. His arm was moving, his hand at his face as if trying to brush away his brain fog.

My fingers had lost all sensation of the glass shard. I tried to pinch harder just to reawaken awareness. I was still making sawing motions. Or at least, I thought I was.

I paused and tried to reposition the shard, more to establish the sense of feeling it than anything else. I began sawing again. But I wasn't able to cut the cord. Had I even nicked it? Was I really holding a broken shard of glass? Was I making motions, or was I imagining it? I felt like I was beginning to hallucinate.

Then it occurred to me that, if I had made even a little abrasion on the cord, perhaps that would weaken it.

Even though I was upside down and tied at the ankles and elbows, maybe I could create a breaking force just by jerking hard. So I took a deep breath, tensed all of my muscles, and made a total body jerk, trying to drive my elbows away from my body.

The cord around my chest broke.

My arms were now free, but I was still hanging from my ankles.

Lynn made a louder moan.

To cut the cord at my ankles would mean I'd have to tense my stomach muscles enough to reach up and grab the rope that suspended me. I'd already been doing the upside down sit-up move so much that my abdomen felt paralyzed. I didn't know if I could do a major crunch again. To make it worse, if I succeeded in cutting myself free, I'd fall to the floor and land on my butt or even my head. At the lowest part of my arc, my head was five feet above the floor. At the highest part of my arc, eight or nine feet. Even if I could make my arms work and get my hands out first, I might not be able to absorb the force of the fall enough to prevent me from breaking my neck and paralyzing me or killing me immediately.

There was a couch in front of the fireplace. If I could alter my ellipse enough, maybe I could cut myself down at the precise moment that would allow me to fall onto the couch.

I had no other choices.

The man moaned again, then rolled onto his side, pushed himself up to a sitting position, and looked up at me. Holding onto the workbench, he pulled himself to his feet. He reached under the bench to a shelf I hadn't seen. Moving too fast for me to see, he pulled out a Taser gun, pointed it up at me, and fired. There was a percussive burst of compressed gas as the cartridge shot its load. Maybe I could have shouted "Weapon Hand" to Spot, but it was too late. Two sharp, electroshock darts, each trailing thin wires that supplied fifty thousand volts of electricity, arced through the air toward me.

FIFTY-NINE

One of the electroshock darts speared into my shoulder. The other grazed my neck as it shot past. As it brushed my neck, I felt a brilliant, shocking, lightning bolt of pain that lasted for a camera-flash moment. It focused all of my attention, but it was over so fast that it didn't paralyze me.

I pulled the dart out of my shoulder.

Lynn picked up a piece of two-by-four lumber about six feet long.

Maybe he intended to bludgeon me with it and then fill my lungs with wasp killer. But I was distracted by movement beyond him, outside the windows. In my oscillating view, I saw Aubrey Blackwood's van going past her bungalow parking place and pulling up the drive to Giuseppe's barn. Her van came to a stop near the door, close enough that she was out of view from where I swung.

I didn't have a clear view out the windows, but I sensed that Aubrey had gotten out of her van and was coming up toward the front entrance to the barn.

Was she working with Lynn? Had she been in on his plan from the beginning?

If I called out to her and she was his employee, nothing would change. But if she was innocent, it might give her a few extra moments to get away.

I shouted out as loud as I could. "Aubrey! Go away! Don't come in, it's dangerous!"

I didn't know if she would be able to hear me, but I had to try.

There was a knock at the door and then it opened.

"Professor?" she called out. "It's your neighbor Aubrey." I saw her crutches reaching in the open doorway and clicking on the floor. "Professor, I saw the light and I wanted to tell you that I brought you a..."

"Aubrey!" I said. "Run! Get out of here. Hurry. You're in danger! This man is a killer."

Aubrey Blackwood looked up and saw me swinging through the air. Her face showed puzzlement and confusion.

"Aubrey, the professor is the murderer we've been looking for. He killed the men in Kings Beach and Truckee and the South Shore. He's going to kill me, and now he'll come after you. RUN!"

It was clear that Aubrey didn't comprehend. Maybe she hadn't heard about the murders. Maybe her world was so focused on painting that it was hard to shift gears and absorb such shocking news. She stared at me and then at Lynn, who was holding himself up with his grip on the workbench. Her face showed no comprehension of threat, as if the only things that registered were what she talked about when I helped her carry her art supplies. Color and shape and value and emotion. A focus on beauty. An innocent pursuit that helped to shut out the meanness of the world.

But what I couldn't do to impress the danger on her, Lynn did.

He leaned on the two-by-four, then pushed himself up away from the workbench. His face was running with blood as he stumbled toward Aubrey.

"You have bad timing, neighbor," he said. He sounded mean and focused and terrifying. "Now I have to silence you, same as I have to silence McKenna." He turned away from me, focused on Aubrey, and lurched toward her.

"Run, Aubrey!" I shouted.

Aubrey seemed all at once to realize what was happening. Her eyes showed terror. She swung her crutches around, turned, moved her crutches farther. In a few moments, she got out the door of the barn and started toward her van.

I heard whimpering cries of fear, the innocent sounds of horrible distress that someone makes when they realize that they are about to die at the hands of an evil person they thought was benign.

Lynn took several awkward steps, using one hand to guide him along the workbench and the other on the piece of lumber.

He paused and hung his head as if to prevent a bout of fainting. Then he seemed to find his balance. He began moving toward the door. His motion smoothed out. He let go of the workbench and moved faster.

Aubrey struggled toward her van, crutches stabbing the ground, her scissors gait going at a fast rate and making her lean back and forth precariously.

My oscillating, partial view gave me some hope. It looked like she'd make it to her van before Lynn could get to her.

Then she fell.

Aubrey sprawled out face down on the path, still ten feet from her driver's door. She held onto one crutch, but the other skittered away.

Her motions were frantic. She lifted her head off the ground, trying to see. She reached out for the wayward crutch, but her fingers couldn't grab it. With great effort, she rolled onto her side, raised her knees, pushed herself back so that she was supporting herself on her hands and knees. She got the one crutch jammed down into the dirt and leaned on it to pull herself up so she was supported on her knees.

I saw her make a great jerking motion. I couldn't tell why, but then I realized that she was trying to jerk one leg forward and get her knee up high enough to plant her foot on the dirt.

Lynn got to the barn door, hitting his shoulder against it, almost losing his balance. Then he pushed outside after Aubrey. His lurching made him grab the door as he went out. It slammed behind him, shutting Spot inside with me.

Through the window, I saw Aubrey get her foot planted. She put both hands on her one crutch and pushed. I thought I heard her yelling at herself, screaming for motion. She got to her feet.

Lynn stumbled toward her, closing the gap.

Aubrey got her door open. Got into the driver's seat. Started the engine. She backed up, turning the wheel. Shifted into drive, turned the wheel the other way.

The van started forward, curving back toward the street. I stared from where I still hung, my vision of Aubrey's escape going in and out of view.

In the far distance, barely even registering in my consciousness,

I saw something else. Something familiar. It took me a couple of swings back and forth to recognize what was coming in and out of my focus. Douglas Fairbanks was down on the street, still walking his bicycle, his head still held low, heading back to where he would catch the shuttle bus. Because the barn was largely out of view, he was oblivious to what was happening.

Aubrey drove toward the street.

Lynn found his strength and took two running steps toward Aubrey's van. He brought the piece of lumber back over his shoulder, then hurled it toward Aubrey's driver's window as if it were a javelin. The wood smashed through the glass.

From where I swung by my ankles, I couldn't see if it hit Aubrey. But the van's horn sounded and didn't stop. The van seemed to speed up and drive straight for the street. It hit the pavement, bouncing up and over the crown of the street, then continued across to the field on the other side, speeding up as if Aubrey's foot was on the accelerator. Lynn watched as the van headed straight for the drop-off, its horn still honking.

Fairbanks continued to move slowly. Then he noticed the van. It took him long moments to realize what was happening.

He jumped on his bicycle and began pedaling fast. He got up some speed and then arced off the pavement and into the field of tall grass, angling for the van. Aubrey's van went faster. But Fairbanks closed in on it from the side like they were two vehicles merging together on the freeway. As he was about to crash into the van, he thrust his hand through the broken driver's window and hung on. He got his other arm through the window. His bicycle fell away from him, then veered away.

I couldn't clearly see what happened next. But I could tell that the bouncing van slowly began to turn. The turn became more pronounced, and the van veered away from the cliff. The bicycle, still rolling, tracked a straight path, crossed behind Aubrey's van, and shot off the cliff into the air.

The van continued to curve and went out of my view.

But Lynn came back into my view, returning toward the barn.

SIXTY

I didn't know if Aubrey had survived or what had happened to Fairbanks. Maybe Lynn was coming back inside because he saw that Aubrey had died. Either way, he was determined to finish me off.

I took another look down toward the couch, gauging my movement. I gyrated enough to bring my orbit closer to the couch.

Then I did a quick countdown practice, trying to figure out just when I should perform the super-human sit-up motion so that I could reach one hand up to the cord at my ankles and use the other hand to swipe at the cord with the broken glass and attempt to cut myself free.

Because my weight was stretching the cord very tight, I reasoned that it might cut more easily than the one that had bound my arms to my sides.

My hands were still numb. I shook my arms to try to get more circulation into my hands.

I doubted I had the strength to bend up against gravity far enough to grab the cord at my ankles. It seemed like something only a young, accomplished gymnast could do. And it seemed clear that whatever strength it would take to do it was not something I could produce more than once.

But I had motivation that few gymnasts ever had. Either I would succeed at this, or I would die by wasp killer and ankle hanging or bludgeoning with another piece of wood.

I got ready. I tensed my muscles. As I began my backswing away from the couch, I did the hardest abdominal crunch of my life, lifting up, reaching up, straining.

My left index and middle finger wrapped around the paracord. I pulled and got my ring finger around it. Next, I got the other hand up, wrist hooked over the fingers of the first hand. I took care to look carefully at the glass shard and position it at a good angle to cut into the paracord.

I came to the apex of my backswing and started back the other way toward the couch.

I positioned my glass shard between my ankles where the paracord was taut between them, then cut into it as hard as I could. I felt fibers part. I saw the cord fray, strands spinning and growing.

But it didn't cut through.

My timing was destroyed. I swung past the couch.

I heard Lynn stumble through the door.

I got to the other end of my swing. The cord frayed further. It seemed the cord casing was melting before my eyes. I took the glass shard and held it away from the cord, then swiped at the cord in a hard motion, changing my sawing motion to a machete hack.

The cord broke, snaked free from my ankles, and seemed to disappear as I fell away.

I didn't fall where I wanted.

I'd been arcing back on another trip to the couch, but I wasn't quite there.

I got my hands in front of my head before I hit. They hit the arm of the couch. My body crumpled and went off the end. I hit the floor hard.

I was bruised. Maybe even broken in places.

But I was alive. I clawed my way up onto hands and knees. I tried to stand, but my feet felt dead. I couldn't even feel pinpricks. It was like I had peglegs, wooden stubs, no feeling, no balance.

Spot was jumping around me, excited to have me back on the ground.

Lynn came toward me.

Still kneeling, I put my arm over Spot's shoulder and gave him a vibration, the prep for a command. I pointed toward Lynn who was reaching for the wasp killer, which lay on the floor between us.

With my head next to Spot's, I spoke in my meanest, growling voice. "Spot, that's the suspect! Do you see the suspect? Do you? I want you to take him down, boy. Take him down hard!"

In a moment, Lynn transformed from angry to fearful, from

confident to nearly frozen with terror. But then he sprinted toward the door and slammed it shut before Spot got to it.

I tried again to stand on my peglegs. Pain was starting to replace numbness. I got up on my feet. I was standing on electric pinpricks. I reached out with my hands for stabilizing holds. Hand-walked from the couch arm to the couch back. Transferred to an end table. Made a jerky, stumbling, falling motion toward the closest wall. Caught myself. Took a breath. Hand-walked along the wall toward the door.

Spot stayed next to me. I leaned on his back. Together we got to the front door. There was a jacket on a hook. Probably Lynn's. I grabbed it and went out.

Lynn was running across the street and heading into the field. He must have decided that his house was too far away, and instead he could seek shelter by climbing down the cliff.

I took Lynn's jacket and put it over Spot's nose. "Spot! Smell this scent! This is the suspect. Do you have it?" I shook his chest, raised my hand next to the side of his head and said, "Find the suspect and take him down!" I dropped my hand in the takedown motion, pointed at the running man, and hit Spot on his rear with my other hand.

Spot took off running. He went down the drive and across the street, a blur of black-and-white motion, 170 pounds at 30 miles per hour.

Spot probably now knew that Lynn was a bad guy. He'd seen Lynn's threatening moves toward me.

From the side came Fairbanks, running hard.

Lynn saw Fairbanks in his peripheral vision. He reached into his pocket and pulled out something black. I realized it was the stun gun. Even though he'd already fired the electroshock darts at me, the gun could still be used like a cattle prod, where you push it up against your target and then pull the trigger.

He held the stun gun out, preparing. He kept running toward the cliff, desperate to get to the drop-off and climb down among the rocks of the cliff to escape.

Lynn again glanced over at Fairbanks, getting ready to fire his stun gun. He never saw that Spot was coming from behind him and much faster than Fairbanks.

When Spot was ten feet away, he leaped. At the same moment, Lynn raised the stun gun.

I cupped my hands around my mouth and shouted as loud as I could. "WEAPON HAND!"

It was a lesson in one of those laws of motion that the real Giuseppe studied. Spot probably outweighed the man by twenty pounds. And he was going the speed of a race horse when his jaws locked onto the arm that held the stun gun.

Once Spot had a grip on Lynn, his motion jerked the man forward and launched him into the air.

Maybe Spot had been aware all along of the cliff edge. Or maybe he saw the edge only at the last moment.

But Spot let go of Lynn's arm in time to land all four paws on solid ground and skid to a stop, while Lynn flew off the cliff.

SIXTY-ONE

I struggled across the street on my pinprick peglegs. Aubrey's van was on one side of the open area. Fairbanks was already trotting back to the open driver's door. He reached in. As I got closer, I saw him holding tissue to Aubrey's face. The bright red blood stains were obvious, but it didn't look like a lot of volume. Spot was next to Fairbanks.

"How is she?" I said when I got to the van.

"She seems okay," Fairbanks said. "Dazed but…"

"I'm fine," Aubrey said.

I looked in the door. Aubrey had her hand on Spot's neck for support, physical or emotional or both. "You sure you're okay?" I said.

She nodded. "The board cut my face. But I don't think any bones are broken."

"I called nine one one," Fairbanks said. "Was that right to do?"

"Yes, that's good," I said.

"You're walking funny," Fairbanks said. "Are you wounded?"

"He was upside down," Aubrey said. "Hanging by a real skinny rope. His feet are probably half cut off."

"I'll be okay," I said. "I'm going to see what happened."

"I tried to catch the man," Fairbanks said. "But Spot got him first. I think the guy might be dead."

"I'll be right back." I hobbled on pinprick feet over to the edge of the drop-off and looked down. Lynn was about 50 feet down, his head mashed face first onto a boulder, and his body turned at an impossible angle. I saw no movement and would have been surprised if I had. I walked back to Aubrey's van.

"The man won't give us any more trouble," I said.

"Aubrey just told me that the man was going to kill you. Does that mean he was the murderer?"

"Dory was killed by the daughter of a man whom she

scammed. The other three victims were killed by this man."

Two Washoe County patrol units came down the street and turned off onto the open, grassy area. Washoe Sergeant Lori Lanzen got out and saw me as she walked over.

"We meet again just a short time after you saved those women on the boat. Mia and Evan, the girl who had dreams of going to law school. And now you've got what?"

I gestured toward Aubrey. "Sergeant, meet watercolorist extraordinaire Aubrey Blackwood. She and I just escaped being killed by a man who is down on the rocks below this cliff." I pointed to where Lynn had gone off. "A man named Lynn, AKA Giuseppe Calvarenna. The real Calvarenna was a famous scientist who died a year ago, and Lynn took his identity and moved into his house. Lynn is the one who murdered the victims in Kings Beach and Truckee, and at the park in South Lake Tahoe."

A fire truck and rescue vehicle came down the street next, sirens blasting.

Lanzen and the EMTs dealt with Aubrey and the body down on the rocks. I gave a brief statement as did Aubrey and Fairbanks. After many questions and understandings that there would be more questions in the future, Lanzen said she'd contact Sergeants Martinez and Santiago and Bains. Then she let us go.

Aubrey had multiple butterfly bandages on her face. But she was adamant that she did not need ongoing medical attention. So Fairbanks and I helped get Aubrey back to her house. Spot stayed next to her as if he knew what would help her most.

When we were confident that Aubrey would be okay, Spot and I drove Fairbanks to his condo, then headed back home through advancing twilight.

It was dark outside when I got to my cabin. My phone rang as I turned on the lights.

"Hello?"

"Owen! He's here! Tom Casey! He's trying to kill me!" It was Street, her words sharp cries of fear. She was panting. Gasping from stress, or, possibly, she was running.

SIXTY-TWO

"Where are you?"

"I'm running." Heavy breaths. "Up the road to your cabin."

"I can be down there in one minute," I said, moving fast toward the front door. Spot jumped to his feet. "I'll pick you up."

"No!" More panting. "I want him to... follow me. Your Jeep will scare him away. If he keeps after me... you could get him." She was breathing like a sprinter.

"That's dangerous! He might..."

"He's running, too." Her strong breathing in her cell phone made the words difficult to understand. "He can't catch me on foot. You can hide. Below your cabin. Waiting. Let me run by. You grab him."

"Where are you now?"

"At the second tight curve. I'm coming to the long straight section." She hung up.

"Spot, come!" I said.

We ran out into the dark, my hand on his collar. The time might come to let him go and give him the command to take down the suspect. Until then, holding his collar meant I could keep him from growling or barking. You can communicate better with a dog when you're touching them.

We sprinted down the dark private road that I shared with my vacation-home neighbors. All of those homes were dark, the residents waiting until the real warmth of summer came in July.

I thought about the dark forest as we went down the same road that Street was running up. It wasn't clear to me where she'd be at this point. But I guessed that she was now in the middle of the straightaway. Near the top of that section, the road made a hard right. If I could be in the dense woods near that point, I would be invisible to a person trying to navigate the dark road.

As we came to that hard curve, we slowed, and I let Spot guide me into the trees, using his see-in-the-dark nose to keep us from walking into tree trunks.

I got us positioned behind a group of fir trees, their dense foliage being a visual block. We stood still and waited. The only noise was Spot's panting, which seemed loud to me, but was below the hearing threshold of anyone doing their own panting as they trudged up the mountain.

Street's description of her situation sounded dangerous, even if she claimed it wasn't. Yet I was in no position to second guess her. But if her father really was running after her, then Street was right. By any measure, she was a serious athlete, skinny like a long-distance runner, and very strong. No way any man old enough to be her father could catch her running up a mountain at 7000 feet of elevation. I couldn't either.

But an arrogant man who thought women were for decor and cooking might think he could tough it out and catch any woman after she wore out her pretty little feet. Some men wouldn't face the truth of a woman's abilities despite all evidence.

In a few moments, Spot tensed. Leaning out from the trees, it seemed like there was nothing. Then I saw a lithe form moving past us, on up the road toward my cabin.

Street.

Next to her ran Blondie. I heard Blondie's toenails click on the asphalt. But Street, despite her hard breathing, was silent. Blondie turned her head toward us but stayed silent as they ran by.

We waited. I had no idea how far behind her Tom Casey was. As the man who blamed her for his long prison sentence despite his obvious guilt in the beating death of Street's younger brother, he might have more than the usual stamina.

Spot stopped panting, listened a bit, then started panting again.

After a few minutes of no sound, I walked Spot to the edge of the road and stared down into the darkness. There was no sign of any person.

Then I had an unsettling thought. There were trails in the forest. What if Tom Casey had explored them during the day?

He might have found one of several ways to hike from near Street's condo up to my cabin without walking on the road. He might know where my cabin is. It was also possible that he would anticipate that Street might run to my cabin.

But even if he had taken a trail, he would still be far behind her. The trails were no more direct than the road, and there was still 1000 feet of vertical elevation rise.

It seemed likely he hadn't followed Street, or, if he had, he'd given up.

"Let's go, boy," I whispered.

We ran back up the road. I kept my hand in Spot's collar.

As we approached my cabin, we slowed. Street would be near. If she was hiding, tucked into the trees or under my deck, Blondie would alert her to our presence.

"Street," I whispered toward the cabin, from which the only lights were the ones I'd left on as we left. "Street, where are you?"

There was a motion in the trees to the side of my cabin. Blondie trotted out and ran to Spot, tail wagging. Street ran out of the darkness, hesitating, glancing left and right as if to gauge the dangers. I bent down and hugged her, and she gripped me as if hanging onto a life raft. Spot pushed up next to us, sniffing Street hard.

"Are you okay?" I said. Her head was tucked under my chin, and I felt her nod.

The scents of physical effort rose from Street's hair just beneath my nose. Another scent was mixed in, slightly pungent and bitter, the scent of fear.

SIXTY-THREE

"Where was this when it happened?"

"Near my condo parking lot."

"And you think he chased you?"

"I know he did. He was behind me, shouting that he was going to kill me. That I was going to pay with my life."

"How far do you think you went while he was shouting?"

"A long way. A quarter mile. Then he stopped shouting. Probably because he was breathless. But I still heard him panting and grunting behind me. It was like you said. I think he couldn't accept the fact that he couldn't catch a girl. So he ran himself down trying."

"Then he could still be near, walking back to his vehicle, trying to catch his breath. We might be able to catch him."

Street looked horrified. She looked down. She stood stiff with fear and shock. Her hands were balled into tight fists as if she was trying to contain rage and fear.

"Hurry!" I said. I put my arm around her shoulder and pushed her forward through the dark.

We ran to the Jeep. I got both Spot and Blondie in the back seat as Street got in the front. I started it and raced down the road. "Tell me where you think he might have come to before he gave up."

Street stared out at the dark road and the narrow swath that the headlights illuminated. "I don't know. I think it was maybe half way up. But then he would have turned and run back, right?" Her words were shakier than ever. Getting closer to the monster was scarier. She looked back and forth toward the dark forest. "He could be anywhere. We'll never see him."

"Dogs can see with their noses."

I assumed that Tom Casey had run or walked a good distance back toward his vehicle, which he would have probably left near Street's condo, maybe pulled off into the woods. So I drove a fair distance past the point where Street thought he'd run to, then stopped.

I let the dogs out.

"Spot!" I said in a loud whisper. "Spot, I need you to do another search." I gave him a shake. "Spot, find the suspect! Find him." I dropped my open hand in a point next to his head and smacked his rear. He took off down the road. Blondie followed.

"How will he know what scent to look for?" Street asked, her voice terrified and shaky.

"He might not. But there is only one human in the woods besides you and me. I think he'll figure it out."

"You think Blondie will understand?" Street asked. Her worry and fear made her voice waver.

"Dogs learn very well from other dogs." I gestured at the dogs, streaking away down the road, moving out of the range of the headlights.

"But she won't bite my father. I already learned that."

"No. Spot will be better at that. Even if she doesn't fully get it yet, the presence of a second dog will help unnerve your father. Let's follow in the Jeep."

We got back in, and I drove after the dogs, rolling down my window so I could hear.

About a hundred yards down, I heard an engine start up.

I hit the gas and sped up. Headlights came on up ahead where the road curved.

"He's going to get away!" Street said.

"I know a shortcut trail through the woods. But it's going to be rough. Hold on."

I swerved off the road and plunged between trees where there was an old, rutted trail. I braked, shoved the shifter into four-wheel-drive, stomped on the accelerator.

In the dim glow of dashboard lights, I sensed that Street reached out for support, her hands still in fists, jammed against the dashboard and door handle. The Jeep shook violently as we bounced over tree roots and rocks. At one point the Jeep hit a tree with the right front fender. We ricocheted away and kept going.

Through the trees, I saw the other headlights. We were

gaining, but just barely. Tom Casey's vehicle was ahead of us. In the red taillight glow, I sensed moving shadows.

The dogs chasing him.

I gave the Jeep another burst of speed. "Okay, hang on," I said to Street. "The trail curves back to the road right up here. I'm going to turn hard."

A moment later, I sensed the turn. I cranked the wheel and we skidded around the curve. Another burst of speed brought us even with Casey as the trail approached the road. I held my course, playing chicken. He gave up first and turned off the road just as we got onto the asphalt.

Maybe he thought he could drive through the trees the same as we did. But there was no trail there.

His car hit a dip, then bounced up over a sharp little rise. It came down hard onto a rock with a loud crunching sound. I slowed as I heard his engine roaring and one of his wheels spinning. He was high-centered on the rock, and he wouldn't be going anywhere.

"Stay in the Jeep," I said to Street.

I got out and ran toward the forest where he'd gotten stuck. Spot ran up to me.

Tom Casey, fully in the mindset of a fleeing fugitive, got out of his car and ran into the forest.

It was a mistake.

"Spot! Find the suspect! Take him down!" I gave Spot the signal. He ran into the darkness.

A moment later, I heard a grunt, the thud of a body hitting the ground, and a muffled scream.

I pulled out my light, walked through the trees, and saw Spot standing there, paws spread wide for stability. His head was reaching down to the ground.

Tom Casey was face down in the dirt, his head turned slightly to the side. Spot's jaws fully encased the man's neck from behind. Casey, as if traumatized by the classic attack mode of a mountain lion, lay frozen. He didn't know that Spot wouldn't kill him by crushing his neck. But he realized it would be easy for a dog of that size to put him down permanently with just one bite, and Casey wasn't taking any chances.

Nearby, Blondie watched us, making no noise or movement. Behind Blondie came movement. Street's dark form approached, stopped, stared at Tom Casey lying at my feet.

I leaned over so my mouth was next to Spot's ear. I made a little growling sound and tapped on Spot's throat, the signal.

Spot growled deep and loud.

"Good boy, Spot. Keep holding him." I tapped his throat again.

Spot upped his growl louder. In addition to the vibration from the growl, Spot's jaws did little spasmodic jerks. I could see Casey go rigid with terror. But it was still nothing compared to what he did to Street.

Then, for Casey's benefit, I said to Spot, "If this scumbag even twitches, bite his head off."

I put a knee in the middle of Casey's back and put weight on it. There was a loud squeak and snapping sound from his vertebra. The man screamed. I jerked his arms back and cuffed him by putting two zip ties around his wrists, pulling them both very tight. Then I did the same with his ankles.

"Okay, Spot, you can let go."

I turned Casey onto his side, then pulled his ankles back and out, arching the man's back, and zip-tied his ankles to his wrists.

I patted Casey down. He had no weapon. Before I stood up, I leaned forward in the dark and whispered, my voice airy and very mean.

"You picked the wrong woman to attack. I'm very close to deciding that when I caught you, your head got accidentally caved in on a rock. Remember that, Tom Casey. If you even look at her, I'll make that decision."

I gave Spot a pat. "Watch him, boy. If he makes the tiniest move, bite his face off."

I left them, went to Street and Blondie, and we walked back to the Jeep. Street opened her door a few tentative inches. Street was obviously very wary. She and Blondie got in.

I rubbed her leg. "The suspect is captured and subdued."

I pulled out my phone and dialed 911.

SIXTY-FOUR

After Diamond and his men came and took the suspect away, I took Street and the dogs up to my cabin. Diamond said he'd come up the mountain when he finished processing the crime scene.

When we were inside, I locked the door, turned the cabin lights down low, and made certain the blinds were closed tight. As always at 7200 feet in June, it was cold at night. So I built a fire in the wood stove. Street sat in the big leather chair, her knees up at her chest, arms around her knees, fists still balled with tension. She shivered violently. I found a blanket and draped it over her.

Spot lay down next to her chair. Blondie took her other side. I knew that was the best reassurance of all. Dogs in a protective position around the cave fire. People have always treasured dogs for uncountable reasons. But knowing that dogs have no fear and that no predator can get to us without having to fight the dogs is near the top of the list.

I wanted to give Street a neck and shoulder rub. But I was afraid that having me step behind her chair and touch her neck might give her flashback fear. It was better to wait. So I sat down in the rocker, available but not pressing. I reached out and rubbed her knee.

After long minutes, she said, "He attacked me just as I got out of my car." Her words were rushed and filled with tears, and her teeth chattered. "It was exactly what you had worried about. Blondie hadn't even followed me out of the car yet."

"I'm so sorry," I said, and squeezed her knee. I had a hundred questions, but I knew she'd tell me when she was ready.

"He grabbed me from behind. So I did like we practiced. I tried to stomp down on his foot. I hit something. Maybe it was his foot, but it didn't seem to do anything. I went limp to give him that false sense of security, then twisted suddenly. I elbowed him in the gut. But he clamped his arm around my neck and began choking me. I could tell that he wanted to kill me."

She paused.

I waited.

"So I went for his eyeballs like we practiced. I reached both hands up behind my head, feeling with my fingers. I was totally determined to take out an eye. Both of them if I could."

Another pause, longer this time.

"But he put his face against the back of my head. As I searched with my fingers, he turned his head to keep me from getting to his face. I couldn't feel an eyeball. Not even for a moment. Meanwhile, I was blacking out. His arm was bent so that it shut off the blood flow in my neck. I was desperate. I thought maybe I could get a finger into his nose and push back into his sinuses. Anything. I was blacking out when I finally found a target."

"His eyes?"

"No. His ear."

"You jammed your finger into his ear?"

"No," she said. "I didn't stick my finger into his ear. I tore the ear off. At least, I tore part of it off."

SIXTY-FIVE

Street looked down at her closed fists. She held them both up, then slowly opened her left hand. It was empty. She kept her right fist closed.

"You tore off his ear and then started running," I said.

Street nodded. "When my hand landed on his ear, my fingertips were at the top of it. So I dug my nails into the skin right where the upper ear meets the head."

Street stared down at her right fist, still clenched, white-knuckled. It must have been seriously cramping. I imagined it was like pulling the pin on a grenade and then holding the lever closed, afraid to let go because of what would emerge, explosive and, in this case, disgusting.

She continued, "I didn't have time to ponder it. I just wanted to cut his skin with my nails, to cut in deep. Then I squeezed his ear, pinching it like my hand was a pliers, and I jerked down as hard as I could. There was a squeak and a mushy tearing sound, like ripping soft leather. He screamed and pushed me away. I yelled Blondie's name and started running."

Blondie raised her head and looked at Street, who was breathing hard all over again.

"After I'd run up the road maybe a hundred yards, I thought I should call you. I was about to pull the velcro tab on my phone pocket when I realized that my fist was closed on his ear. It made me gag, and I almost vomited. But then I focused on my anger, my rage at being attacked. I kept my grip on his ear. I got my phone out with my left hand and called you."

She stopped to breathe hard. I could see that she was still shivering, violent, full-body jerking. "When Diamond comes here, can you tell him to come alone? Or maybe leave the other cops outside? Can they not turn on sirens and red lights?" Her words, coming through clenched teeth and cold lips, were thick and hard to understand.

"I'll tell him," I said, understanding that the trauma of an attack is intensified by noise. First Responders are trained to be calm. But light bars on emergency vehicles are anything but. Sirens are the worst for a victim who is not currently being assaulted. I thought that Diamond's crew would not use them in this situation. But I walked into my kitchen nook and used my landline phone so I wouldn't have to fight the poor quality connection of my cell. I dialed Diamond directly and spoke in a soft voice, not hiding my words from Street, just being respectfully low key.

"One more thing," I said to Diamond. "Street tore off part of her attacker's ear. You'll want to take that with you when you leave."

When I was done, I made a cup of hot tea in the microwave and carried it to Street, who was still staring at her clenched hand.

She picked it up with her left hand and sipped.

"Diamond will be here soon," I said. I glanced at her closed fist and saw for the first time the dried blood between her fingers. "Do you want to get cleaned up?"

Street closed her eyes hard as if to shut off her thoughts. "Maybe when Diamond comes."

"Sounds good."

The fire grew bright behind the glass of the wood stove. Little pops and cracks resonated inside the metal box. Street was still shivering, still in a kind of shock. The fire was hot now and would help with radiant heat as well as psychological warmth. I considered putting on some calming music, soft, slow classical. But quiet seemed best.

Ten minutes later, I heard vehicle sounds. An engine arriving, then going silent. A car door. A second car door. There was a soft knock at the door. Spot jumped up, not surprised, but eager. Blondie raised her head to watch, her floppy ears perked forward.

I opened the door and let Diamond in. Spot sniffed him and wagged as Diamond gave him a rough pet. When Blondie realized what was going on, she jumped up to get her share of attention.

Diamond turned toward Street and just looked without speaking.

When Diamond speaks with his perfect command of words, you can still hear the faint accent that indicates that English is his second language. But silent emotional communication, given or received, is the same in any language, and Diamond is a master at that. He nodded at Street as he walked over to the side of the leather chair. He squatted down next to her, balancing on the balls of his feet. Street was still tense, still shaking, her left hand gripping the arm of the chair. Her right fist still clutched the chunk of her father's ear.

Diamond put his hand on her left forearm. "You okay?"

She nodded.

He gently rubbed her arm. "You're safe now."

She nodded again.

"McKenna says you are a hell of a fighter and you don't let anyone attack you without a physical quid pro quo."

Street made the tiniest of smiles.

"I could arrange a trade," Diamond said. "Be like a prisoner exchange on the Bridge of Spies." He pulled out his wallet as he gestured toward her right fist. "You give me your Tom Casey trophy, I give you my mother's photo, which has been imprisoned in this wallet for twenty years." He slipped the photo out and reached it out toward Street.

Street's smile became a millimeter less tiny.

"Of course, you have to give the photo back after you've had her for awhile."

Street took the photo with her left hand and stared at it. "She's beautiful. Look at her eyes."

Diamond spread a handkerchief over his other hand and held it out, palm up. "Yes, her eyes were like yours, almost black, like cave pools that go to the center of the Earth."

As Diamond spoke, he reached for Street's clenched fist, set it knuckles-down onto the handkerchief, rubbing her fingers to relieve them of their stiffness. Then he opened her fingers slowly, so that her hand always covered the object it contained. During this, Diamond kept talking about his mother, kept Street focused on the photo.

"And check out mama's hair. It was brown like dark chocolate, thick as you can imagine. Now it is mostly white, but still just as thick and heavy."

It was a brilliant display of comfort and empathy and understanding. Diamond got the ear wrapped in his handkerchief without Street ever having looked at it. He pocketed the handkerchief while he segued to his mother's baking.

"Is she still alive?" Street asked.

"Mi madre? Oh Dios mío, she'll outlive me. Her apartment is on the sixth floor in Mexico City. Mexico City is over seven thousand feet. Just like Owen's cabin. Do you know how she gets her groceries? She carries them up the stairs. Seventy-eight years old, and she never takes the elevator. She'll be a pallbearer at my funeral."

Street's smile was now full. She handed the photo back to Diamond. Street's right hand was closed again, but not clenched into a fist. She slowly stood up. I joined her as she walked to my little bathroom.

"Do you need anything?" I asked in a soft voice before she closed the door.

She shook her head. "No, thanks." She paused. "I have to give Diamond a statement, right?"

I nodded. "Only when you're ready. It can be tomorrow."

"Okay." She seemed to look off into space.

Street touched the tip of her left index finger to my lips, then looked down at her bloody right hand, which was still closed but no longer holding anything. She stepped into the bathroom and closed the door.

I took four steps back to the living room.

Diamond was sitting on the rocker, both of his arms out petting the dogs, Spot to his right, Blondie to his left.

"That was masterful," I said.

He shrugged. "Just trying to feel my way to a place where she can tell us what happened and give us the goods on this creep father of hers. Although, I guess she already gave me the goods." He patted his pocket where he'd put the handkerchief. "Ear flesh is surprisingly lightweight," he said. "But it looks like she mostly just got the rim, so to speak. So I shouldn't expect any more heft."

Diamond gave me a serious look. "The woman's been through hell."

"Street is an icon of self-sufficiency and strength," I said. "But this is going to stress her out for some time."

Diamond said, "It would stress out anyone, no matter how self-sufficient. Anyway, John Donne said No Man Is An Island."

"The poet, right?"

"Sí.

"I know about him," I said. "'Love built on beauty, soon as beauty, dies.'"

Diamond raised his eyebrows. "You surprise me."

"I learned it from Street," I said. "One time when I told her she was beautiful, she protested vigorously saying that she obviously was not. And then, as if to feel better about it, she quoted Donne."

"Smart girl," Diamond said.

"Who are you talking about?" Street said as she emerged from the bathroom, hands and face looking freshly scrubbed.

"You," Diamond said. "McKenna was saying that your awareness of John Donne's poetry helps mitigate your tendency toward self-critique."

"I didn't say that," I said.

"Then you should have."

EPILOGUE

For all of his obvious awkwardness, Douglas Fairbanks nevertheless understood the basics of how to put on a good private party, even if he went overboard on his decorations and enthusiasm.

He told us to meet him at Heavenly Village on the South Shore.

Spot and I picked up Street and Blondie. We parked in the ramp at Heavenly Village and walked over to the gondola base station. We held Spot and Blondie by collar and leash, and they behaved, eager to sit and take time for people watching, and, no doubt, people smelling. Although, because it wasn't yet July, the summer tourist crush hadn't yet begun. There were just scattered couples strolling the village.

The blue-gray gondolas came out of the base station at regular intervals, clamped onto the big cable, and lofted up the mountain at high speed. The passengers inside plastered their faces to the acrylic windows.

"Are you okay with this?" I asked Street.

She made a small nod. "It will be a good distraction."

Just a few minutes later, Sergeant Diamond Martinez and Sergeants Bains and Santiago all walked up, side-by-side, looking like three scruffy gunmen out of the Magnificent Seven. All three wore cowboy hats, black for Diamond, brown for Bains and Santiago. All three wore cowboy boots beneath their jeans, black for Diamond, and brown for the other two. They stopped together and stood in a line, with Diamond in the center, as if they'd rehearsed like a chorus line.

"Three counties worth of lawmen," I said. "Imposing show of force."

"Three hombres ready to rumble," Bains said.

"Kick some ass," Santiago said.

"Recite some cowboy poetry," Diamond said.

"Fairbanks is gonna love that," I said. "You guys got the look, I'll give you that. You packing to back it up?"

"Try us and find out," Santiago said. He didn't even crack a smile. Impressive.

Spot and Blondie both turned their heads and looked past the sergeants.

Douglas Fairbanks appeared. He wore a formal, black dinner jacket and under it his dayglo road bike outfit, the blue and yellow stripes catching the setting sun, the spandex material revealing every curve of his musculature and his not-so-musculature. He looked gloriously goofy and out-of-place. He was obviously comfortable making a joke with his uniform.

Next to Fairbanks was Aubrey Blackwood, looking radiant and stylish in a maroon pantsuit with magenta shirt and maroon jacket. She'd tied maroon ribbons around her crutches and curled the ends so they bounced and waved.

The black-and-blue swelling on her jaw from the blow that Lynn, the Giuseppe imposter, gave her with the two-by-four through the car window had gone down. Aubrey had covered the discoloration with makeup, and the other bruises from her fall didn't show at all. She looked quite snappy as she worked her crutches, clacking left and right, doing the scissors walk with her stiff legs, moving forward at a good speed.

As Fairbanks and Aubrey approached and Fairbanks gave us a big grin, I realized I'd never seen him smile. He said, "Men and women and hound dogs, I'd like you all to meet Aubrey Blackwood, someone I think is very special. This party is for her."

Street smiled, and the three lawmen all took off their hats and bowed before Aubrey.

Aubrey made a sudden huge smile, and tears rolled down her cheeks.

"Please don't get upset, Ms. Blackwood," Diamond said. "We respect strength and beauty. And we can see that you have a surfeit of both."

"It's true ma'am," Santiago said. "We know you've been through a tough gig, and we applaud your focus and resolve."

Bains put his hat back on, put his hands together palm-to-palm, his fingertips touching his chin, and bowed again, his silence seeming significant.

Fairbanks said, "I'll be just a minute." He trotted away toward the gondola.

The dogs were very affectionate with Aubrey, and we all chatted. I told Aubrey that she probably couldn't trust lawmen as scruffy as the three who were with us. The three hombres sneered at me. Then Fairbanks came back and waved us over.

I don't know what kind of bribe he paid to the gondola operators, but they stopped the gondola as Fairbanks helped Aubrey approach the loading dock. And when she was ready to board, the gondola that approached was dressed in white roses. They were inserted into the ski compartments. There was a bouquet of white roses attached to the gondola's front and another attached to its rear. Inside the gondola was a small table and on it a vase of white roses and a bottle of champagne in a cooler and two long-stemmed glasses. I noticed a book next to the vase of flowers. My guess was that it was a poetry collection.

Fairbanks helped Aubrey inside and helped her sit down. Their gondola began to move forward, then latched onto the high-speed cable and accelerated out of the base station and up the mountain.

The gondola operators looked the other way as Street and I ushered the dogs into the next gondola. The three scruffy lawmen followed in the next one.

Once the gondola doors shut, Street said to me, "Aubrey kind of glows, doesn't she?"

"Yes, she has a warmth you don't want to turn away from."

"Even the dogs noticed."

"I saw that, too," I said.

We were all whisked up into the sky where we got off at the observation platform at 9100 feet. We walked around to where the deck projected out over the mountain and looked down on the giant blue lake surrounded by a rim of snow-capped peaks.

Fairbanks had worked more magic. There was a table spread with white linen and chairs with white cushions, and on the table were more bouquets of white roses surrounded by a large buffet of hors d'oeuvres and champagne and glasses for all of us.

To one side sat two men in tuxedos, one playing guitar and the other playing keyboards, jazz standards.

Fairbanks even had doggie bowl treats of de-boned chicken wings, which Blondie chewed appreciatively, while Spot inhaled them and looked around for the next serving.

As the sun set behind the Sierra Crest, we insisted that Fairbanks pose with Aubrey for photographs, she looking very sophisticated and he, in his garish biking outfit, looking like the stylistic satire of the decade. Aubrey made her beautiful grin, and her eyes crinkled, and we probably all felt a bit plain next to her.

Later, as we were walking back toward the gondola for the return trip down, I found myself next to Aubrey. We moved quietly through the twilight. The spring songbirds had gone silent. The only sound was the clicking of Aubrey's crutches on the metal decking. The alpen glow was fading, and the stars were coming out. Three thousand feet below us, the lake was turning black, and the ring of lights around it, 75 miles in circumference, shimmered.

"I'm so glad to have met you," I said to Aubrey.

"I'm so glad Douglas Fairbanks asked me to join you all," Aubrey said.

We walked a bit without talking.

"I think he's a good man," I said. "Kind of different. But he's into poetry, which is a lot like art. Trying to find meaning in a world that's focused on shallow ideals and silly priorities."

"Like many of us," Aubrey said.

"You think you'll see him again?" I asked.

"If he's interested," Aubrey said.

"He's interested," I said.

The next afternoon, Street and I took the dogs and drove up the East Shore. We parked on the highway, put on packs with food and barbecue supplies, and hiked down to one of the secret beaches that are popular with nudists during warmer weather. In the cool weather at the end of June, we had the place to ourselves.

When we got to the beach, Blondie immediately waded into the lake. Spot walked over to the water and drank some of it.

Street threw a stick out into the lake. Blondie leaped in and swam out to get it. Spot stepped far enough into the water to get his paws thoroughly wet with ice water, then decided that Blondie should have the stick to herself.

Spot came to watch me as I pulled out the miniature folding barbecue, put in charcoal, and lit it. He knew what barbecues meant. And much as sticks had their own special attraction, he knew that the allure of grilled treats was an order of magnitude greater.

When the charcoal was ready, I put a six-pack of pork brats on for me and the dogs and a single turkey wild rice pretend brat for Street.

Street opened the Tusk 'n Red wine I'd gotten from Trader Joe's. It was produced in Ukiah and seemed appropriate because what I'd learned in Ukiah had helped in solving the case. Street poured a generous inch and a half into the repurposed jam jars. They had embossed grapes on the surface and were relatively indestructible compared to the long-stemmed, large-bell, singing glassware favored by sommeliers and not favored by backpacking beachgoers.

Although we missed it by three squares on the calendar, we toasted the summer solstice.

"To Helios, the Sun god on the summer solstice," Street said.

"To Helios," I said.

We clicked glasses. I drank. Street tasted.

The sun on the water was like an arc-welding light shining through blue diamonds. The flickering waves scintillated as if to stop the world and proclaim Tahoe the center of the Earth and Helios the center of the universe.

Soon, we ate. The food was as good as Spot and Blondie's enthusiasm indicated.

Afterward, they lay in the sand and snoozed as the sun lowered behind the mountains across the lake. Street and I leaned back against a giant, angled boulder, our knees up, and looked out at the turquoise water that was fast becoming shades of purple gray.

After a period of quiet, I could tell by Street's breathing that she was tense. I put my hand on her knee.

"Your father is in jail. Diamond assured me that they are giving him no privileges, no opportunities. I think you can relax."

"You'd think," Street said. She sounded tentative, worried, stressed.

"Will you be okay?"

She paused before answering. "I don't know. It seems there's a cumulative effect with periods of major stress. Each time you fight your way through a big problem, it leaves an ugly residue. Like successive waterlines after repeated floods. Every time it happens, you realize that things can never go back to your previous innocence. Does that make any sense?"

"Yeah. For many people, much of the time, the world isn't an easy place," I said. "Some people, some lives, the stars don't line up and make it simple. You've gone through your entire life never making a problem for anyone, never doing anything to make someone think that you stand between them and what they want. You've always just done your very best in every situation you were dropped into. I can understand that other people, failing by the same measure, might resent that. But those who hate people who've never done them wrong are sick. When we're presented with their hate, we're tempted to put up barricades in front of the castle gate, tuck-point the loopholes, sharpen the arrowheads, load the cannons, and double check that the black powder is dry. But it won't succeed in doing anything other than locking us inside the tower."

"Precisely," Street said. "I can't have a worthwhile life if I seal myself off from every possible threat."

"I agree." I propped my jam jar in the sand so it wouldn't tip, reached for the bottle, added a tiny bit to Street's glass, then refilled mine. "But having said that, if you ever want, short term or long term, the security of Spot nearby or even me, you know what the answer is."

"I know," she said. "Thanks. Don't ever think that's not important and appreciated."

"But," I said.

"But there is great value in being independent, being able to fend for yourself. Having others to depend on is a huge gift. But having to depend on others is very difficult. Imagine it for yourself. You're as independent as a person can be. If that weren't the case, it would permanently alter your worldview in a debilitating way. You need no help from others. Physical, financial, psychological."

"Emotionally," I said. "I need you emotionally."

"I believe you want that, but not that you need it. You may not always want to manage everything by yourself, but you can if need be. There's tremendous value in that. I want that, too. I demand it of myself. I don't expect others to see things the same way. And I don't always see it that way as applied to others. But it's okay for me to see it that way regarding myself. I don't ask for other people's approval. I just want my own approval of how I go through life."

She paused to take a deep breath, sipped a bit of wine, reached out and ran a fingertip down the top of Blondie's nose.

"We both knew these things about the other before we got close, right?"

"Right," I said.

"So you understand my need to be independent."

"Indeed," I said. "I expect it."

"And you understand why I probably won't ever live with you on a full-time basis."

I nodded.

"But you know I love you."

"And I love you, too."

She held her glass up and looked through the wine toward the lake. The last of the sunlight flashed rose-colored beams across her face. "We'll still spend time together. Dinner. Hiking. Skiing. Vacations sometimes. Occasional sleepovers."

"I like that last part. Sleepovers."

She raised her glass again. "To sleepovers," she said.

We clicked our glasses.

About The Author

Todd Borg and his wife live in Lake Tahoe, where they write and paint. To contact Todd or learn more about the Owen McKenna mysteries, please visit toddborg.com.

A message from the author:

Dear Reader,

If you enjoyed this novel, please consider posting a short review on any book website you like to use. Reviews help authors a great deal, and that in turn allows us to write more stories for you.

Thank you very much for your interest and support!

Todd